Spelling

How to use this book with your child:

It is recommended that an adult spends time with a child while doing any kind of school practice, to offer encouragement and guidance. Find a quiet place to work, preferably at a table, and encourage your child to hold his or her pen or pencil correctly.

Try to work at your child's pace and avoid spending too long on any one page or activity. Most of all, emphasise the fun element of what you are doing and enjoy this special and exciting time!

Don't forget to add your reward sticker to each page you complete!

Reward sticker!

Designed by Plum5
Illustrations by Sue King, Sharon Smart and Andy Geeson
Educational consultant Chris Andrew and Nina Filipek

www.autumnchildrensbooks.co.uk

Days of the week

Put the days of the week in order starting with Sunday.

Friday	Tuesday	Sunday
Wednesday	Saturday	
Thursday	Monday	

____

____

____

____

____

____

____

Reward sticker!

Months of the year

It is important that you know the months of the year and how to spell them. It is also important that you know the seasons and when each month falls. Place the name of the month in the correct box.

January · November · March · June

May · February · December · August

September · July · April · October

Spring	Summer
______	______
______	______
______	______

Autumn	Winter
______	______
______	______
______	______

Reward sticker!

The village bridge

Some words end in **ge** or **dge**. Complete the spellings below using the first two words in each column to help you.

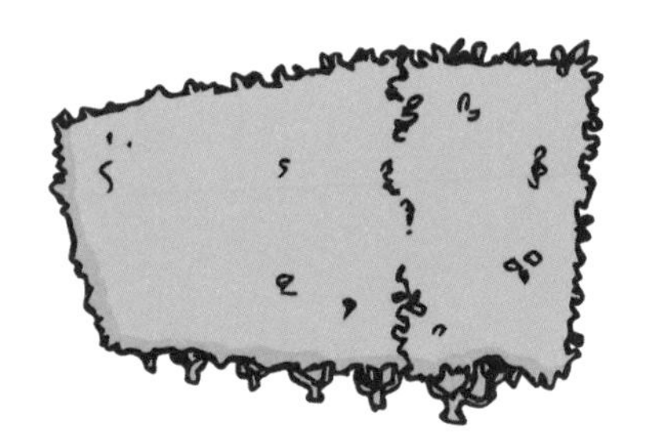

badge	change
dodge	charge
bri____	pa____
he____	villa____
fu____	hu____
sle____	a____

Reward sticker!

Sounds like s

The answers to this crossword all have a **c** in them that sounds like an **s**. Complete the crossword by writing in the answers below. One of the answers has been written in to start you off.

circus

lace

race

ice

rice

space

circle

cinema

city

Reward sticker!

Words with kn and gn

Words with **kn** and **gn** are tricky! The **k** and the **g** are there but not sounded – they are silent. Look at the story below. Circle all of the **kn** and **gn** words with a silent **k** or **g**.

Maria walked through the park with a knapsack on her back. She thought she saw something odd peeping from behind a tree. She was so distracted that she didn't see the sign until she had knocked her knee on it. It hurt, so she knelt down. She swatted a gnat that buzzed around her face. After she had got comfortable with her back against the trunk of the tree, Maria reached into her knapsack and pulled out her knitting. Just as she did, she heard a voice muttering behind her. She slowly looked over her shoulder and in a hole in the trunk she saw a small face looking out. It was a gnome! Now, to Maria's knowledge, gnomes didn't exist, except, this one clearly did! And he was gnawing on her sandwiches, gnashing his teeth ferociously!

Reward sticker!

Words with w

Some words with **w** are another case of the silent letter – the **w** is so shy that it doesn't speak! When **w** comes in front of **r** we only ever sound the **r**! Sometimes it hides in the middle of words too!

These words are all missing their silent partner! Can you help them by adding the **w**?

__rite	ans__er
__restle	__reck
__rong	__ritten
__rapped	__ren
__rote	s__ord
__rist	__riggle

Reward sticker!

Word search fun

The **le** spelling is the most common for this sound. Find the **le** words in the word search. Look out! Some of the words may be diagonal or backwards!

e	r	s	j	e	y	r	x	e	v	e	g	u	e	e
y	l	v	a	u	l	q	l	d	q	p	q	l	f	h
v	i	d	f	m	b	g	h	d	v	s	c	a	d	x
u	i	f	d	e	p	b	a	w	n	n	p	m	z	x
m	u	v	b	i	l	l	l	e	u	p	p	f	g	r
i	g	r	w	k	m	t	e	e	l	e	e	t	p	q
n	z	k	f	e	e	c	s	e	z	e	o	v	r	e
t	o	p	p	l	e	w	h	a	j	l	p	x	t	l
x	x	g	p	l	b	e	p	a	c	p	l	e	t	g
m	y	p	d	o	e	l	b	a	c	a	e	l	a	n
d	i	n	t	e	l	t	t	i	l	t	h	z	b	a
r	a	t	u	m	b	l	e	m	u	s	h	z	l	a
c	l	v	h	i	j	t	d	m	k	i	g	u	e	t
e	y	z	s	b	y	f	n	p	w	k	r	p	g	p
d	s	j	u	n	g	l	e	p	t	q	o	u	b	m

angle
apple
bottle
cable
candle
castle
eagle
jungle
little
middle
people
puzzle
ripple
sample
staple
table
topple
tumble
uncle

Reward sticker!

Words with el

The **el** spelling is much less common than **le**. The **el** spelling is used after the letters **m**, **n**, **r**, **s**, **v**, **w** and more often than not, after **s**. Add the **el** ending to these words.

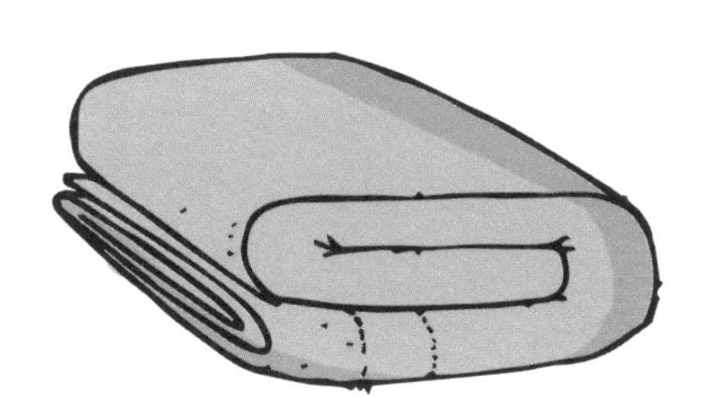

tow____

jew____

tunn____

squirr____

cam____

Reward sticker!

Animal or animil?

Look at each picture and say the word clearly to see if you can hear the sound. Now write in the correct vowel sound.

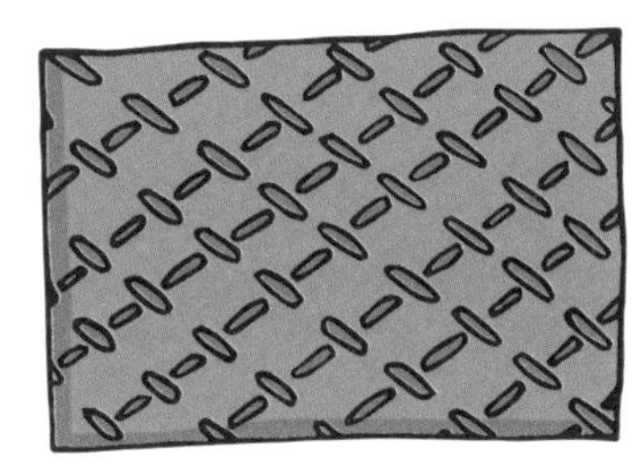

met__l

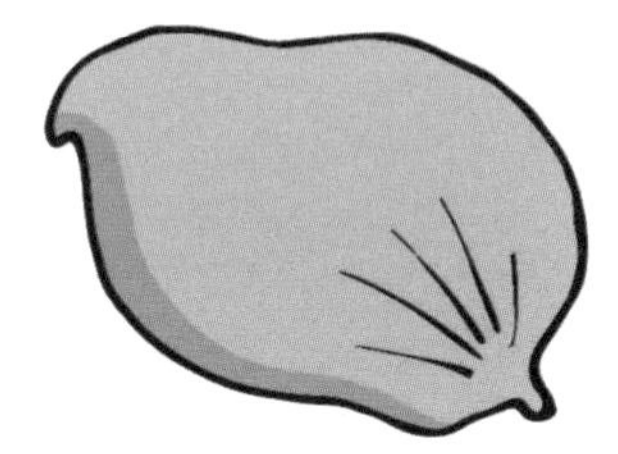

pet__l

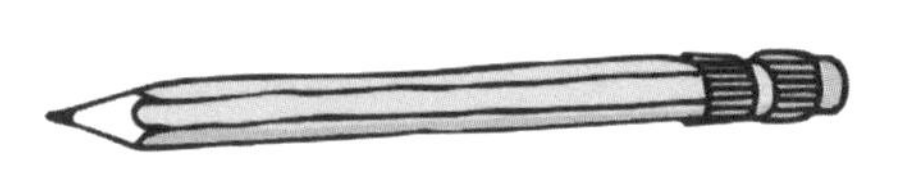

penc__l

anim__l

pup__l

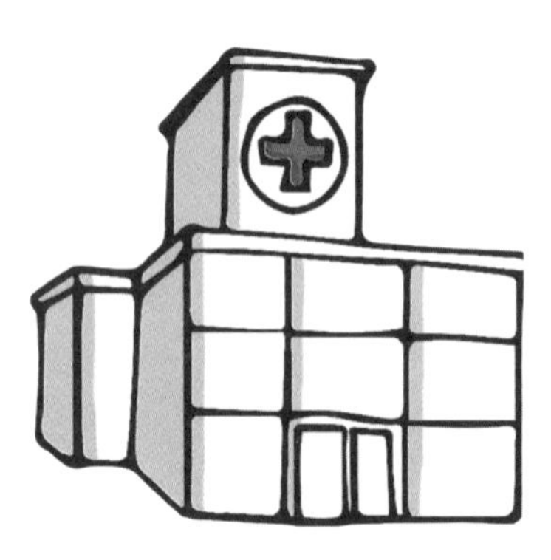

hospit__l

Reward sticker!

Testing endings

Choose which of these word endings belong at the end of each word.

al

le

hot____

app____

peop____

pet____

jew____

gerb____

tins____

met____

capit____

cam____

tunn____

penc____

midd____

foss____

hospit____

tow____

Reward sticker!

Y like an eye!

Look at the words below. Circle the ones that have a **y** in them but make the same sound as in eye! These are normally at the end of words! e.g. **shy**

drop	hit	run
cry	fly	castle
metal	dry	sky
pencil	sly	park
circle	why	defy
brown	sigh	reply
dog	try	fry
finish	clown	write

Reward sticker!

Plurals

A **plural** is when you have more than one of something.
Add **ies** to the end of each of these words ending in **y** to make them plural. e.g. baby → babies. Remember **ies** replaces the **y**.

diary diar______

city cit______

party part______

army arm______

jelly jell______

fairy fair______

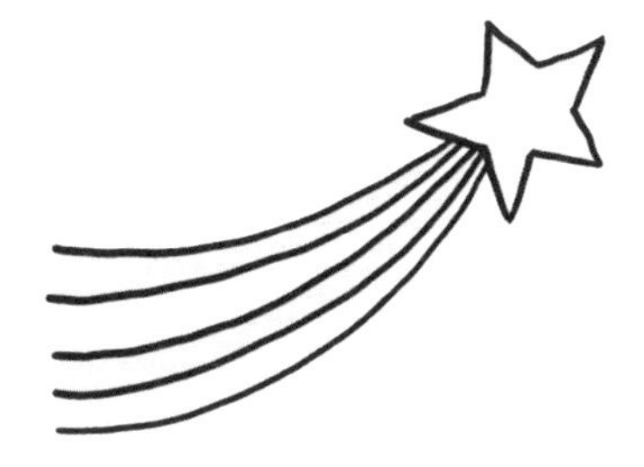

Reward sticker!

Tense times

Put these words in the correct tense speech bubble.

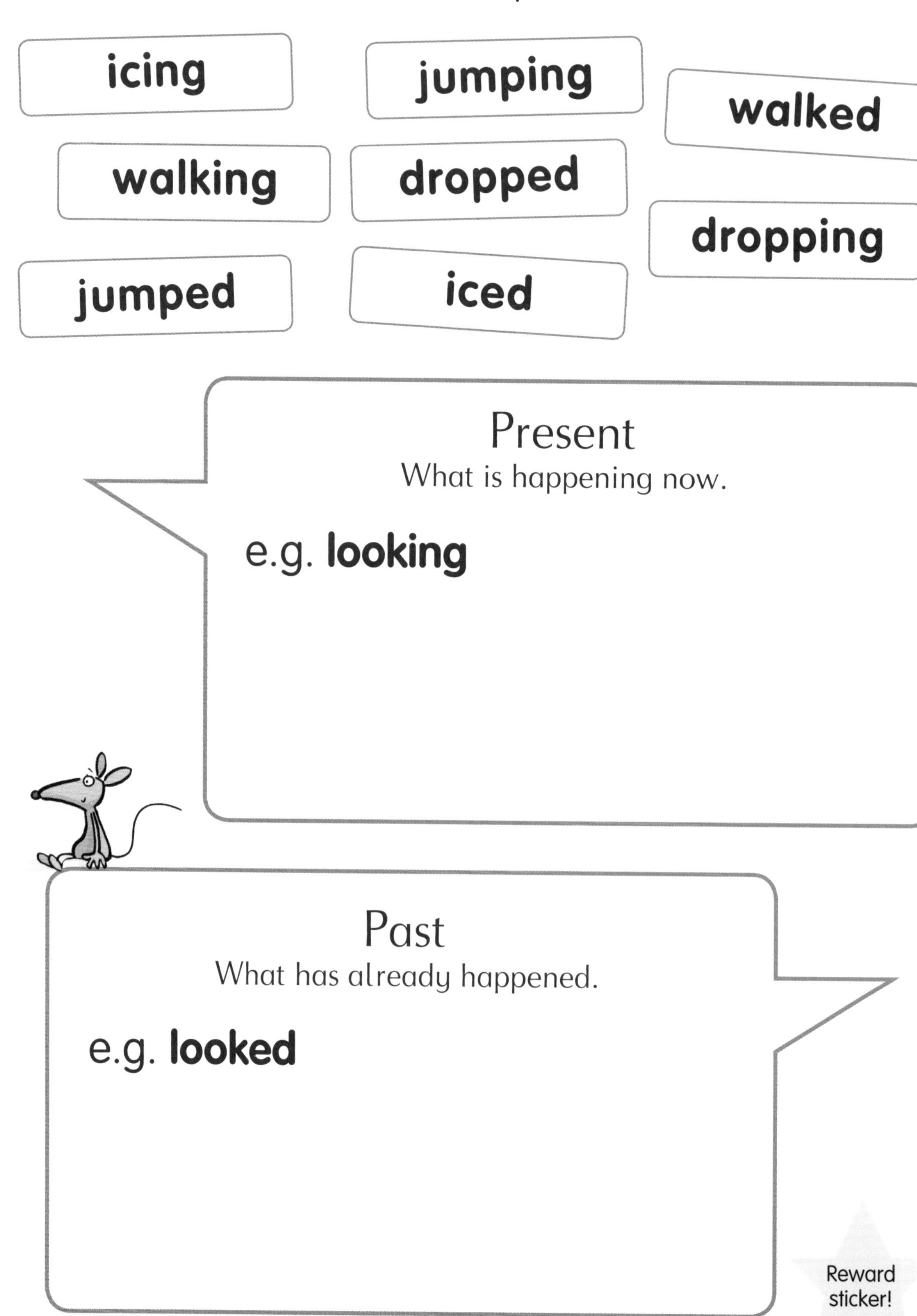

icing
jumping
walked
walking
dropped
dropping
jumped
iced
Present
What is happening now.
e.g. looking
Past
What has already happened.
e.g. looked
Reward sticker!

Comparing

Look at the words below – we add on **er** or **est** to the endings to show comparisons.
e.g. short – short**er** – short**est**.
Add **er** and **est** on to these words.

fast fast____ fast______

tall tall____ tall______

wide wid____ wid______

kind __________ __________

These next three are trickier because they end in **y**. It doesn't work to add **er** or **est**, you need to drop the **y** and replace it with **i** first.

hungry __________ __________

funny __________ __________

tasty __________ __________

Reward sticker!

Seeing double

Some words have double consonants – like words with **ll** in them. Unscramble the words with double consonants below.

awll _ _ _ _   llca _ _ _ _

flla _ _ _ _   ahll _ _ _ _

wlli _ _ _ _   tlal _ _ _ _

Some words need an extra consonant to be added before you can add extra letters. These words are usually verbs.
Hum becomes humming or hummed.
e.g. cla**p** → cla**pp**ing, cla**pp**ed

Add an extra consonant to each root word below before adding **ing** or **ed**.

ing 

drop   drop______   drop______

stop   stop______   stop______

travel   ______   ______

 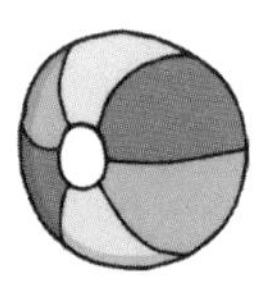

Reward sticker!

I did it!

Clever me!

That's right!

Good job!

Clever me!

I did it!

Clever me!

That's right!

Good job!

Well done!

I did it!

Clever me!

That's right!

Good job!

Well done!

I did it!

Well done!

Clever me!

That's right!

Good job!

Well done!

I did it!

One l or two?

Put these words in the right box depending on whether they have a single or double **l**.

ball	tall	talk
walk	almighty	wall
always	adult	almost
all	call	hall

l

ll

Reward sticker!

Missing vowels

Vowels are **a**, **e**, **i**, **o**, **u**. Write in the missing vowel for each word.

m__ther

c__me

oth__r

hon__y

br__ther

m__ney

noth__ng

doz__n

Mond__y

__bove

don__t

don__

glov__

s__me

Reward sticker!

Monkey business

The **ey** sound at the end of words makes your mouth stretch wide, like a monkey! Think up some more examples.

valley

monkey

Reward sticker!

Quick question

The **qu** spelling sounds like **kw**. Draw a line to link the words to the images below.

queen

quiet

question

quack

quarrel

a.

b.

c.

d.

e.

How many more **qu** words can you think of?

____

____

____

Reward sticker!

Wor words

There are not many **wor** words, but you need to know the letter pattern is always **wor**, not wer.
Finish off these **wor** words, with the endings **d**, **m**, **th**, **thy**, **ld** and **k**.

d   m   thy

k   th   ld

wor___   wor___

wor___   wor___

wor___   wor___

Reward sticker!

Suffixes

Suffixes are letters, or groups of letters, added to the ends of words. By adding a suffix you make a new word and often change the meaning of the root word.
e.g. Adding **less** makes the word mean the opposite.
Add **less** to the end of each of these words to change the meaning.

This homework seems end____________.

This pen is use____________.

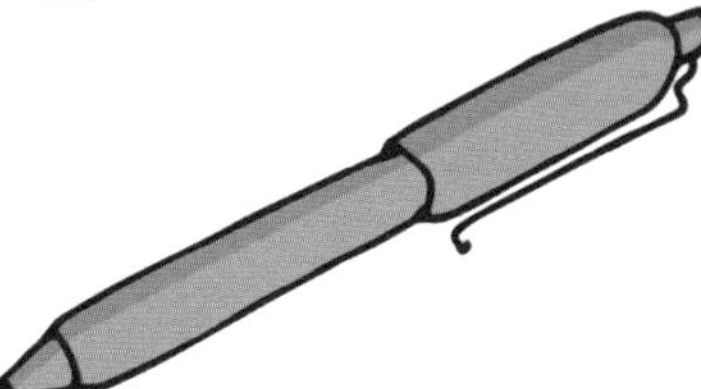

The man was home____________.

The trip to the dentist was pain____________.

ly, **ment**, **ful** or **ness** are other suffixes you will come across. Add the correct ones to the following words:

thank____________ dark____________

move____________ quiet____________

pay____________ loud____________

Reward sticker!

Tion and sion word search

Find the words ending in **tion** and **sion** in the word search.
Look out! Some of the words may be diagonal or backwards!

d	e	s	t	i	n	a	t	i	o	n	z	n	q	d
n	h	x	s	t	n	o	r	l	f	z	o	q	j	e
s	o	c	p	o	a	e	i	o	j	i	m	c	r	c
q	t	i	i	e	v	z	u	s	s	q	o	o	m	i
z	u	t	t	i	c	n	l	n	n	n	d	m	b	s
p	o	e	s	n	d	t	e	q	o	e	o	p	n	i
l	c	i	s	a	e	h	a	i	z	n	p	l	o	o
d	o	r	t	t	e	v	t	t	l	o	y	e	i	n
n	q	i	m	r	i	o	n	x	i	u	s	t	t	o
q	o	m	p	g	m	o	f	i	v	o	c	i	u	i
n	c	m	v	m	v	z	n	z	q	b	n	o	l	t
l	o	n	o	i	t	c	e	r	i	d	i	n	l	o
c	p	c	e	x	p	l	o	s	i	o	n	o	o	m
n	o	i	s	a	v	n	i	w	i	z	j	v	p	e
o	g	x	p	m	c	t	w	i	x	u	s	g	d	i

commotion
completion
comprehension
decision
destination
direction
emotion
expectation
explosion
foundation
invasion
invention
lotion
pension
pollution
question
revision

Reward
sticker!

Homophones

Homophones confuse most people! Homphones are when the words sound the same but are spelled differently and have different meanin
Here are some helpful tips – say them out loud and learn them.

T**heir**:	usually you can replace their with **our** in a sentence, if it still makes sense, you're using it correctly.
They**'re**:	you need to just remember the **'** is really in place of an **a**.
T**here**:	here, is a place.
W**itch**:	the witch had an itch on her nose.
Which:	which one? Remember the double w sound.
H**ear**/Here:	the one with **ear** in it is about listening!
Blue/blew:	say the words. You form your lips slightly differently. Blew makes your lips take the shape of blowing.
Piece/peace:	simple, I like a piece of pie.
To/two/**too**:	too has too many o's.
Be/bee:	I like to be, but not with buzzing bees.

Complete the sentences below by filling in the gaps.
Use the information above to help you.

My coat is over __________.

Someone __________ my candles out!

I can't __________ you!

My favourite colour is __________.

Reward sticker!

Look at the pictures below and match the words to the correct pictures.

flour

flower

knight

night

bear

bare

mail

male

leak

leek

a.

b.

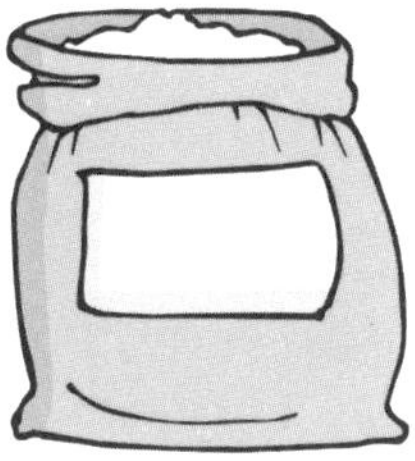

c.

d.

e.

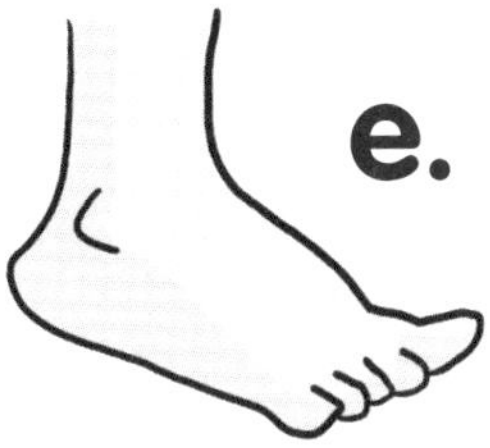

f.

g.

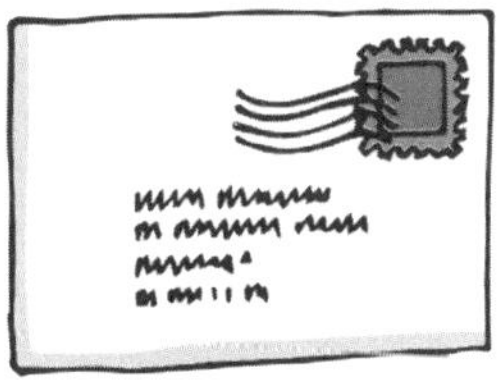

h.

i.

j.

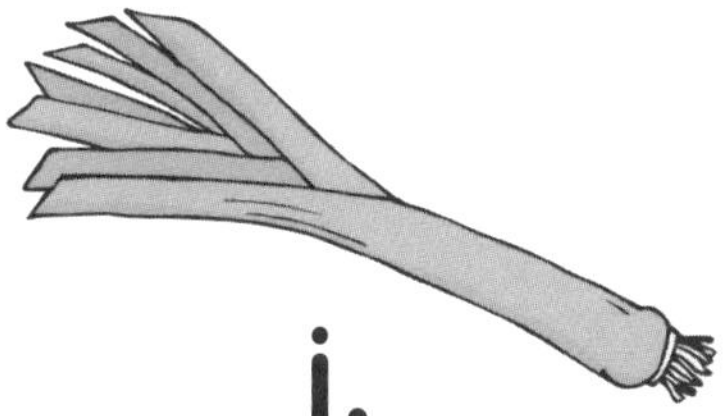

Reward sticker!

Antonyms

Antonym is the name we give to something that means the opposite. e.g. **slow** is an antonym of **fast**.
Write some antonyms for these words.

big ______________________

quiet ______________________

high ______________________

dry ______________________

weak ______________________

light ______________________

long ______________________

soft ______________________

Reward sticker!

Now look at these four sentences.
Carefully fill in the two missing words, which are opposites.
e.g. A hare runs **fast** but a tortoise is **slow**.

1. A mouse is ________________

   but a giraffe is ________________.

2. A rock is ________________

   but silk is ________________.

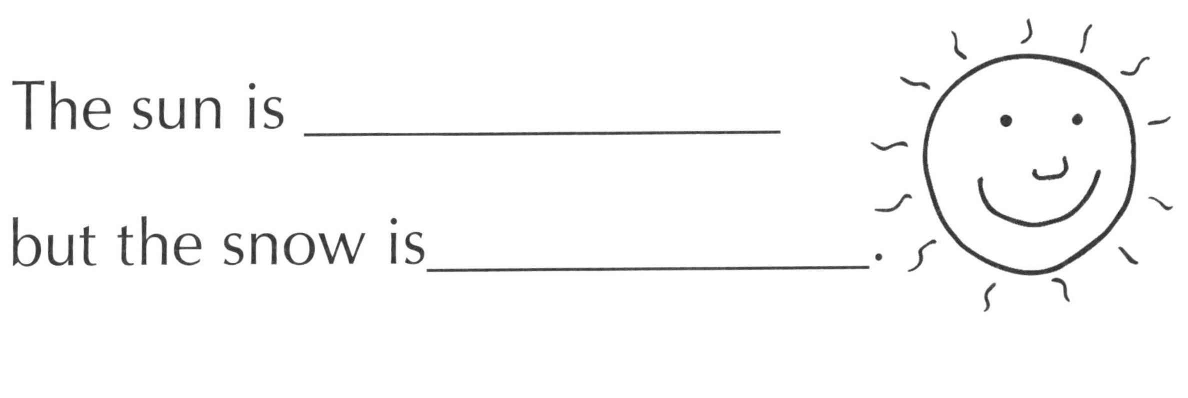

3. The sun is ________________

   but the snow is________________.

4. A lemon is ________________

   but honey is ________________.

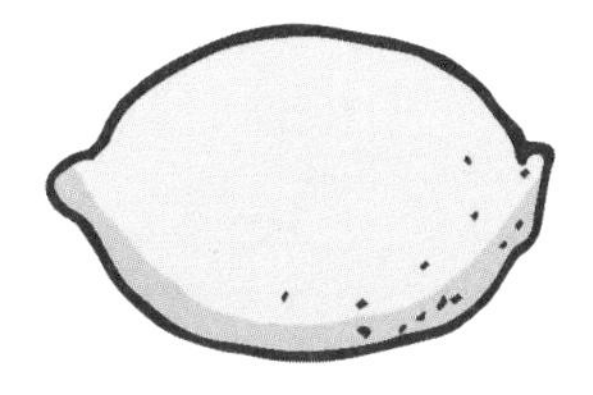

Reward sticker!

Cunning contractions

Sometimes we shorten words – especially when we speak.
We use an apostrophe ’ to replace some letters.

e.g. **is not** can become **isn’t** – the **o** is missed out. This is called a contraction.

Look at the examples below and shade over the letters that have been missed out.

should not ➔ shouldn’t

was not ➔ wasn’t

you have ➔ you’ve

you are ➔ you’re

I would ➔ I’d

shall not ➔ shan’t

Now look at the sentences below. Rewrite them on the line underneath using an apostrophe to shorten the highlighted words.

James could not wait to open his presents.

____

I am not going to the party.

____

Reward sticker!

Weeks and months

Test time! Can you remember how to spell the days of the week? What about the months of the year and the seasons?

Days of the week:

Months of the year:

Seasons:

Reward sticker!

Exceptions

Our language is difficult at times. You can learn all the rules but sometimes there are words that just break them all! Below are some of these words. Ask an adult to help you learn them. Read the words aloud and see which ones you can spell. If there are any you can't spell ask the adult to write the words on a blank sheet of paper. Look at the word, think about it carefully then cover it up and try writing it. Then, check to see if you got it right.

after	could	kind	poor
again	door	last	pretty
any	even	many	prove
bath	every	mind	should
beautiful	everybody	money	steak
because	eye	most	sugar
behind	fast	move	sure
both	father	Mr	told
break	find	Mrs	water
busy	floor	old	who
child	gold	only	whole
children*	grass	parents	wild
Christmas	great	pass	would
class	half	past	
climb	hold	path	
clothes	hour	people	
cold	improve	plant	

*children isn't really an exception, but is included because it is a good idea to learn it at the same time as child.

Reward sticker!

Answers

Days of the week

Sunday, Monday, Tuesday, Wednesday, Thursday, Friday, Saturday

Months of the year

Spring: March, April, May
Summer: June, July, August
Autumn: September, October, November
Winter: December, January, February

The village bridge

bridge	page
hedge	village
fudge	huge
sledge	age

Sounds like s

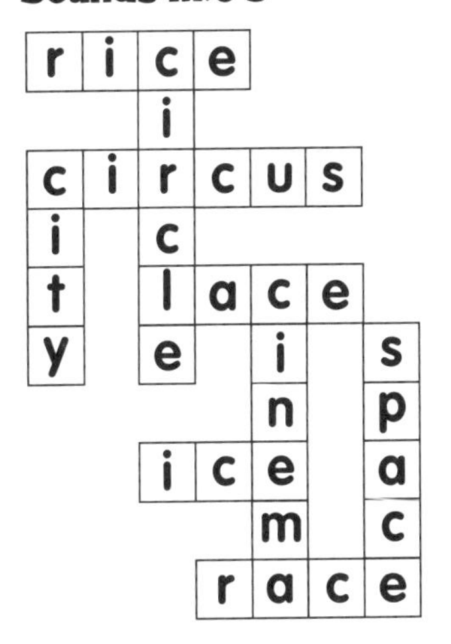

Words with kn and gn

knapsack, sign, knocked, knee, knelt, gnat, knapsack, knitting, gnome, knowledge, gnomes, gnawing, gnashing

Words with w

write	answer
wrestle	wreck
wrong	written
wrapped	wren
wrote	sword
wrist	wriggle

Word search fun

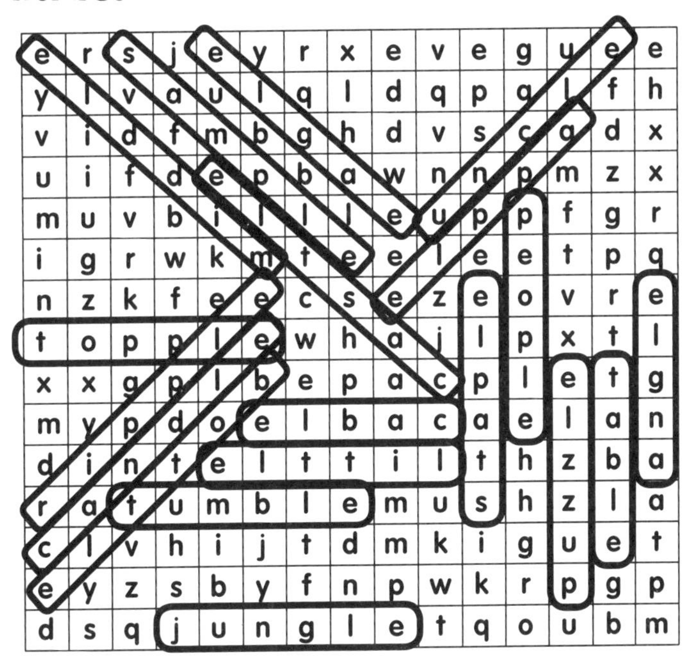

Words with el

towel, jewel, tunnel, squirrel, camel

Animal or animil?

metal, petal, pencil, animal, pupil, hospital

Testing endings

hotel	capital
apple	camel
people	tunnel
petal	pencil
jewel	middle
gerbil	fossil
tinsel	hospital
metal	towel

Y like an eye!

cry, fly, dry, sky, sly, why, defy, reply, try, fry

Plurals

diaries, cities, parties, armies, jellies, fairies

Tense times

present	past
icing	iced
jumping	jumped
walking	walked
dropping	dropped

Comparing

faster	fastest
taller	tallest
wider	widest
kinder	kindest
hungrier	hungriest
funnier	funniest
tastier	tastiest

Seeing double

wall	call
fall	hall
will	tall
dropping	dropped
stopping	stopped
travelling	travelled

One l or two?

l	ll
always	ball
almighty	tall
walk	all
adult	call
talk	wall
almost	hall

Answers

Missing vowels

mother	come or came
other	honey
brother	money
nothing	dozen
Monday	above
donut	done
glove	some or same

Quick question

a. question, **b.** quiet,
c. queen, **d.** quack,
e. quarrel

Wor words

word	worm
worthy	work
worth	world

Suffixes

thankful	darkness/ly
movement	quietness/ly
payment	loudness/ly

Tion and sion word search

d	e	s	t	i	n	a	t	i	o	n	z	n	q	d
n	h	x	s	t	n	o	r	l	f	z	o	q	j	e
s	o	c	p	o	a	e	i	o	j	i	m	c	r	c
q	t	i	i	e	v	z	u	s	s	q	o	o	m	i
z	u	t	t	i	c	n	l	n	n	n	d	m	b	s
p	o	e	s	n	d	t	e	a	o	e	o	p	n	i
l	c	i	s	a	e	h	a	i	z	n	p	l	o	o
d	o	r	t	t	e	v	t	t	l	o	y	e	i	n
h	q	i	m	r	i	o	n	x	i	u	s	t	t	o
q	o	m	p	g	m	o	f	i	v	o	c	i	u	i
n	c	m	v	m	v	z	n	z	q	b	n	o	l	t
l	o	n	o	i	t	c	e	r	i	d	i	n	l	o
c	p	c	e	x	p	l	o	s	i	o	n	o	o	m
n	o	i	s	a	v	n	i	w	i	z	j	v	p	e
o	g	x	p	m	c	t	w	i	x	u	s	g	d	i

Homophones

there, blew, hear, blue
a. flower, **b.** flour
c. knight, **d.** night, **e.** bare,
f. bear, **g.** mail, **h.** male,
i. leak, **j.**leek

Antonyms

e.g. small, loud, low, wet, strong, dark, short, hard

small	tall
hard	soft
hot	cold
sour	sweet

Cunning contractions

should not
was not
you have
you are
I would
shall not
couldn't
I'm

Weeks and months

Sunday, Monday, Tuesday, Wednesday, Thursday, Friday, Saturday

January, February, March, April, May, June, July, August, September, October, November, December

spring, summer, autumn, winter

Year 3 Textb

Series Editor: Tony Staneff

Astrid
Astrid is brave.
She likes to
have a go
at solving
new types of
problems.

Contents

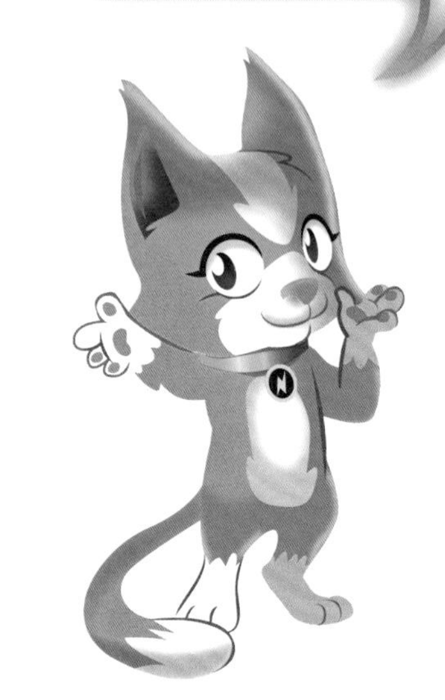

Your teacher will tell you which page you need.

Let's go and find some new maths adventures!

How to use this book

These pages make sure we are ready for the unit ahead. Find out what we will be learning and brush up on your skills!

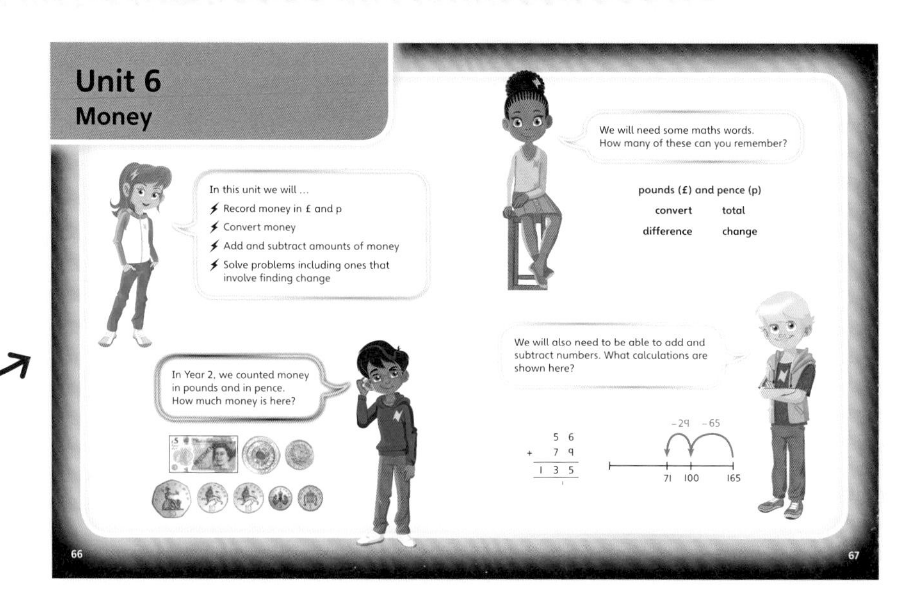

Unit 6
Money
In this unit we will ...
Record money in £ and p
Convert money
Add and subtract amounts of money
Solve problems including ones that involve finding change
We will need some maths words. How many of these can you remember?
pounds (£) and pence (p)
convert
total
difference
change
In Year 2, we counted money in pounds and in pence. How much money is here?
We will also need to be able to add and subtract numbers. What calculations are shown here?
−29
−65
71
100
165
66
67

Discover

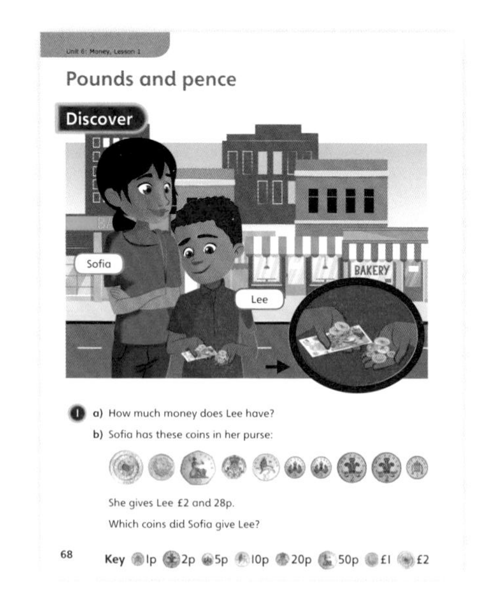

Unit 6: Money, Lesson 1
Pounds and pence
Discover
Sofia
Lee
BAKERY
a) How much money does Lee have?
b) Sofia has these coins in her purse:
She gives Lee £2 and 28p.
Which coins did Sofia give Lee?
68
Key 1p 2p 5p 10p 20p 50p £1 £2

Lessons start with **Discover**.

Here, we explore new maths problems.

Can you work out how to find the answer?

Do not be afraid to make mistakes. Learn from them and try again!

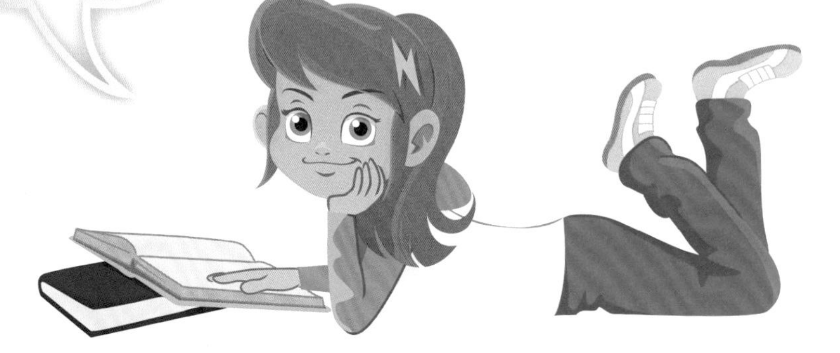

Share

Next, we share our ideas with the class.

Did we all solve the problems the same way? What ideas can you try?

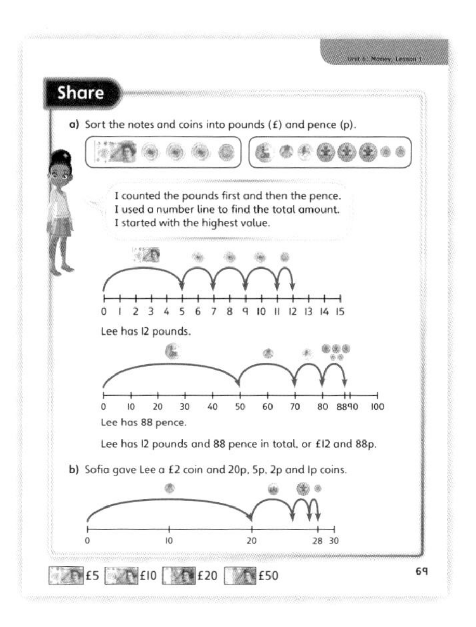
Unit 6: Money, Lesson 1

Share

a) Sort the notes and coins into pounds (£) and pence (p).

I counted the pounds first and then the pence. I used a number line to find the total amount. I started with the highest value.

0 1 2 3 4 5 6 7 8 9 10 11 12 13 14 15

Lee has 12 pounds.

0 10 20 30 40 50 60 70 80 88 90 100

Lee has 88 pence.

Lee has 12 pounds and 88 pence in total, or £12 and 88p.

b) Sofia gave Lee a £2 coin and 20p, 5p, 2p and 1p coins.

0 10 20 28 30

£5 £10 £20 £50 69

Think together

Then we have a go at some more problems together. Use what you have just learnt to help you.

We will try a challenge too!

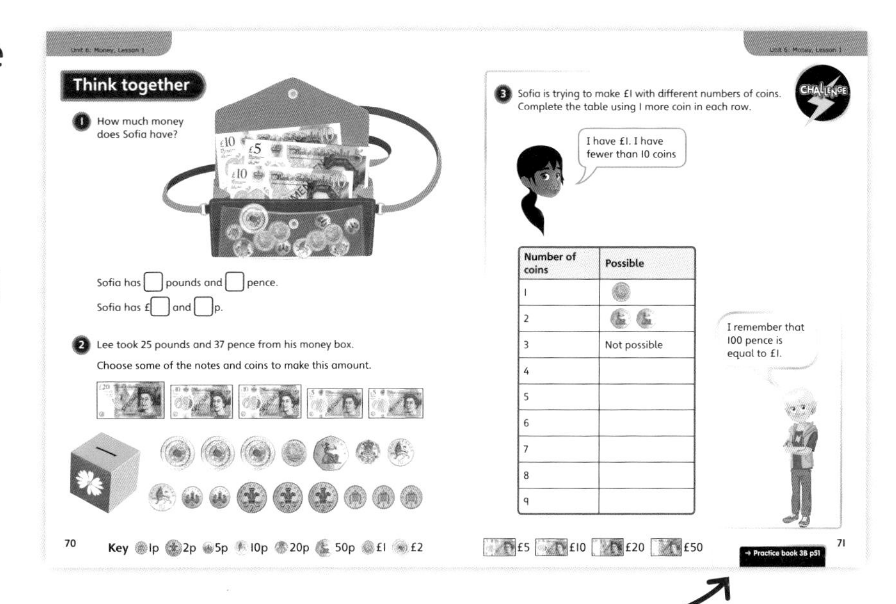
Unit 6: Money, Lesson 1

Think together

1 How much money does Sofia have?

Sofia has ☐ pounds and ☐ pence.

Sofia has £☐ and ☐p.

2 Lee took 25 pounds and 37 pence from his money box.

Choose some of the notes and coins to make this amount.

70 Key 1p 2p 5p 10p 20p 50p £1 £2

3 Sofia is trying to make £1 with different numbers of coins. Complete the table using 1 more coin in each row.

CHALLENGE

I have £1. I have fewer than 10 coins

Number of coins	Possible
1	
2	
3	Not possible
4	
5	
6	
7	
8	
9	

I remember that 100 pence is equal to £1.

£5 £10 £20 £50 → Practice book 3B p51 71

This tells you which page to go to in your **Practice Book**.

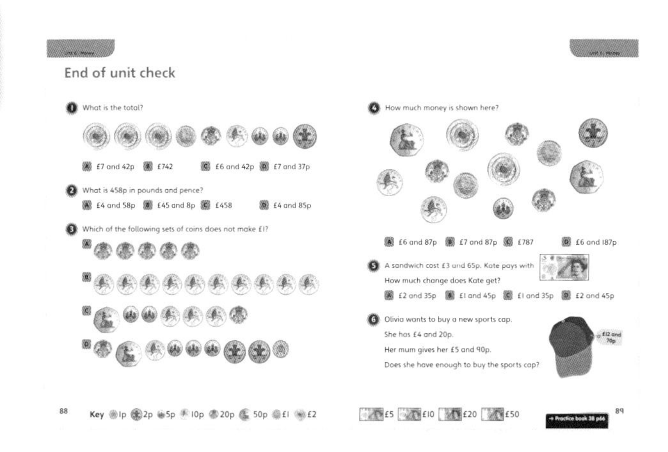
End of unit check

1 What is the total?

A £7 and 42p B £742 C £6 and 42p D £7 and 37p

2 What is 458p in pounds and pence?

A £4 and 58p B £45 and 8p C £458 D £4 and 85p

3 Which of the following sets of coins does not make £1?

4 How much money is shown here?

A £6 and 87p B £7 and 87p C £787 D £6 and 187p

5 A sandwich cost £3 and 65p. Kate pays with

How much change does Kate get?

A £2 and 35p B £1 and 45p C £1 and 35p D £2 and 45p

6 Olivia wants to buy a new sports cap.

She has £4 and 20p.

Her mum gives her £5 and 90p.

Does she have enough to buy the sports cap?

88 Key 1p 2p 5p 10p 20p 50p £1 £2

£5 £10 £20 £50 → Practice book 3B p66 89

At the end of each unit there is an **End of unit check**. This is our chance to show how much we have learnt.

Unit 5
Multiplication and division 2

In this unit we will ...

- Compare multiplication and division statements using inequality signs
- Use known multiplication facts to solve other multiplication problems
- Find multiplication and division fact families
- Learn to multiply and divide by partitioning
- Solve mixed multiplication and division problems including multi-step problems

Do you remember what this is called? We will use it to help partition numbers.

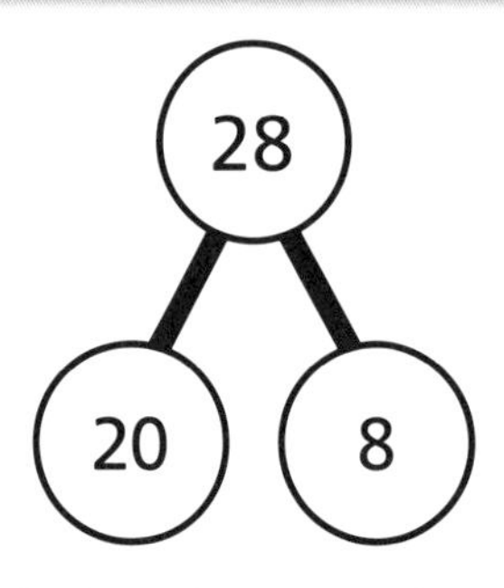

We will need some maths words.
Do you know what they all mean?

multiplication **division** **statement**

number sentence **compare** **more than**

less than (<) **greater than (>)** **equal (=)**

equally **least** **most** **remainder**

share **partition** **multi-step**

We need to use number lines too.
These will help us understand
multiplication and division.

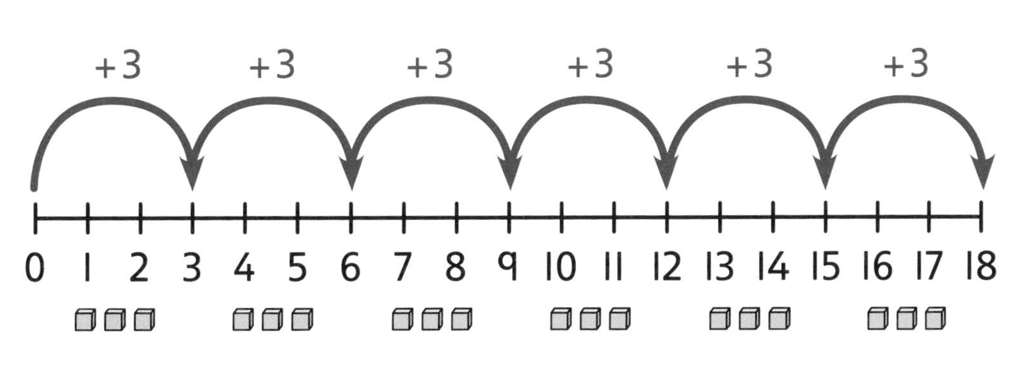

Comparing multiplication and division statements 1

Discover

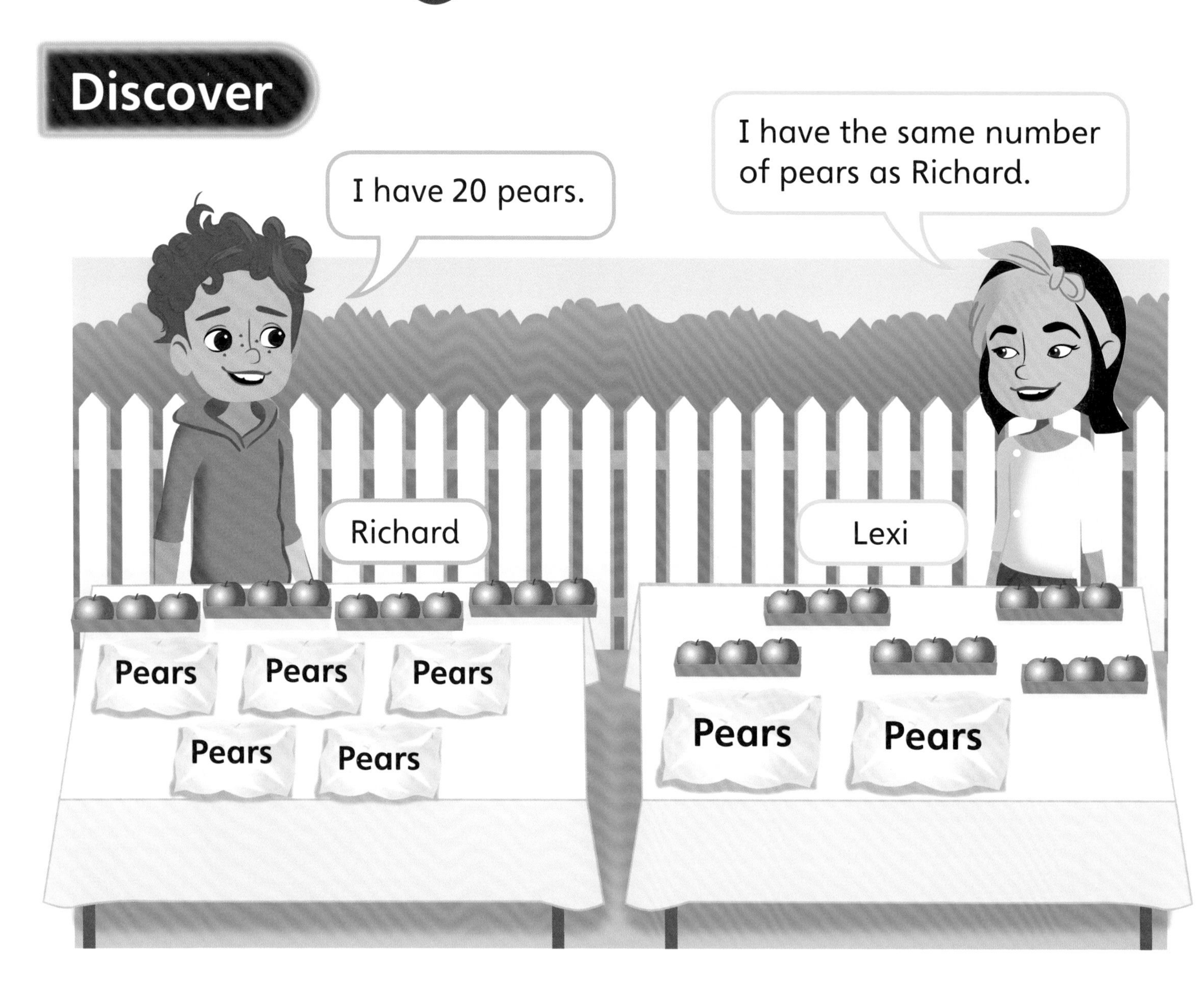

1 **a)** Who has more apples, Richard or Lexi?

b) Richard's bags each have the same number of pears in them.

Each of Lexi's bags have the same number of pears in them.

Whose bags contain the least number of pears?

Share

I worked out the number of apples each child had.

a) There are 3 apples in each pack.

Richard has 4 packs.

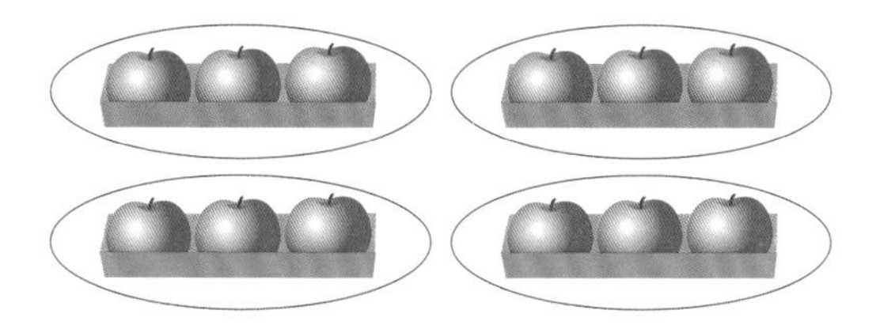

$4 \times 3 = 12$

$5 \times 3 > 4 \times 3$

$15 > 12$

So Lexi has more apples.

Lexi has 5 packs.

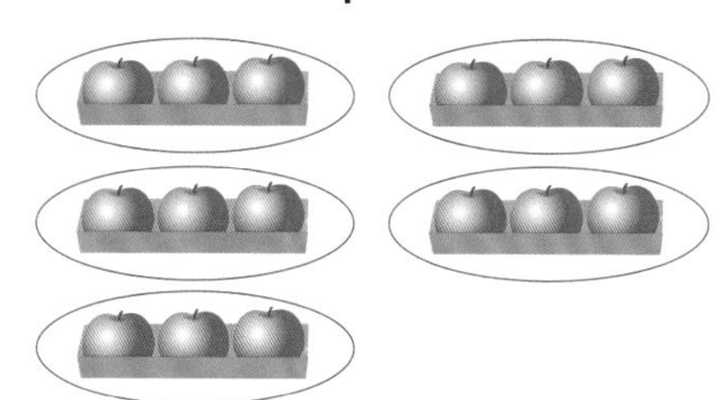

$5 \times 3 = 15$

I did not need to work out the number of apples for each person. All the packs have the same number of apples. Lexi has more packs, so she has more apples.

b) Richard has 20 pears. They are grouped equally in 5 bags.

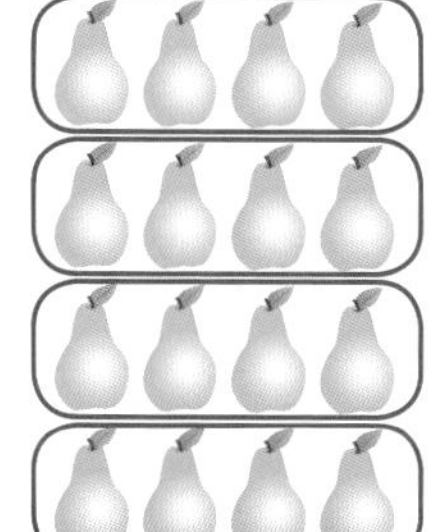

$20 \div 5 = 4$

Each bag contains 4 pears.

Lexi has 20 pears. They are grouped equally in 2 bags.

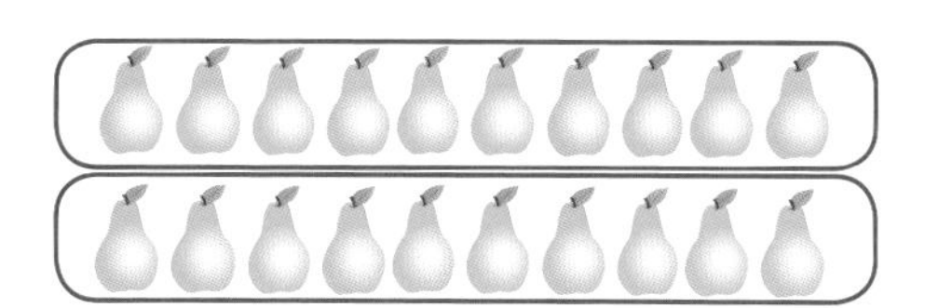

$20 \div 2 = 10$

Each bag contains 10 pears.

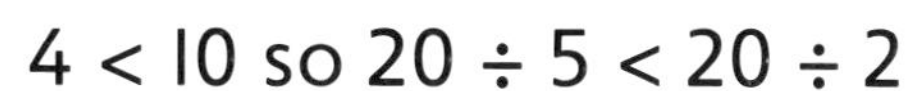

$4 < 10$ so $20 \div 5 < 20 \div 2$

Richard's bags contain the least number of pears.

I can work out the answer without doing a division. Richard and Lexi have the same number of pears. Richard has more bags so he must have fewer pears in each bag than Lexi.

Think together

1 Who has the least number of bananas?

3 × 4 ◯ 2 × 4

__________ has the least number of bananas.

2 Whose boxes of melons weigh the most in total?

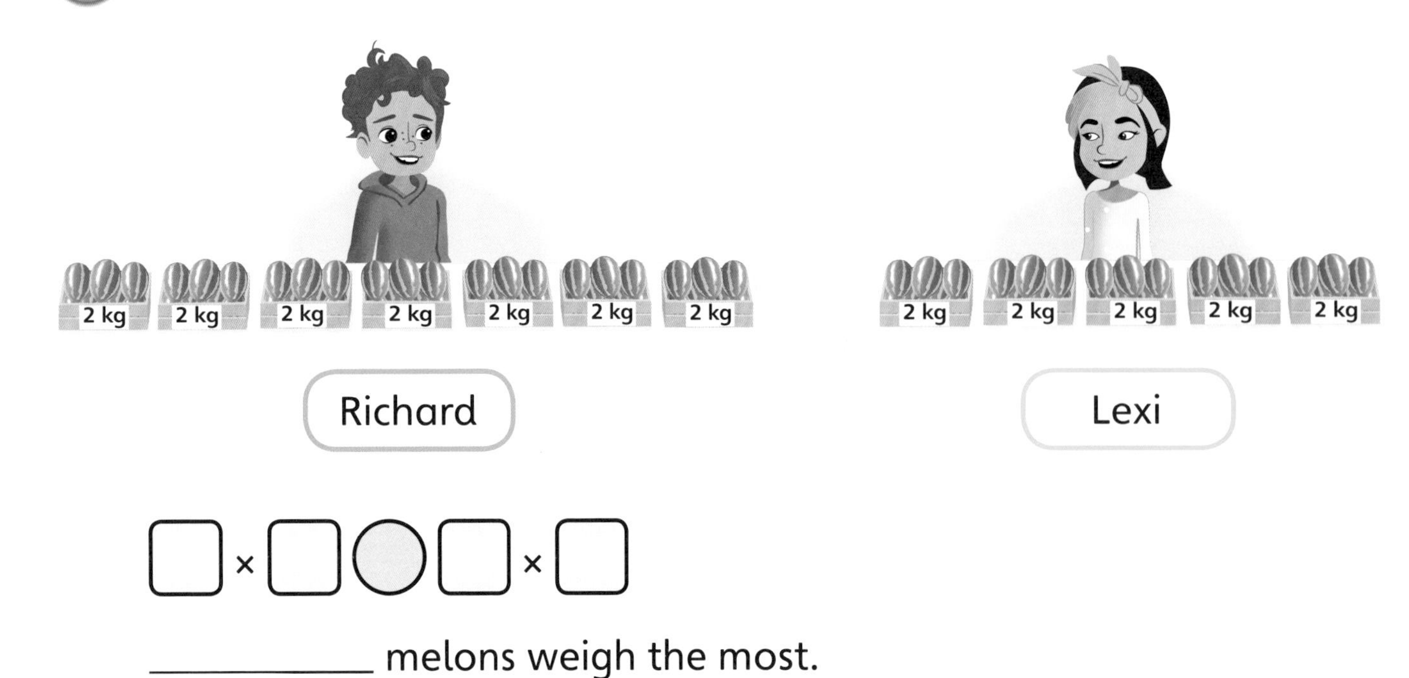

☐ × ☐ ◯ ☐ × ☐

__________ melons weigh the most.

3 Work out how to complete the sentences using <, > or =.

a) 3×5 ◯ 18

b) 5×3 ◯ 3×5

c) 4×5 ◯ 5×3

d) 8×2 ◯ 3×5

e) $24 \div 2$ ◯ 10

f) $24 \div 3$ ◯ $24 \div 4$

g) $24 \div 3$ ◯ $18 \div 3$

h) $24 \div 3$ ◯ $20 \div 5$

Explain, using equipment, how you did this.

Could you complete some of these without working out the calculations?

Some of these have similar numbers in them.

I wonder if those are ones I can compare without working out the answers.

→ Practice book 3B p6

Related multiplication calculations

Discover

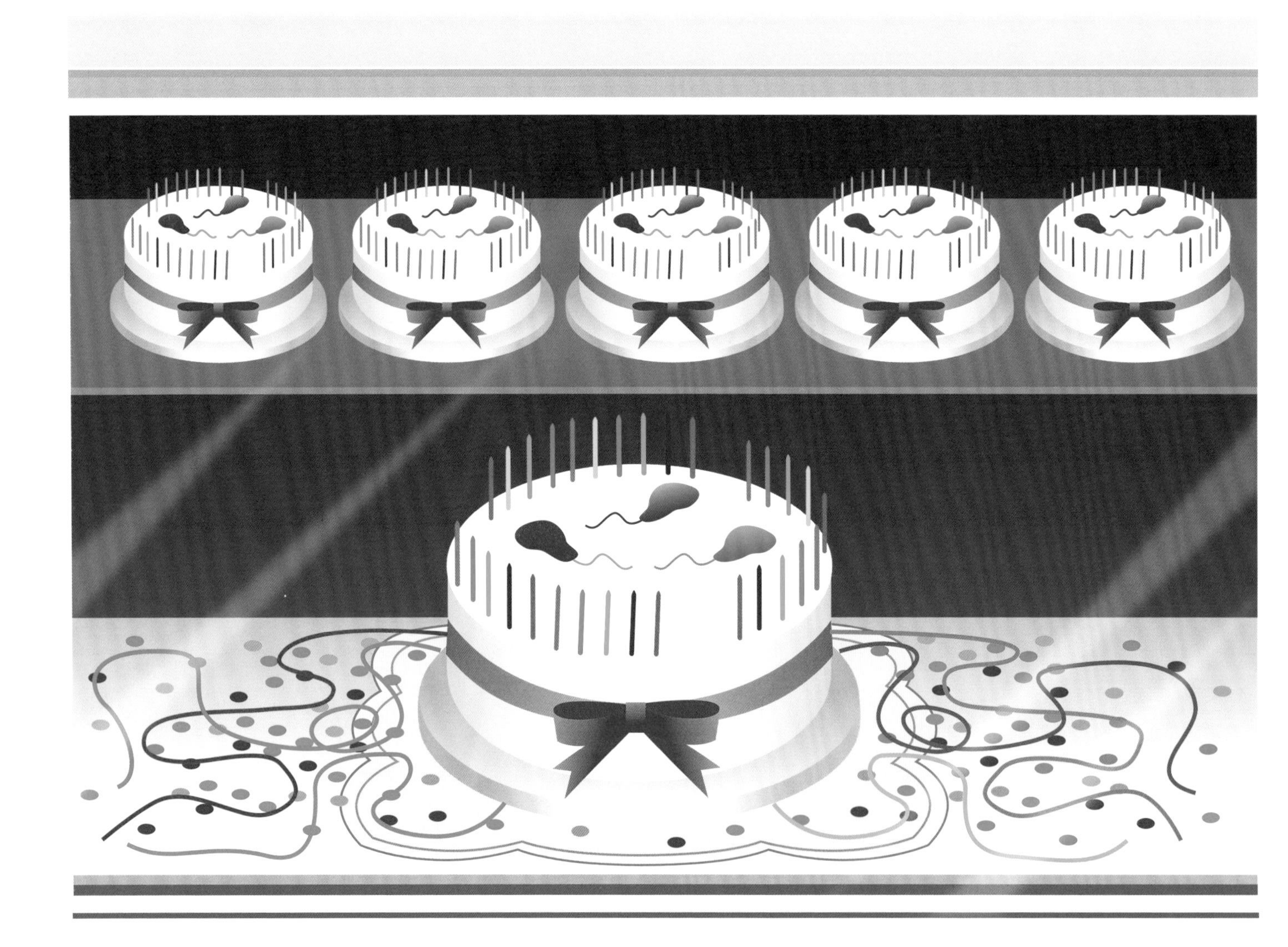

1 a) How many balloons are there on all the cakes in total?

b) How many candles are there on all the cakes in total?

What do you notice about your answers?

Share

Remember to use your times-tables facts if you know them.

a) There are 3 balloons on each cake.

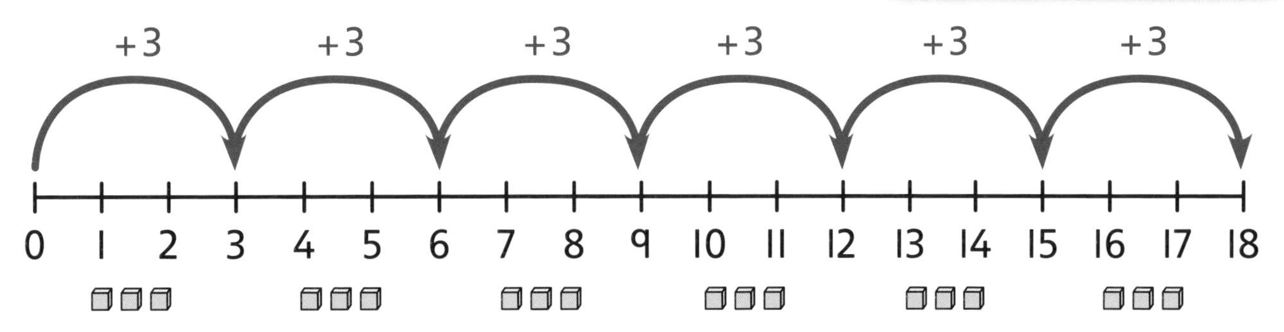

There are 6 cakes in total.

$6 \times 3 = 18$

There are 18 balloons in total.

I used a number line and counted up in 3s.

b) There are 6 cakes.

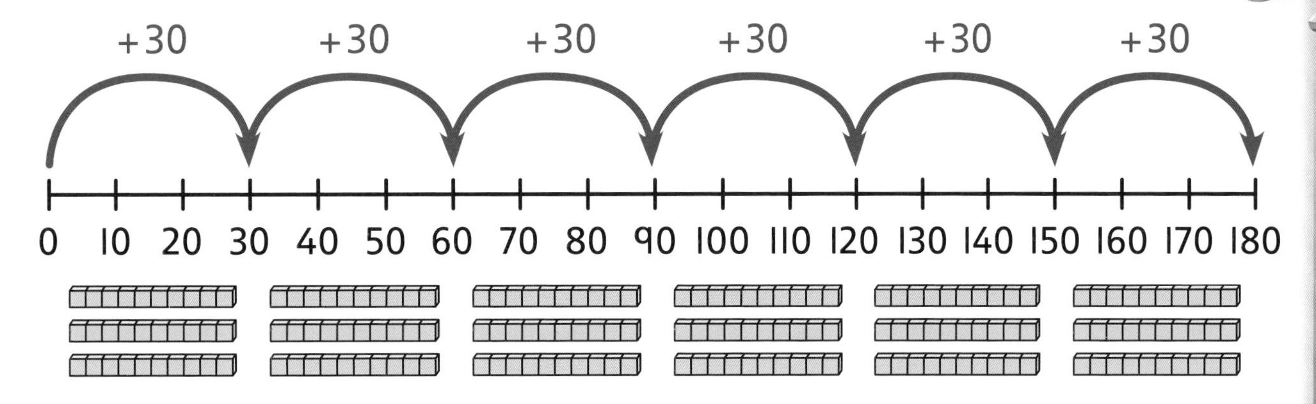

There are 30 candles on each cake.

$6 \times 30 = 180$

There are 180 candles in total.

This answer is 10 times bigger because there are 10 times more candles than balloons.

Think together

1 A baker bakes 8 cakes.

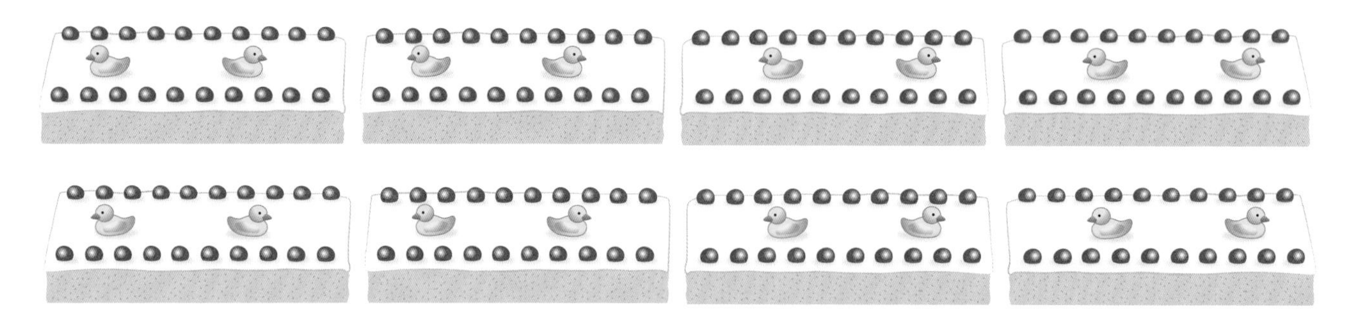

a) How many ducks are there on the cakes in total?

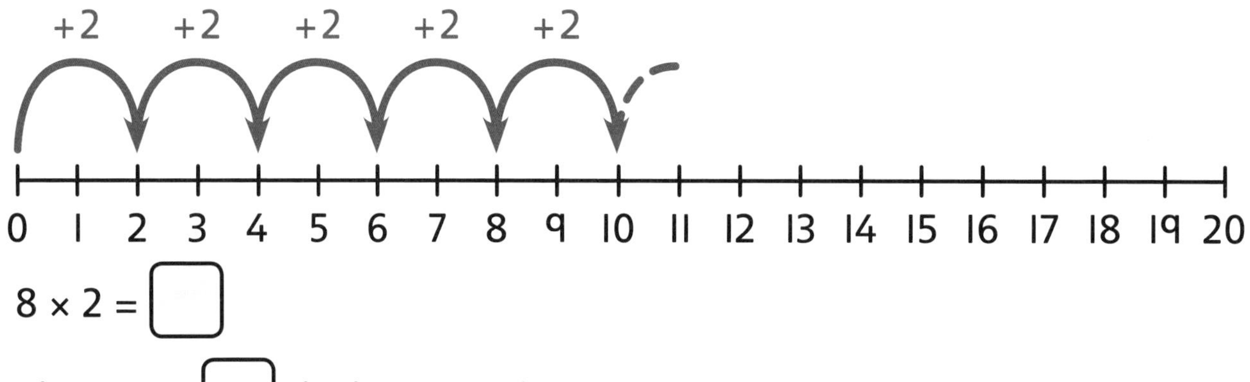

$8 \times 2 = \square$

There are $\square$ ducks in total.

b) How many cherries are there on the cakes in total?

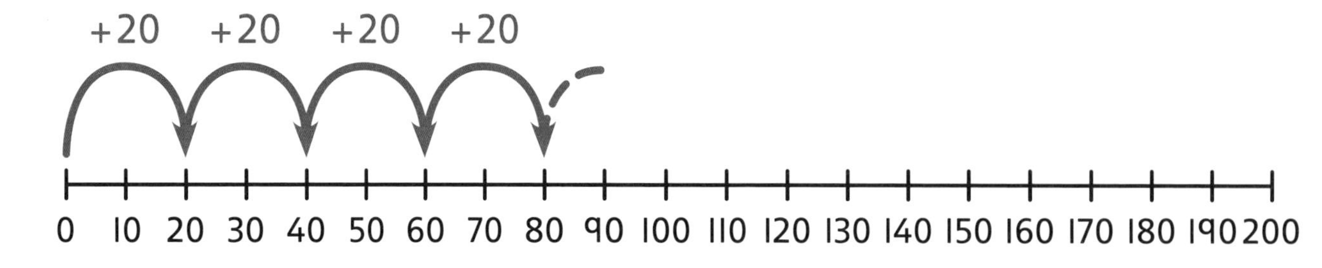

$8 \times 20 = \square$

There are $\square$ cherries in total.

2 How many chocolate circles are there in total?

☐ × ☐ = ☐

There are ☐ chocolate circles in total.

3 **a)** Use base 10 equipment to work out these calculations.

4 × 3 = ☐

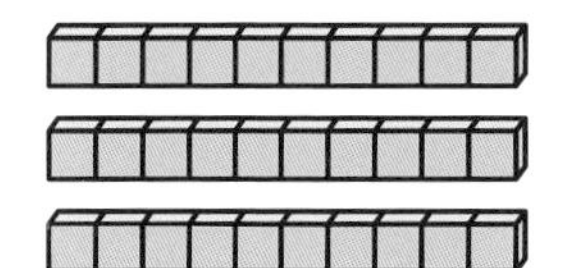
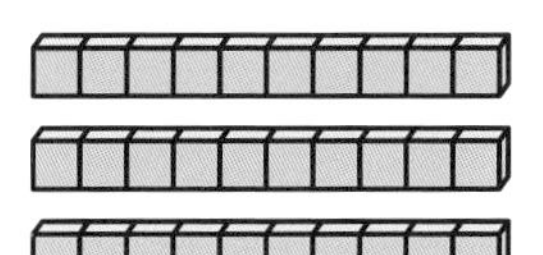
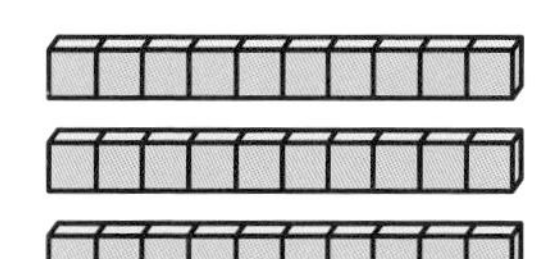
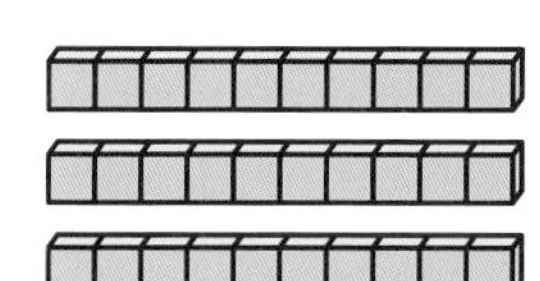

4 × 30 = ☐

b) Work out these calculations.

i) 7 × 5 = ☐

ii) 7 × 50 = ☐

iii) 70 × 5 = ☐

iv) 6 × 4 = ☐

v) 6 × 40 = ☐

vi) 60 × 4 = ☐

I can see a pattern in the answers.

→ Practice book 3B p9

Related multiplication and division calculations

Discover

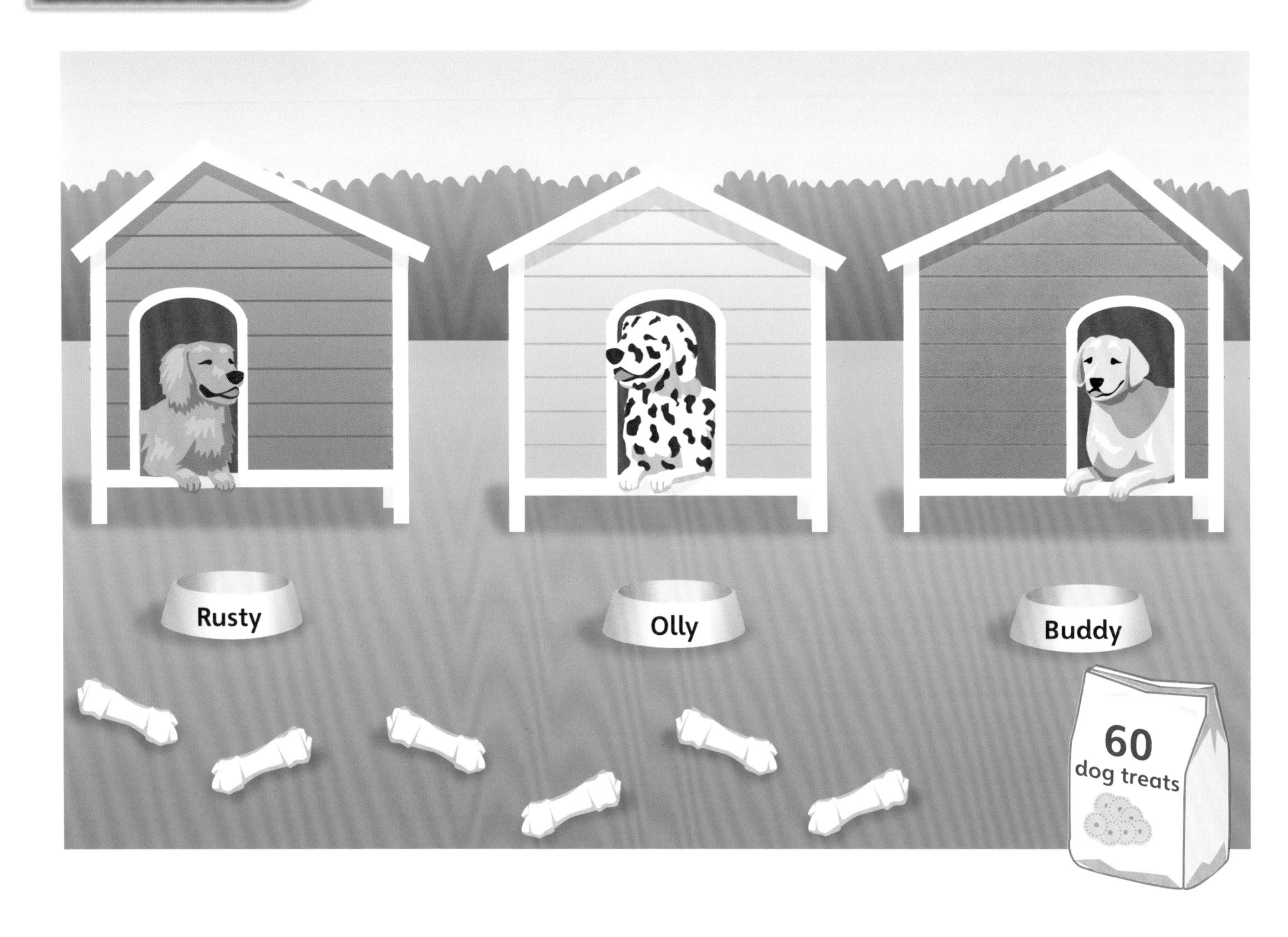

1 **a)** The bones are shared equally between the dogs.

How many bones will each dog get?

b) The dog treats are shared equally between the dogs.

How many dog treats will each dog get?

Share

a) There are 6 bones.

There are 3 dogs.

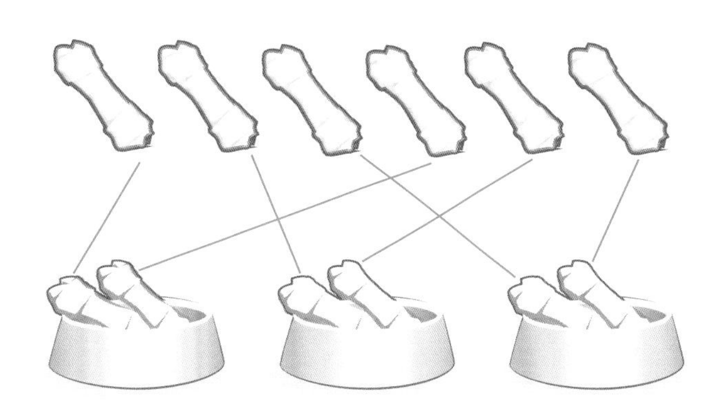

I shared the bones out one at a time.

Each dog will get 2 bones.

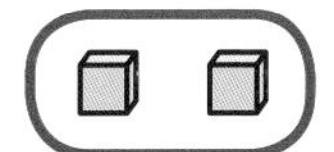 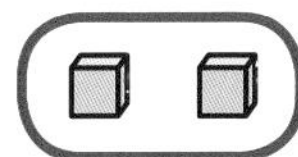 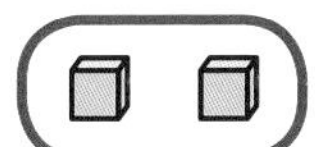

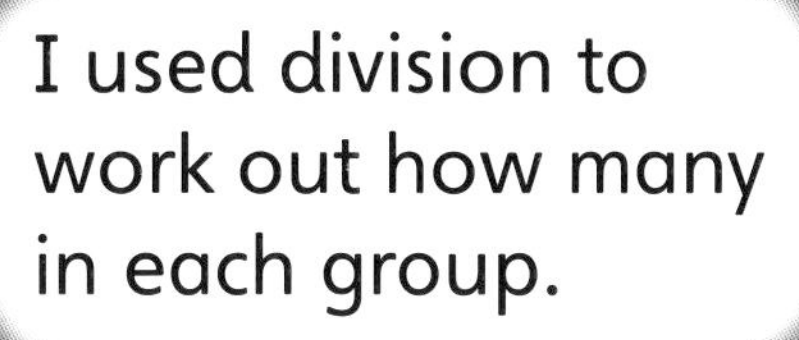

I used division to work out how many in each group.

6 ones ÷ 3 = 2 ones

6 ÷ 3 = 2

Each dog will get 2 bones.

b) There are 60 dog treats.

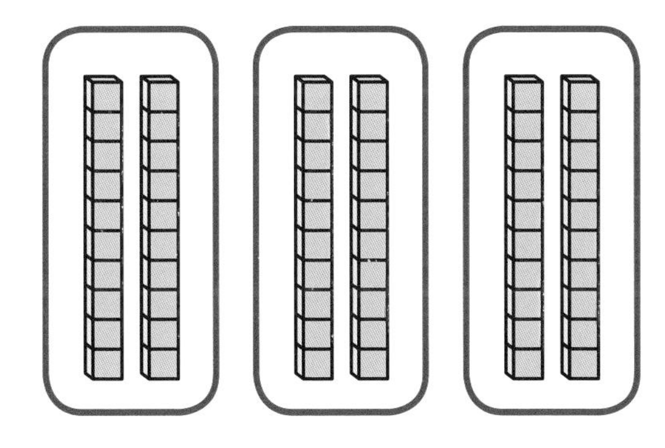

I used base 10 equipment to represent 10 treats.

I shared these between 3 groups.

6 tens ÷ 3 = 2 tens

60 ÷ 3 = 20

Each dog will get 20 treats.

I wonder if I could have used my answer from 6 ÷ 2.

Think together

1 These bones are shared between 4 dogs.

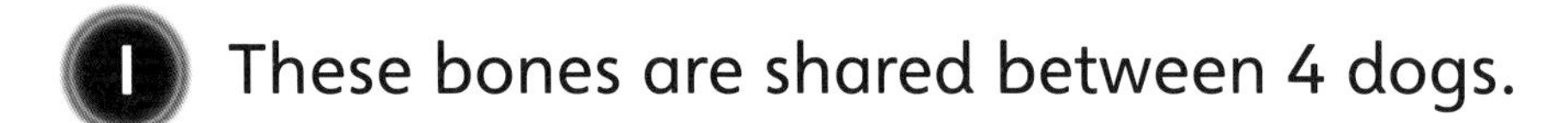

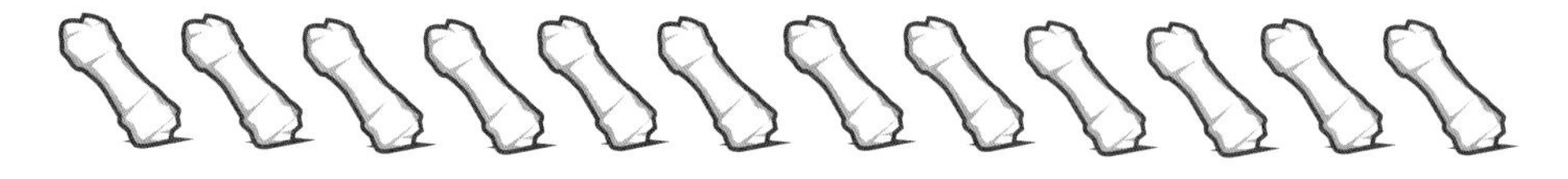

How many bones does each dog receive?

12 ones ÷ 4 = ☐ ones

12 ÷ 4 = ☐

Each dog receives ☐ bones.

2 120 dog treats are shared between 4 dogs.

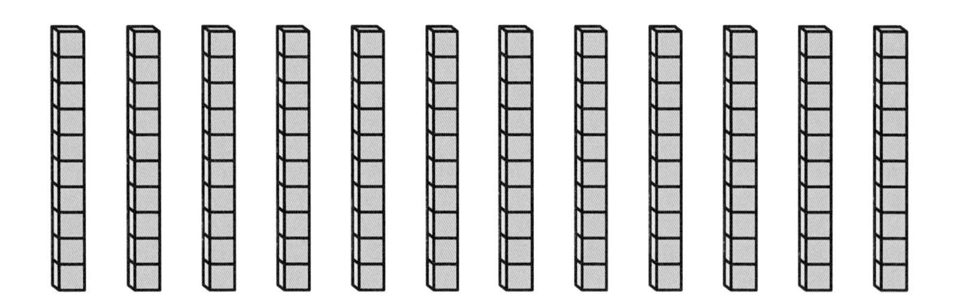

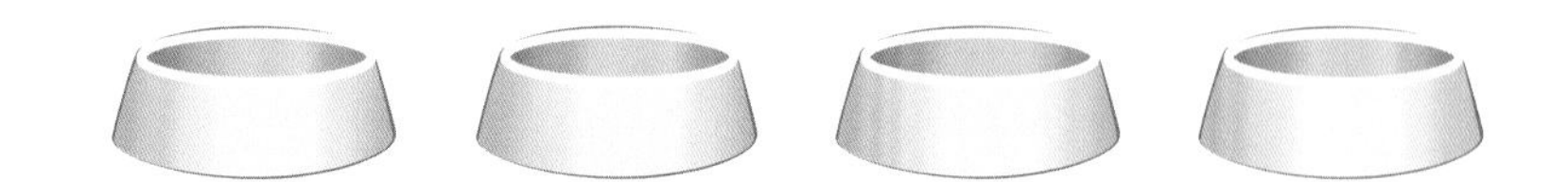

☐ tens ÷ 4 = ☐ tens

☐ ÷ 4 = ☐

Each dog gets ☐ dog treats.

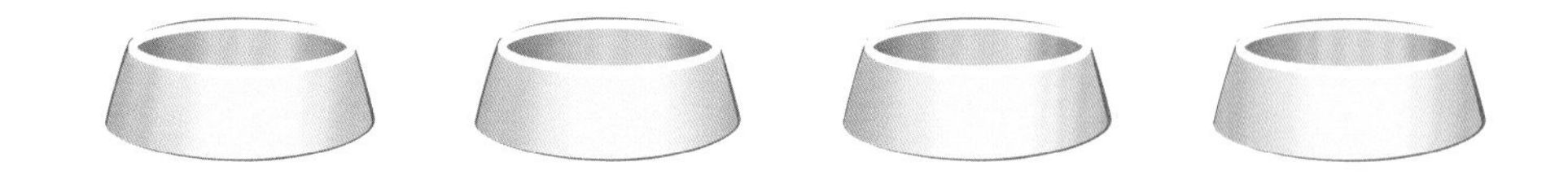

CHALLENGE

3 Aki uses multiplication facts to work out some division facts.

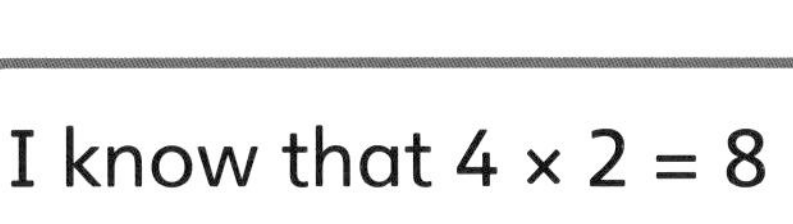
I know that 4 × 2 = 8

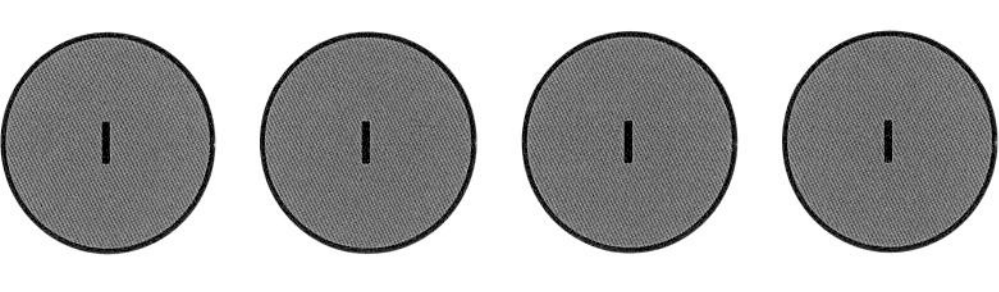

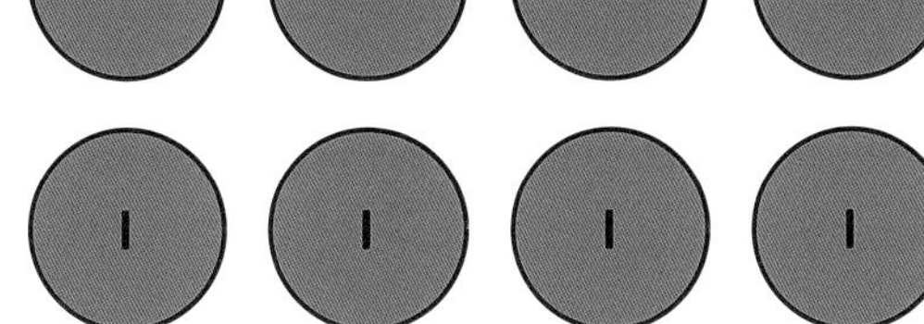

a) Help Aki work out the following facts.

$2 \times 4 = \square$ $8 \div 2 = \square$ $8 \div 4 = \square$

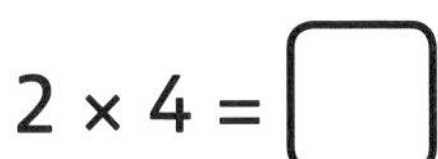

I know that 4 × 20 = 80

b) What other calculations can Aki work out using this fact?

$\square \times \square = \square$ $\square \div \square = \square$ $\square \div \square = \square$

I can use the array in the picture above to help me.

What other multiplication facts do you know? Can you make up your own related multiplication and division facts?

→ Practice book 3B p12

Comparing multiplication and division statements 2

Discover

1 a) Are there more noodles in total in the boxes or the bags?

b) Each jug holds 240 ml of juice.

The first jug of juice is shared equally between the red glasses.

The second jug of juice is shared equally between the blue glasses.

Does one red or one blue glass contain more juice?

Share

A box and a bag hold the same amount. I can see there are more noodles in total in the bags without working anything out.

a) Each bag contains 80 g of noodles.

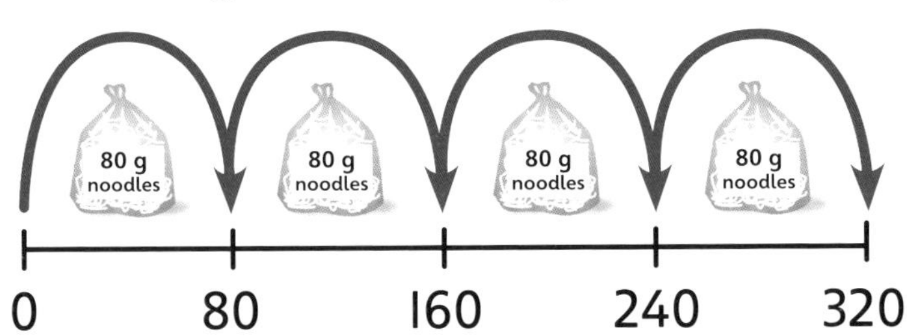

$4 \times 80 = 320$ There are 320 g of noodles in the bags in total.

Each box also contains 80 g of noodles.

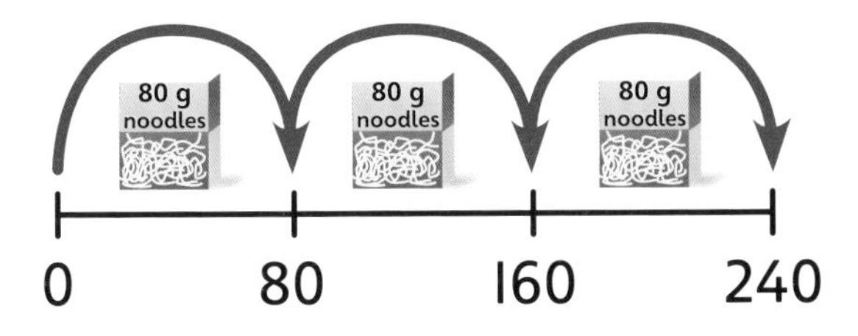

$3 \times 80 = 240$ There are 240 g of noodles in the boxes in total.

$320\text{ g} > 240\text{ g}$ There are more noodles in the bags than the boxes.

$4 \times 80 > 3 \times 80$ There are more noodles in total in the bags.

b) There are 6 red glasses.

There are 2 blue glasses.

If I share 240 ml of juice between more glasses there must be less juice in each glass.

The jugs contain the same amount of juice.

$240 \div 6 < 240 \div 2$

One blue glass contains more juice.

Think together

1 A sack of potatoes weighs 20 kg.

Whose sacks of potatoes weigh the most?

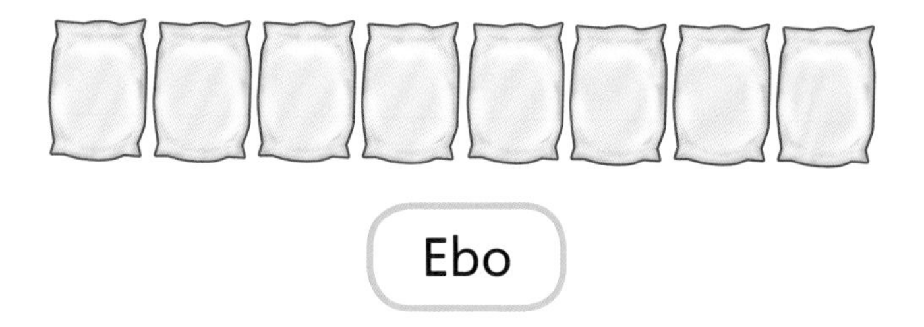

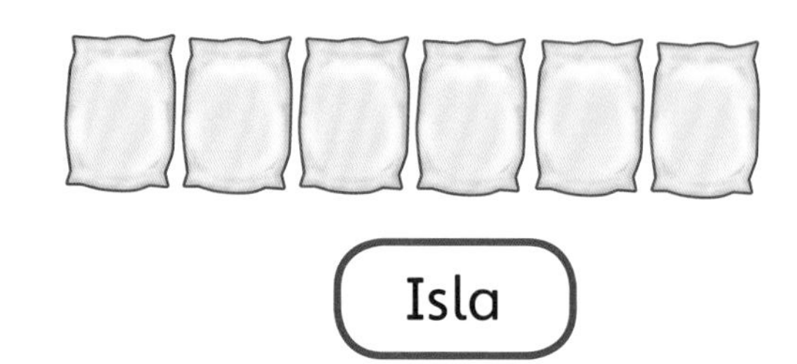

Ebo

Isla

8 × 20 ◯ 6 × 20

__________ potatoes weigh the most.

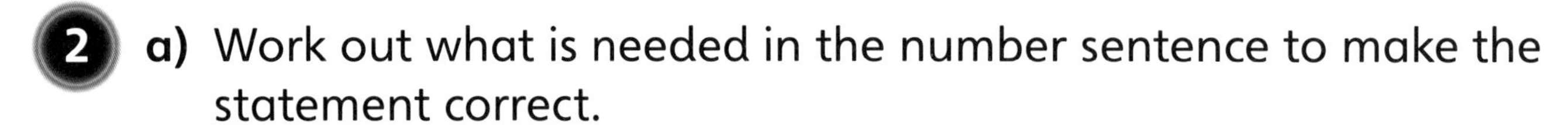

2 **a)** Work out what is needed in the number sentence to make the statement correct.

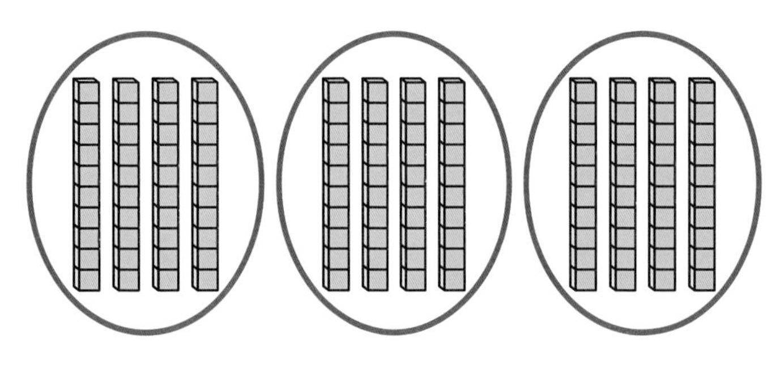

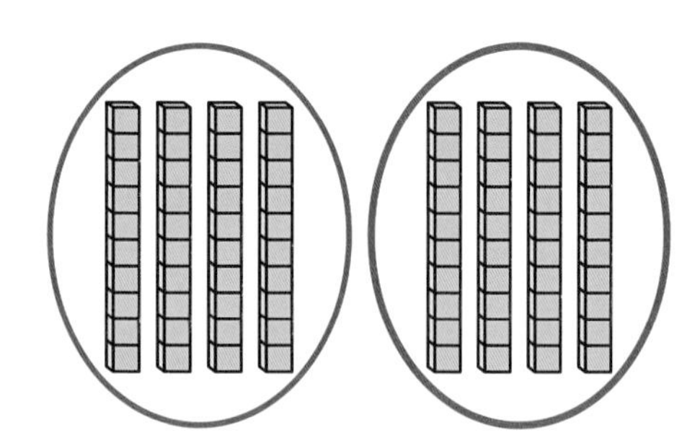

3 × 40 ◯ 2 × 40

b) Can you compare without working out any calculations?

i) 7 × 30 ◯ 30 × 7

ii) 6 × 20 ◯ 3 × 40

iii) 4 × 30 ◯ 5 × 20

3 £360 is shared between three children.

Danny

Then another £360 is shared between these four children.

Ebo

Who receives more money, Zac or Emma?

Explain how you know.

I will work out two divisions and compare the answers.

I do not think you need to do any calculations.

→ Practice book 3B p15

Multiplying a 2-digit number by a 1-digit number 1

Discover

1 a) How many flowers have the people bought in total?

Use a number line to help you work out your answer.

b) Use multiplication to work out how many flowers are bought in total.

Did you get the same answer?

Share

a) Each person bought 23 flowers.

I used a number line. I counted the 10s first and then the 1s.

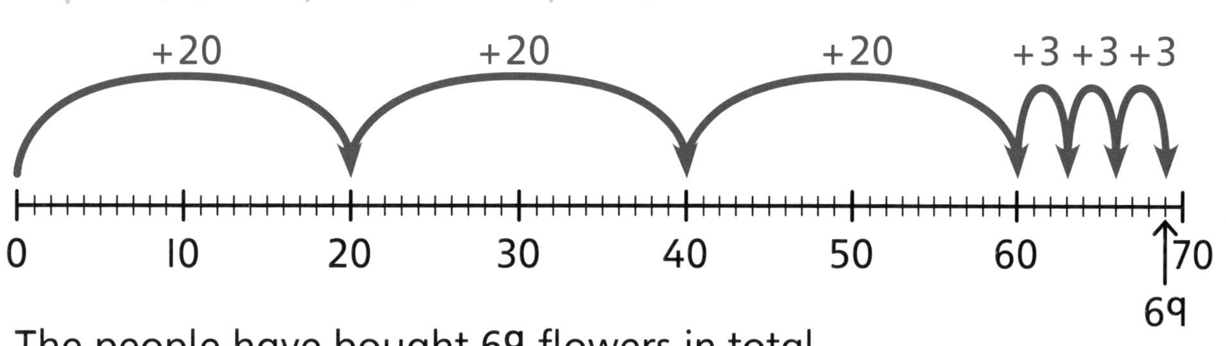

The people have bought 69 flowers in total.

b) To find the total number of flowers, work out 3 × 23.

I put the 3 rows of 23 in a place value grid.

Multiply the ones first.

3 × 3 ones = 9 ones
3 × 3 = 9

T	O

3 × 3 = 9

Now multiply the tens.

3 × 2 tens = 6 tens
3 × 20 = 60

T	O

3 × 20 = 60 3 × 3 = 9

Add the answers together.

60 + 9 = 69
So, 3 × 23 = 69

69 flowers are bought in total.

Think together

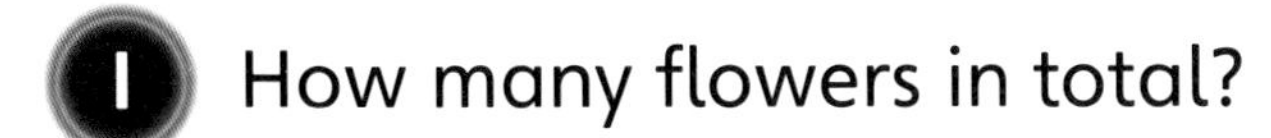

1 How many flowers in total?

4×2 ones = □ ones

$4 \times 2 =$ □

4×1 ten = □ tens

$4 \times 10 =$ □

□ + □ = □

So, $4 \times 12 =$ □

T	O

2 Find the solution to 4×21.

□ × □ one = □ ones

□ × □ = □

□ × □ tens = □ tens

□ × □ = □

□ + □ = □

So, $4 \times 21 =$ □

T	O

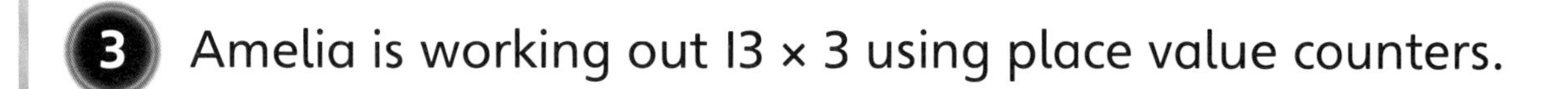

3 Amelia is working out 13 × 3 using place value counters.

☐ × ☐ = ☐
☐ × ☐ = ☐

☐ + ☐ = ☐

So,

☐ × ☐ = ☐

T	O
10	1 1 1
10	1 1 1
10	1 1 1

a) Complete Amelia's calculation.

b) Use counters to work out 34 × 2.

I think you get the same answer if you multiply the 10s first and then the 1s.

Remember, 13 × 3 is the same as 3 × 13.

→ Practice book 3B p18

Multiplying a 2-digit number by a 1-digit number 2

Discover

1 **a)** Which calculation is Max working out?

Is Max correct?

b) Which multiplication is Jamilla working out?

What is the answer to this calculation?

Share

a) Max has 3 rows of 12. He is working out the calculation 12 × 3.

3 × 2 = 6
3 × 10 = 30

30 + 6 = 36
So, 12 × 3 = 36

Max is not correct. He has 36 not 32.

T	O
10	1 1
10	1 1
10	1 1

b) Jamilla is working out 3 × 24.

T	O

=

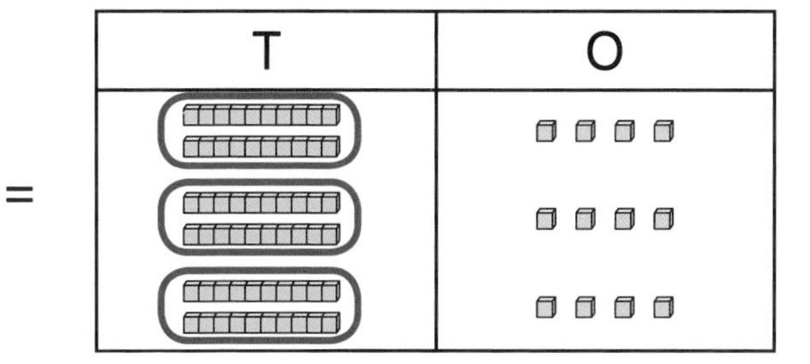

Multiply the 1s first.
3 × 4 = 12

Then multiply the 10s.
3 × 20 = 60

Now add the answers.

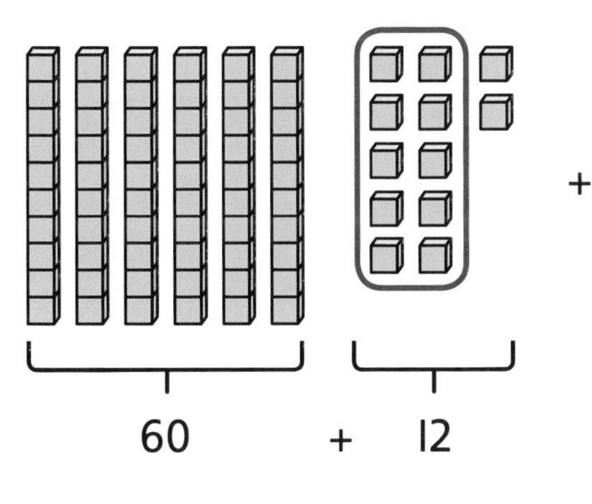

+

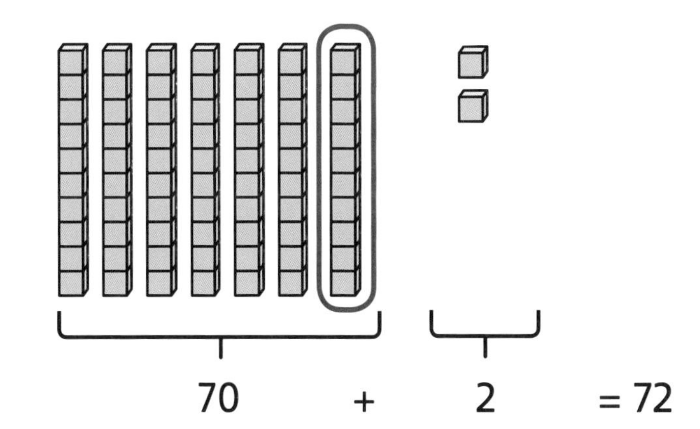

60 + 12 = 72

So, 3 × 24 = 72

Think together

Max is now working out 4×23.

Help Max work out the answer.

$4 \times 3 = \square$

$4 \times 20 = \square$

$\square + \square = \square$

So, $4 \times 23 = \square$

T	O

2 Work out 17×2.

$\square \times \square = \square$

$\square \times \square = \square$

$\square + \square = \square$

So, $17 \times 2 = \square$

T	O

3 What calculation does each place value grid show?

T	O
10 10	1 1 1
10 10	1 1 1
10 10	1 1 1
10 10	1 1 1
10 10	1 1 1

T	O
●	●●●● ●●●●
●	●●●● ●●●●
●	●●●● ●●●●

Work out the answer to each of the calculations.

I think there could be two calculations for each place value grid.

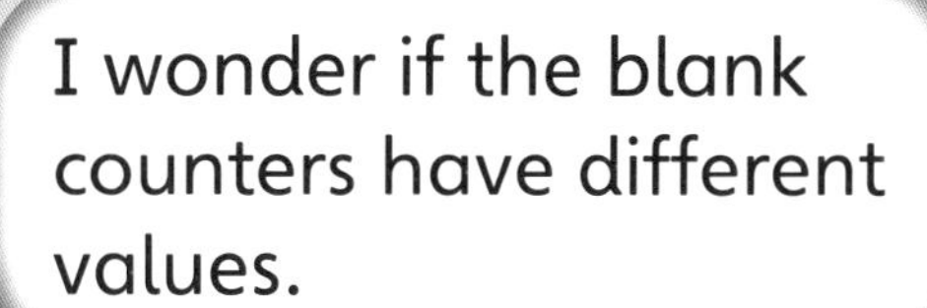

I wonder if the blank counters have different values.

→ Practice book 3B p21

Multiplying a 2-digit number by a 1-digit number 3

Discover

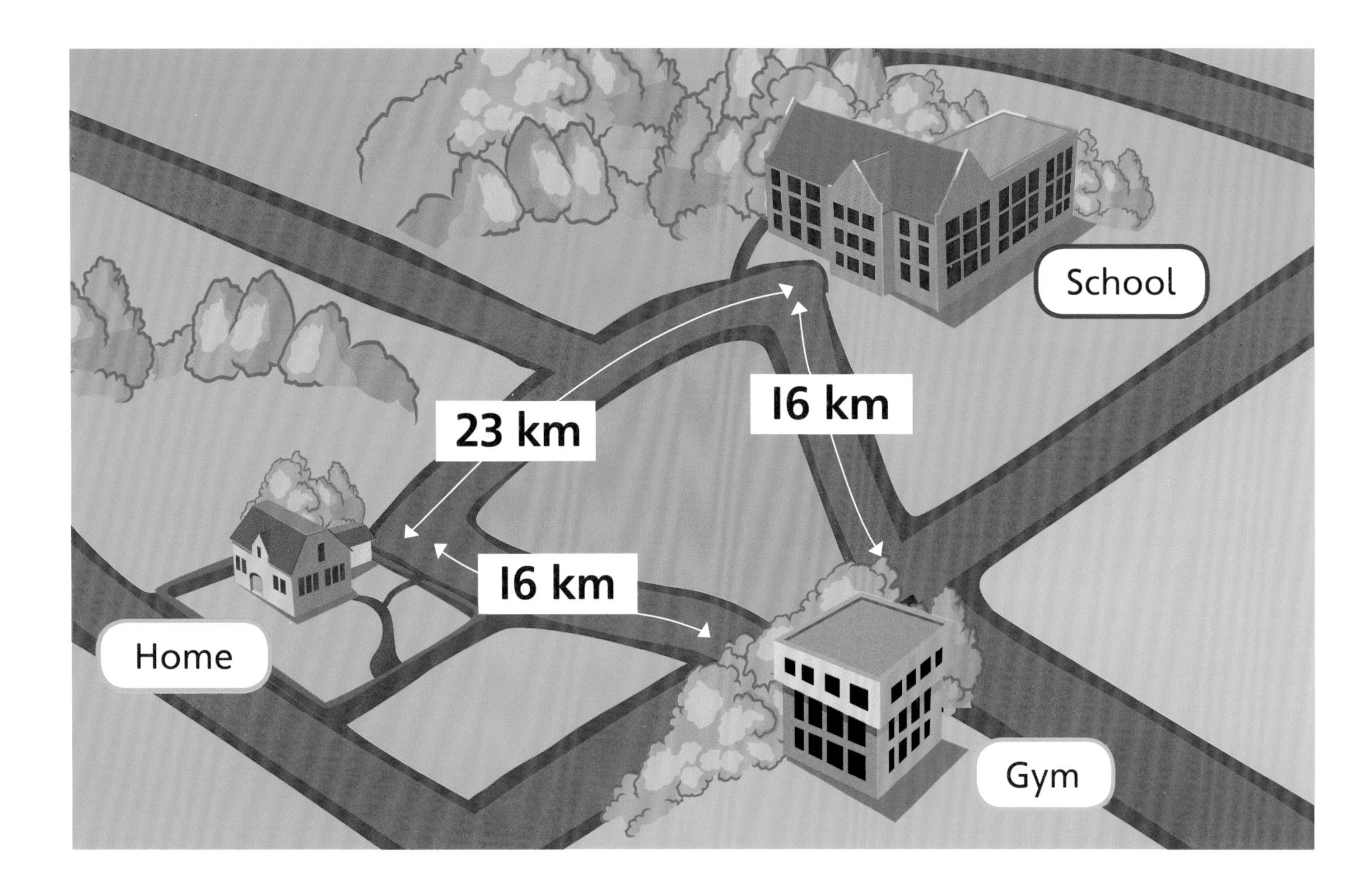

1 **a)** Mrs Dean travels from Home to School and back again on Monday and Tuesday.

How far does she travel?

b) On Wednesday, Mrs Dean goes straight to the Gym and then on to School.

What is the total distance she travels to School on Wednesday?

Share

a) Mrs Dean travels along the road between Home and School 4 times on Monday and Tuesday.

Each time she travels 23 km.

The total distance is 4 × 23.

I will use columns to help me organise my work. 4 × 23 is the same as 23 × 4.

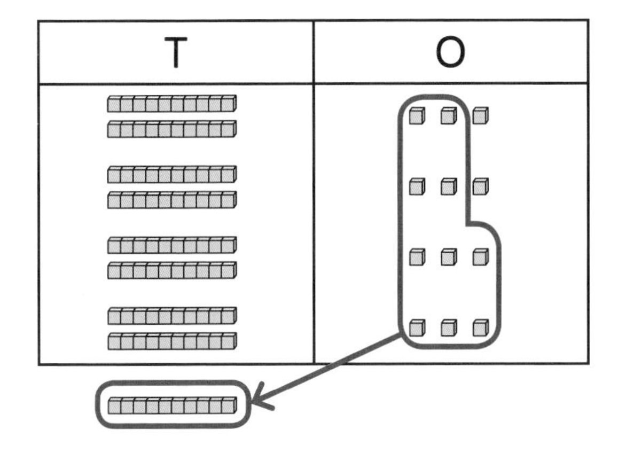

	T	O
	2	3
×		4
	1	2

First work out the total number of 1s.

4 × 3

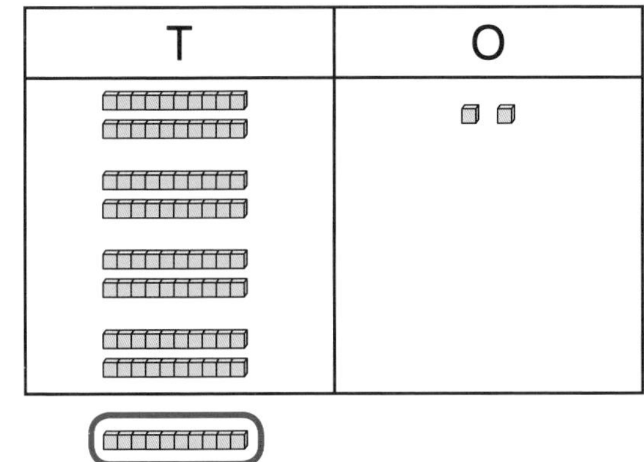

	T	O
	2	3
×		4
	1	2
+	8	0
	9	2

Now work out how many 10s.

4 × 20

Add to find the answer.

Mrs Dean travels 92 km in total.

b) The total distance is 2 × 16 km.

	T	O
	1	6
×		2
	1	2
+	2	0
	3	2

2 × 6

2 × 10

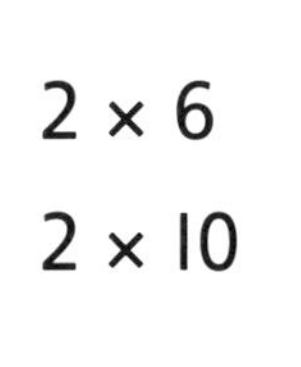

The total distance is 32 km.

I added 16 and 16 to work out the answer.

Think together

1 Mr Jones travels along this road 6 times in a week.

What is the total distance he travels?

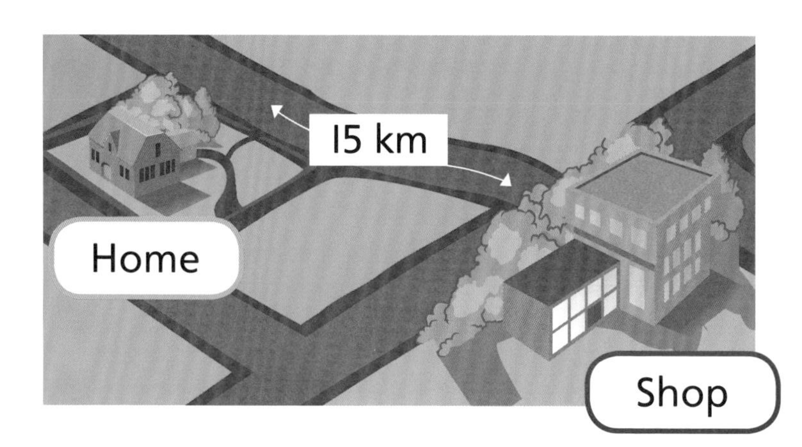

T	O

```
   T O
   1 5
×    6
-----
          6 × 5
+         6 × 10
-----

-----
```

6 × 15 = ☐

2 Work out 15 × 5.

T	O

```
   T O
   1 5
×    5
-----
          ☐ × ☐

+         ☐ × ☐
-----

-----
```

15 × 5 = ☐

3 Mrs Dean is taking boxes from home to school.

She travels along the road 5 times in total.

How far does she travel in total along this road?

Mrs Dean travels ☐ km in total.

There is something different about this question.

I think the answer is above 100.

→ Practice book 3B p24

Dividing a 2-digit number by a 1-digit number 1

Discover

1 a) The sheep are shared equally between the 2 farmers.

How many sheep does each farmer have?

b) The sheep are divided equally between the pens.

How many sheep are in each pen?

Share

a) There are 48 sheep.

There are 2 farmers.

I used a part-whole model to partition my number into 10s and 1s. I shared the 10 first and then the 1s.

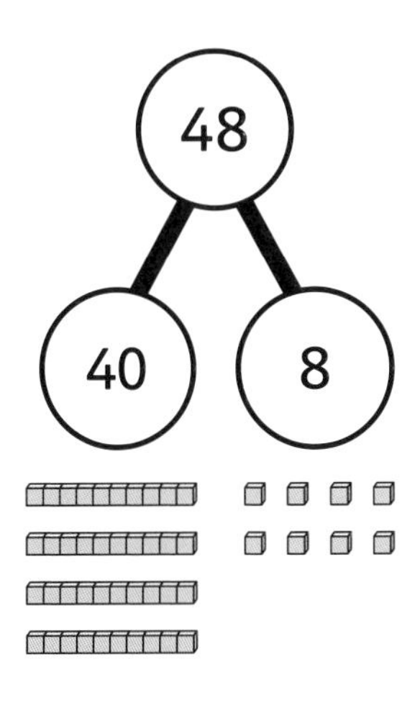

First divide the 10s.

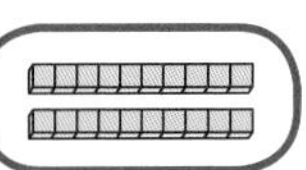

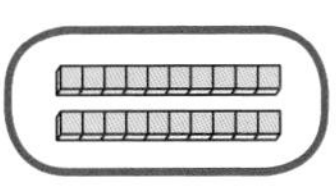

4 tens ÷ 2 = 2 tens

40 ÷ 2 = 20

Now divide the 1s.

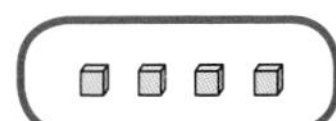

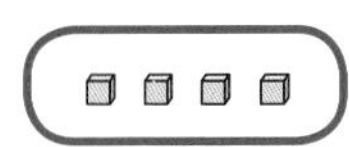

8 ones ÷ 2 = 4 ones

8 ÷ 2 = 4

Now add the answers together.

20 + 4 = 24

So, 48 ÷ 2 = 24

Each farmer has 24 sheep.

b) Each farmer has 24 sheep.

Each farmer has 2 pens.

24 ÷ 2 = 12

There are 12 sheep in each pen.

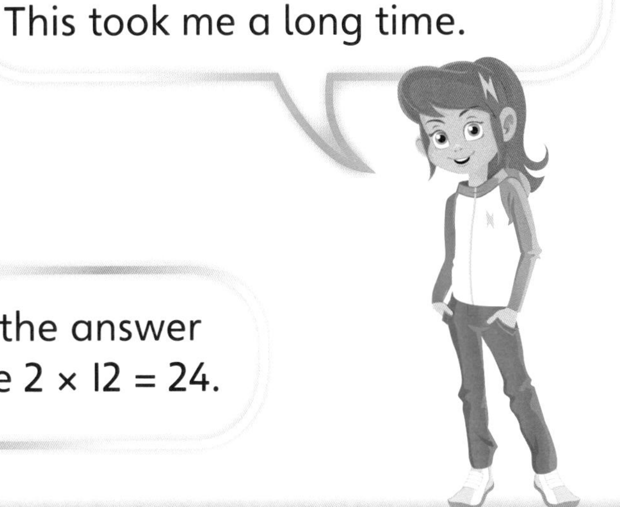

I shared the sheep one by one. This took me a long time.

I know the answer because 2 × 12 = 24.

Think together

Lexi has 39 carrots.

She shares the carrots between 3 horses.

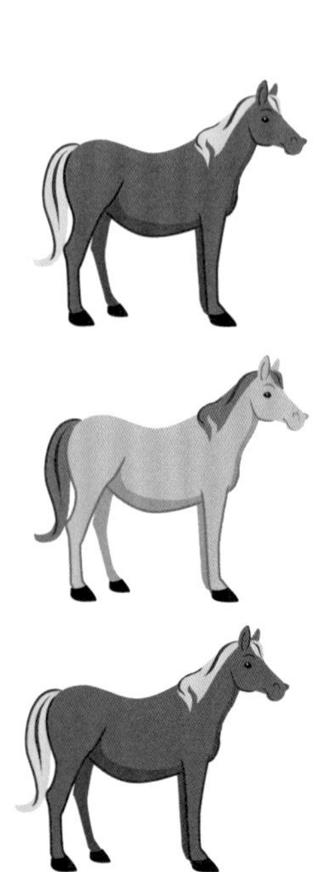

How many carrots does each horse get?

Divide the 10s first.

3 tens ÷ 3 = ☐ ten

30 ÷ 3 = ☐

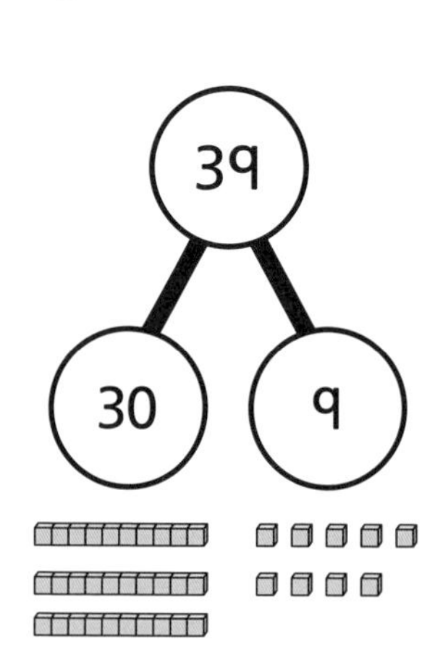

Divide the 1s.

9 ones ÷ 3 = ☐ ones

9 ÷ 3 = ☐

☐ + ☐ = ☐

39 ÷ 3 = ☐

Each horse gets ☐ carrots.

2 Work out 68 ÷ 2.

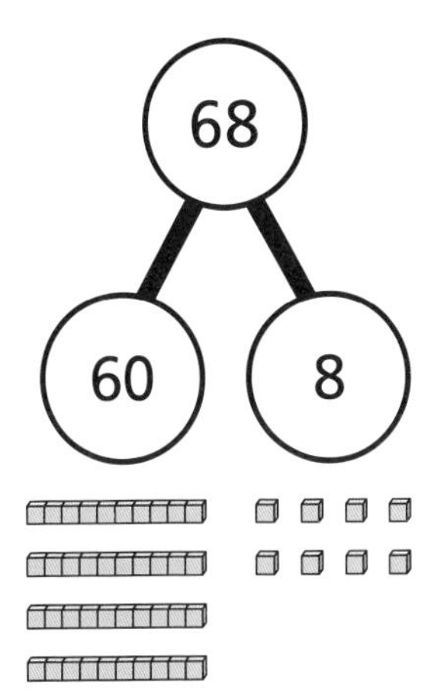

6 tens ÷ 2 = ☐ tens

60 ÷ 2 = ☐

☐ ones ÷ ☐ = ☐ ones

☐ ÷ ☐ = ☐

☐ + ☐ = ☐

So, 68 ÷ 2 = ☐

CHALLENGE

3 Mo and Alex are working out 84 ÷ 4.

I will take 84 cubes and share them into 4 equal piles, one by one.

Mo

I will divide the 10s first and then the 1s.

Whose method do you prefer?

Explain to your partner why.

I think one of these methods is quicker than the other.

I will partition my numbers into 10s and 1s first.

→ Practice book 3B p27

Dividing a 2-digit number by a 1-digit number 2

Discover

1 a) How many lanterns were released by the boats?

Represent the lanterns using base 10 equipment.

b) The same number of lanterns were released by each boat.

How many lanterns were released by each boat?

Share

a) 42 lanterns were released by the boats.

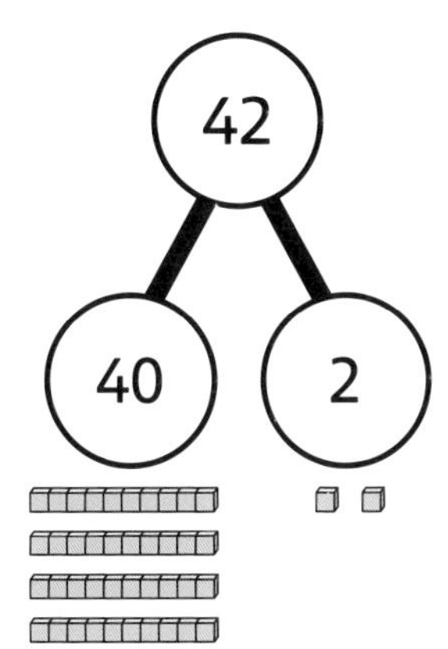

42 is made up of 4 tens and 2 ones.

b) 42 lanterns are shared equally between 3 boats.

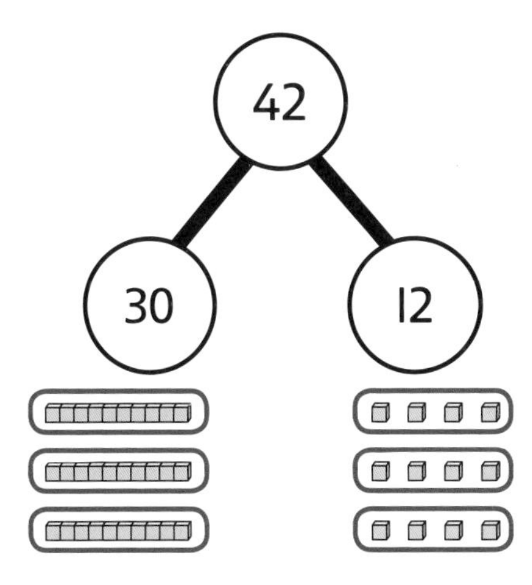

I tried to share the 10s first. They did not share equally. I had 1 ten left over.

I exchanged 1 ten for 10 ones.

Divide the 10s first.

3 tens ÷ 3 = 1 ten

$30 \div 3 = 10$

Now divide the 1s.

12 ones ÷ 3 = 4 ones

$12 \div 3 = 4$

Add up the answers.

$10 + 4 = 14$

So, $42 \div 3 = 14$

14 lanterns were released by each boat.

You can partition 42 into 30 and 12, as the parts both divide by 3.

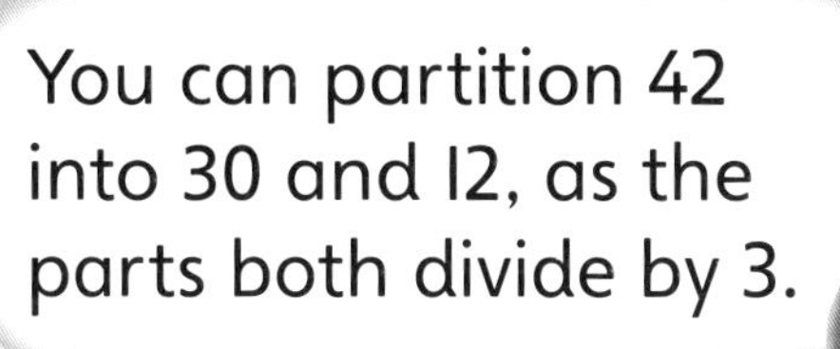

Think together

1 There are 36 people waiting to get on 2 buses.

The same number of people get on each bus.

How many people get on each bus?

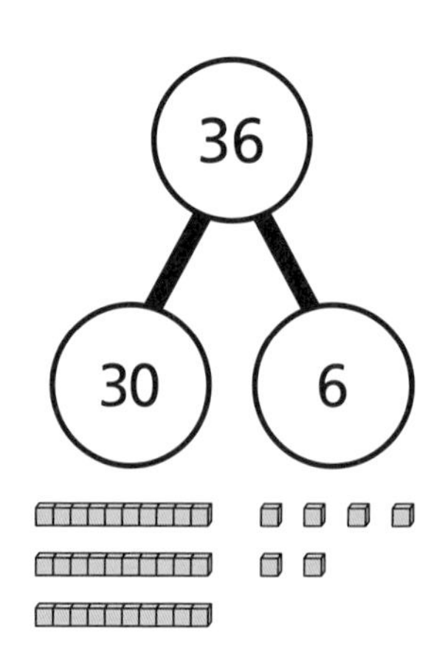

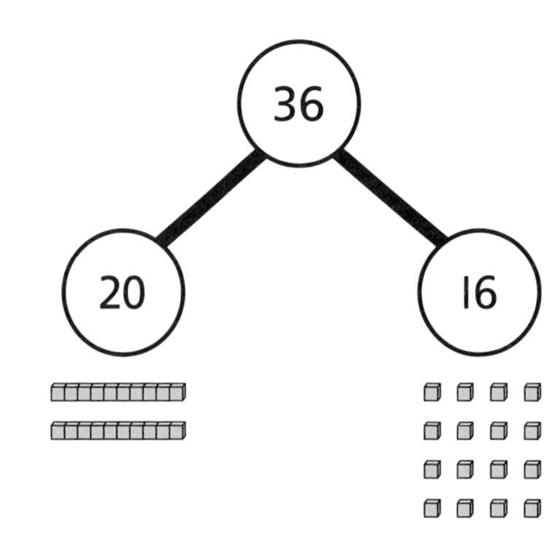

2 tens ÷ 2 = ☐ ten

20 ÷ 2 = ☐

☐ + ☐ = ☐

16 ones ÷ 2 = ☐ ones

16 ÷ 2 = ☐

So, 36 ÷ 2 = ☐

2 Use the part-whole models to help solve the divisions.

a) 65 ÷ 5

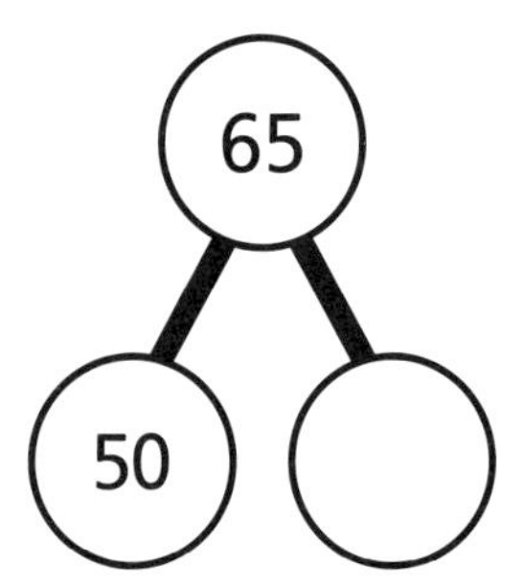

b) 75 ÷ 5

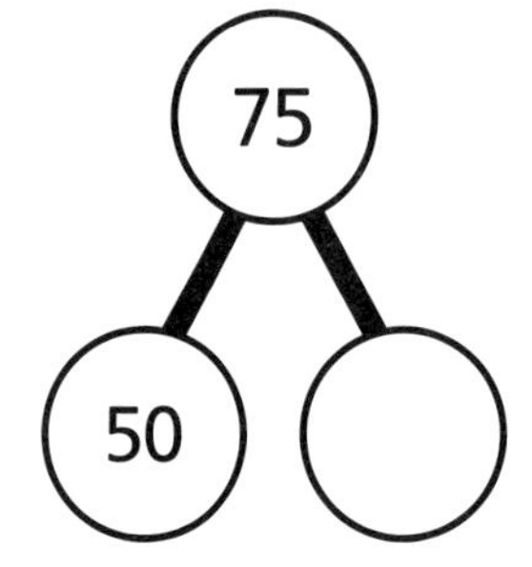

c) 85 ÷ 5

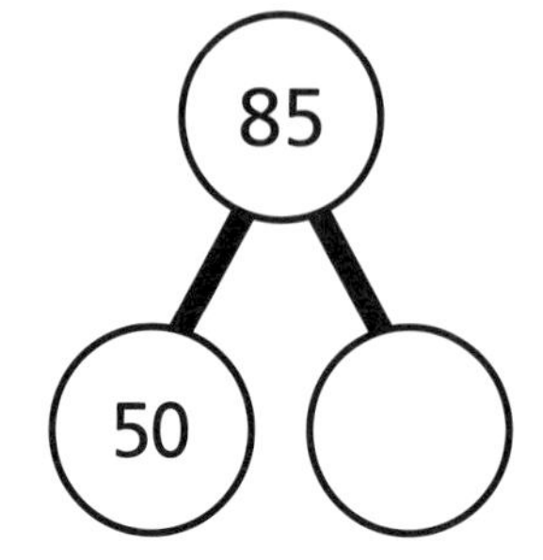

3 Reena and Andy are working out 75 ÷ 3.

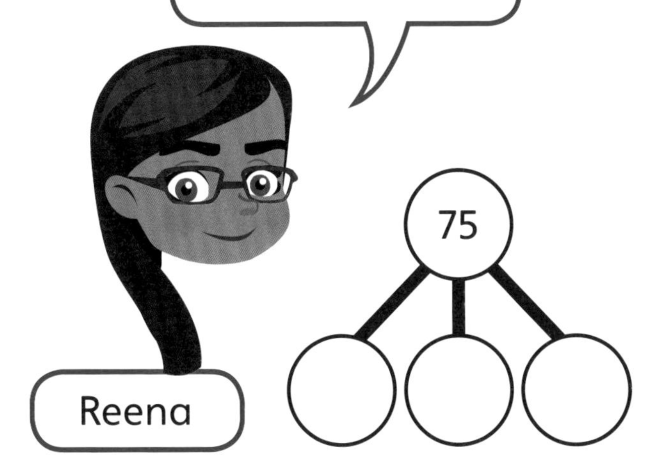

I partitioned 75 into 3 parts.
75
Reena

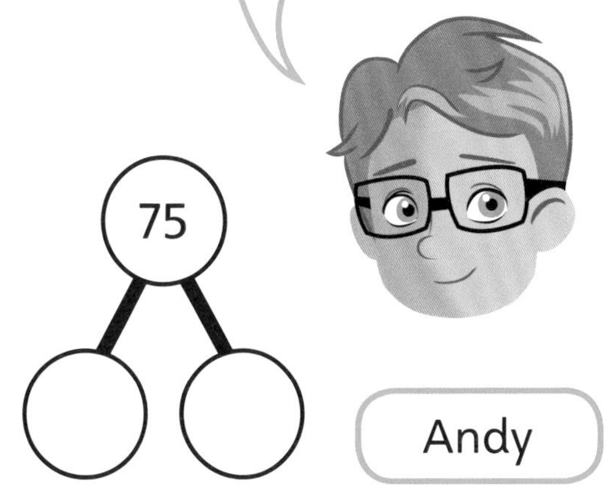

I partitioned 75 into 2 parts.
75
Andy

a) What could the parts have been to help work out 75 ÷ 3?

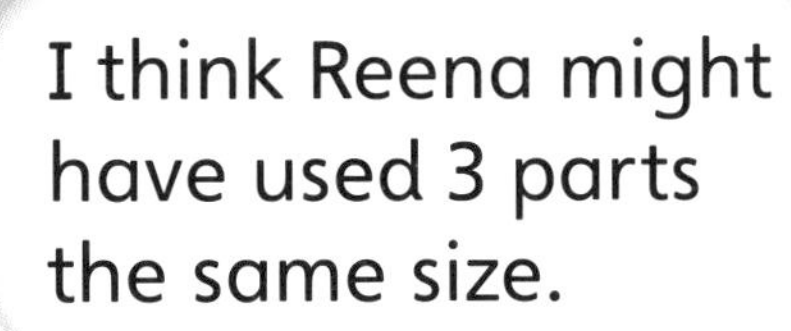

I think Reena might have used 3 parts the same size.

I remember that 3 × 20 = 60. I wonder if this helps me?

b) Explain why this part-whole model does not help you work out 75 ÷ 3.

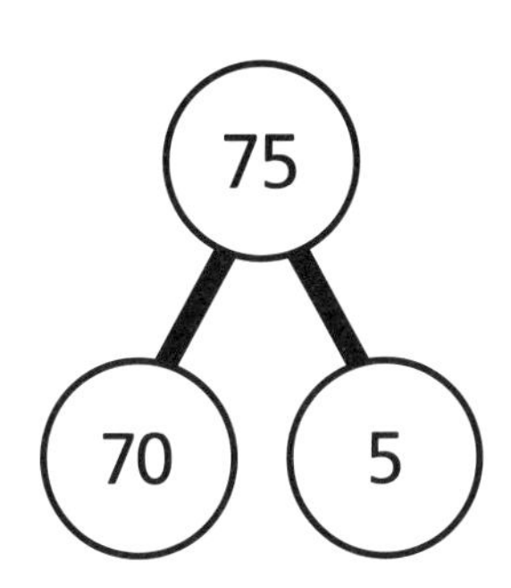

→ Practice book 3B p30

Dividing a 2-digit number by a 1-digit number 3

Discover

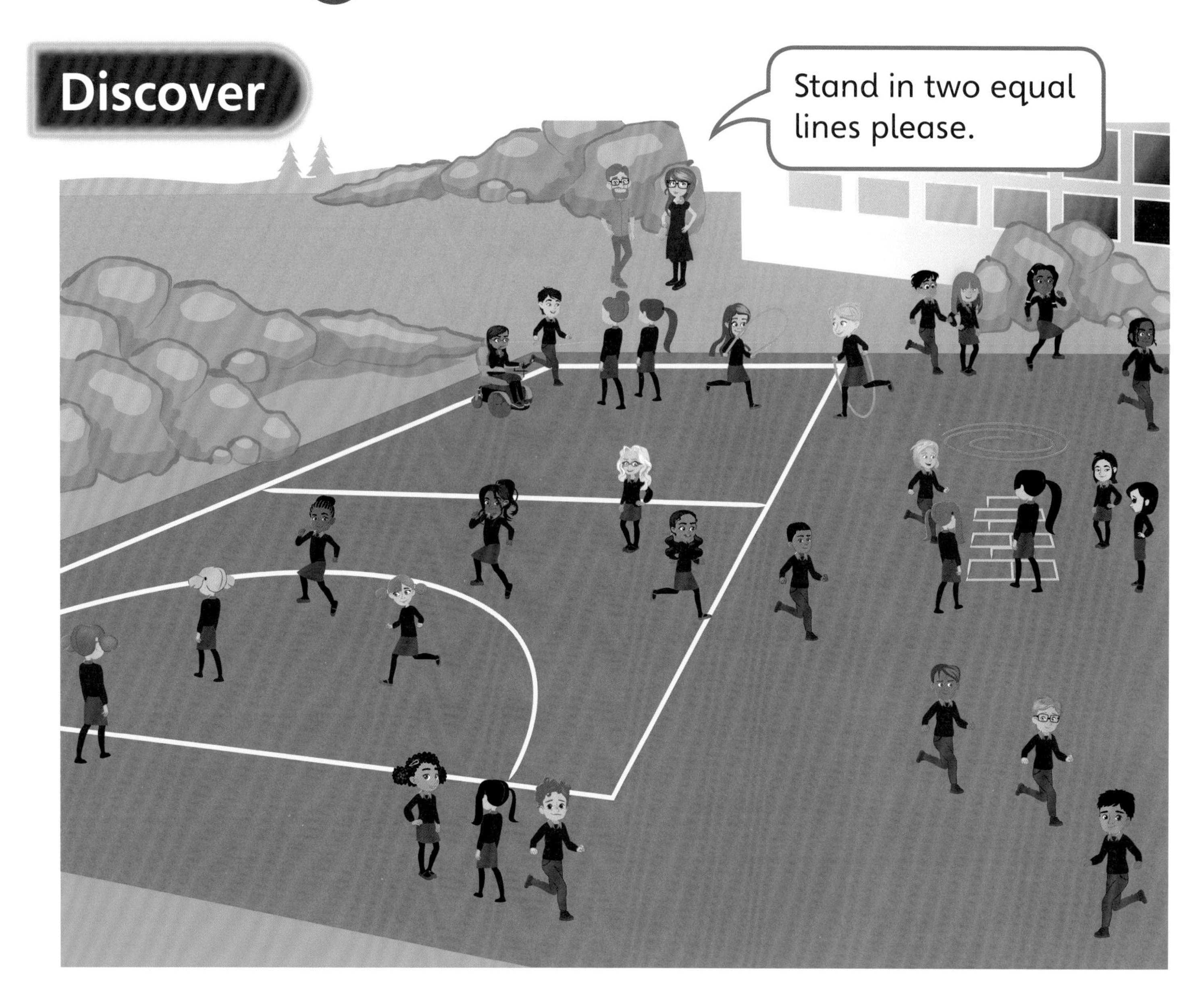
Stand in two equal lines please.

1 a) How do you know that the children cannot form two equal lines?

b) The children try to form two equal lines.

How many will there be in each line?

How many children will be left over?

Share

a) There are 29 children in the playground.

29 is an example of an odd number.

Odd numbers do not divide equally by 2.

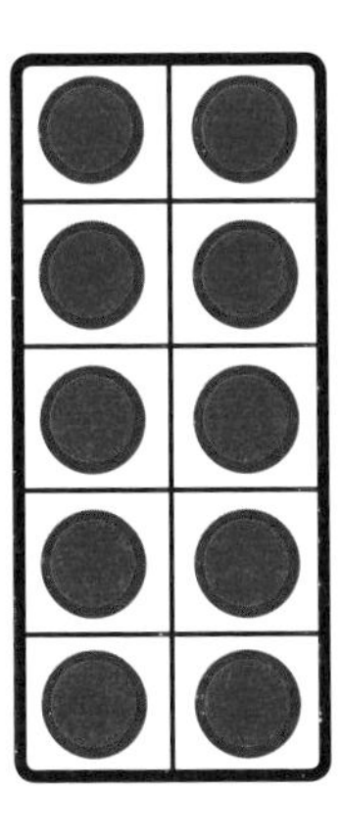
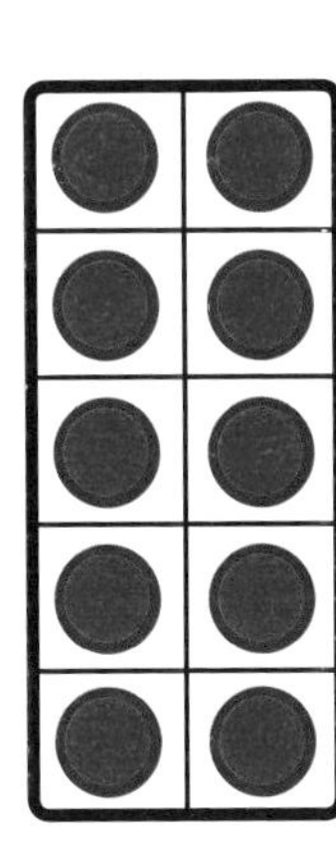
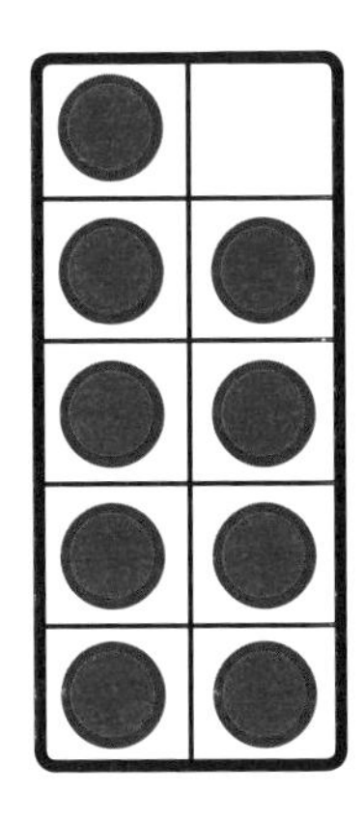

Remember that even numbers end in 0, 2, 4, 6 or 8.

b) There are 29 children. There are 2 lines.

The 29 children need to be shared between the 2 lines.

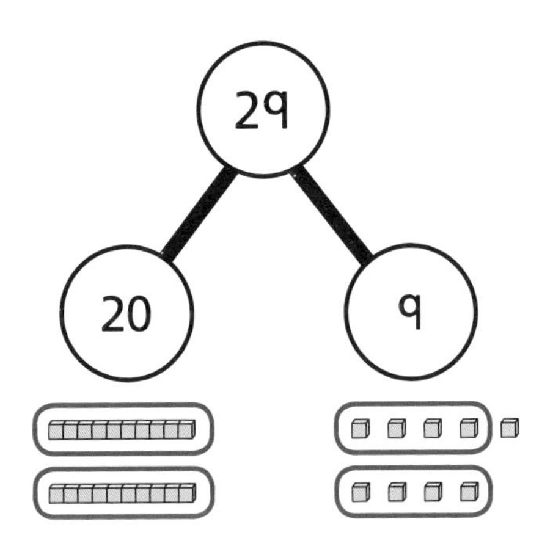

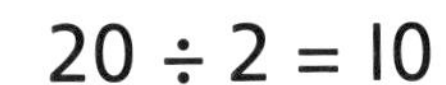

I partitioned my number into 10s and 1s to make the dividing quicker.

20 ÷ 2 = 10   9 ÷ 2 = 4 remainder 1

10 + 4 remainder 1 = 14 remainder 1

29 ÷ 2 = 14 remainder 1

There will be 14 children in each line and 1 child left over.

Think together

1 There are 38 children in a playground.

They need to stand in 3 lines.

Line 1 Line 2 Line 3

a) How many children will stand in each line?

☐ children will stand in each line.

b) How many will be left over?

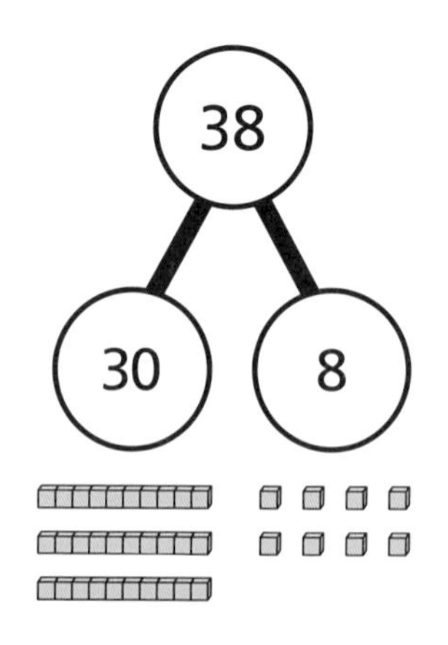

$30 \div 3 =$ ☐

$8 \div 3 =$ ☐ remainder ☐

$38 \div 3 =$ ☐ remainder ☐

There will be ☐ children in each line.

There will be ☐ children left over.

2 There are 67 children in the playground.

They try to make 5 equal lines.

How many children are in each line and how many are left over?

☐ ÷ ☐ = ☐ remainder ☐

67 ÷ 5 = ☐ remainder ☐

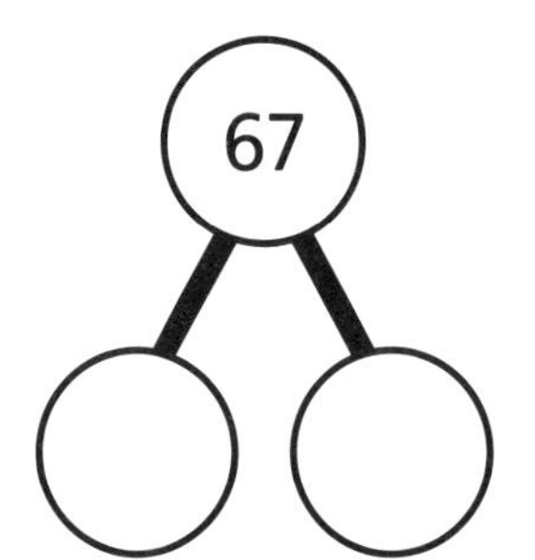

There are ☐ children in each line.

There are ☐ children left over.

3 Mo is working out 89 ÷ 4.

I do not think this divides equally.
I think there will be a remainder.

Is Mo correct? Explain how you know.

Work out the answer to Mo's question.

What do I know about numbers in the 4 times-table?

→ Practice book 3B p33

How many ways?

Discover

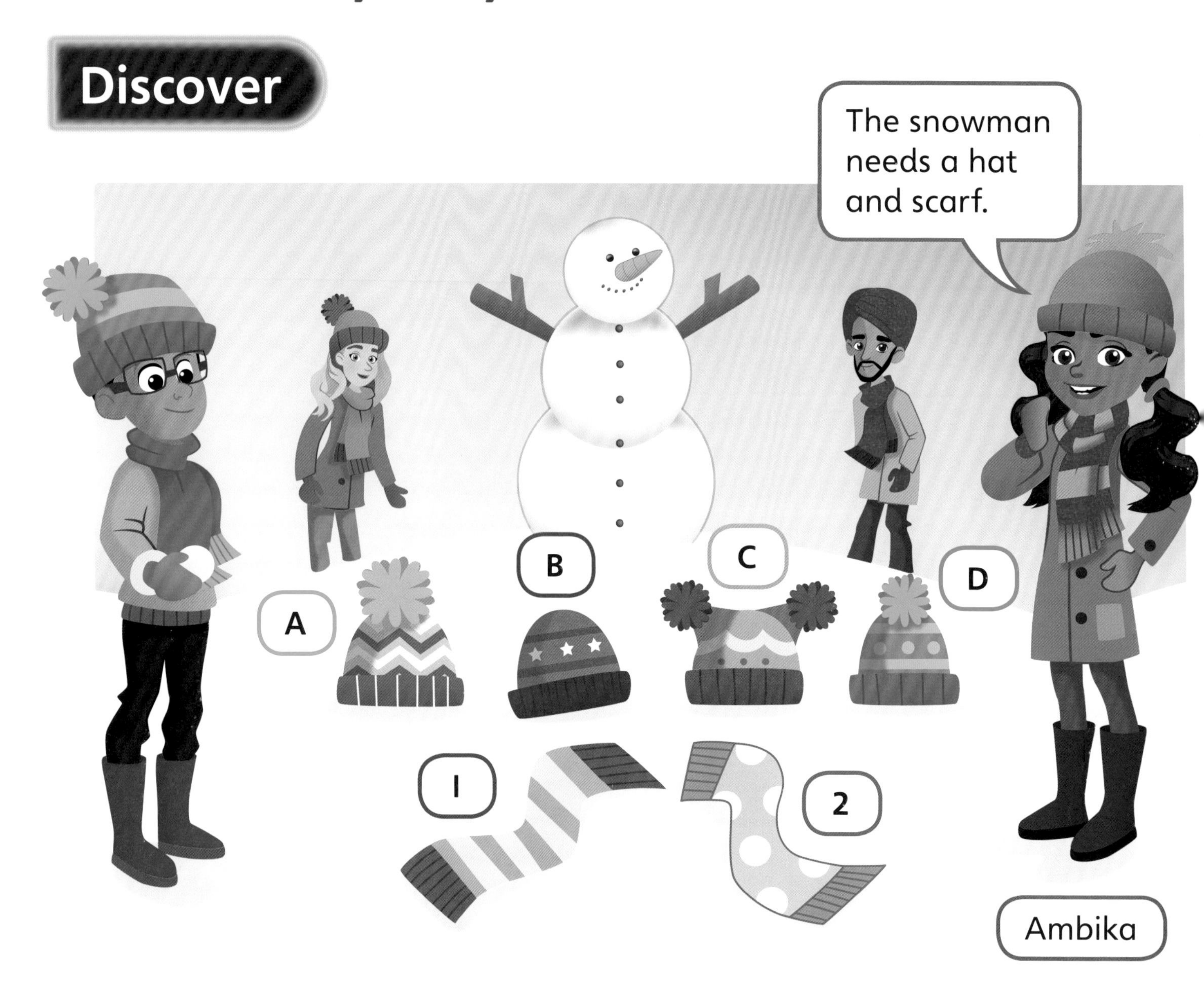
The snowman needs a hat and scarf.
A
B
C
D
1
2
Ambika

1 **a)** How many different ways can Ambika dress the snowman?

Record the ways in a list.

b) Is there a link between the number of hats and scarves and the number of ways to dress the snowman?

Share

I just used trial and error.

a) The snowman needs a hat and a scarf.

I think there is a better way. Start with the first hat and then put on each scarf. Then do the same for each hat. This way you will know you have them all. I put the results in a table.

I used lines to match them up. There were 8 ways to dress the snowman.

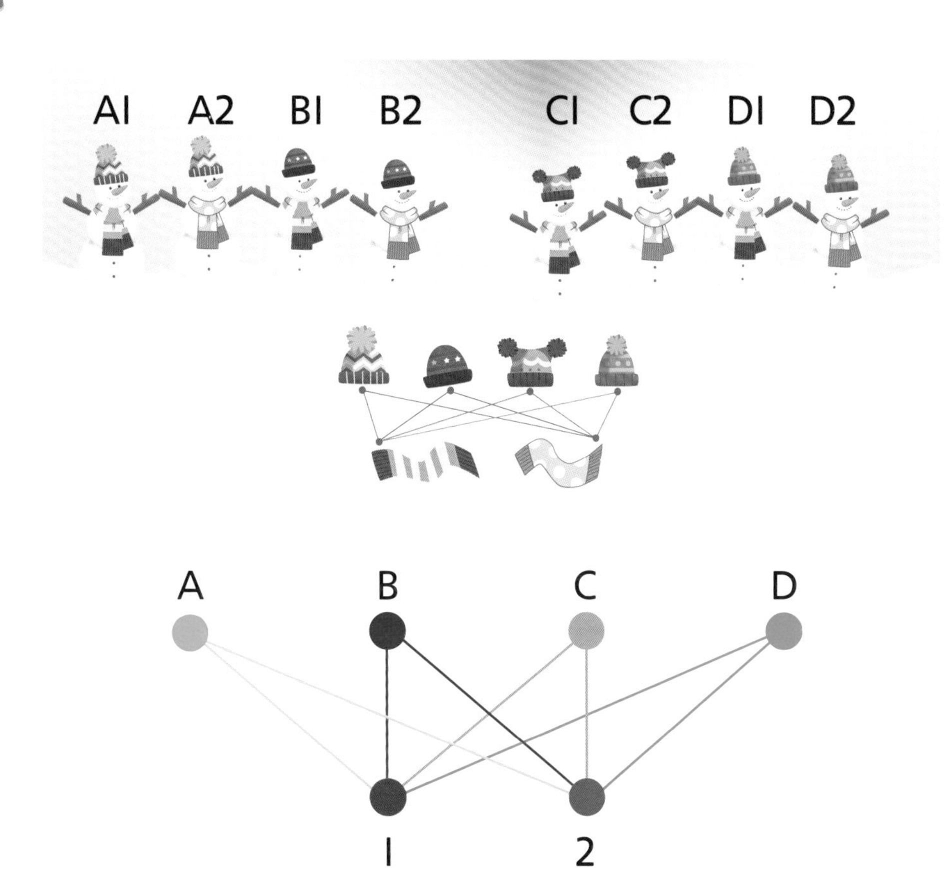

Hat	Scarf
Hat A	Scarf 1
Hat A	Scarf 2
Hat B	Scarf 1
Hat B	Scarf 2
Hat C	Scarf 1
Hat C	Scarf 2
Hat D	Scarf 1
Hat D	Scarf 2

b) There are 4 possible hats. For each hat there could be 2 possible scarves. To find the number of ways you can multiply the numbers.

The total number of ways to dress the snowman is $4 \times 2 = 8$ ways.

Think together

1 Lexi is choosing a pair of shoes and coat for her teddy bear.

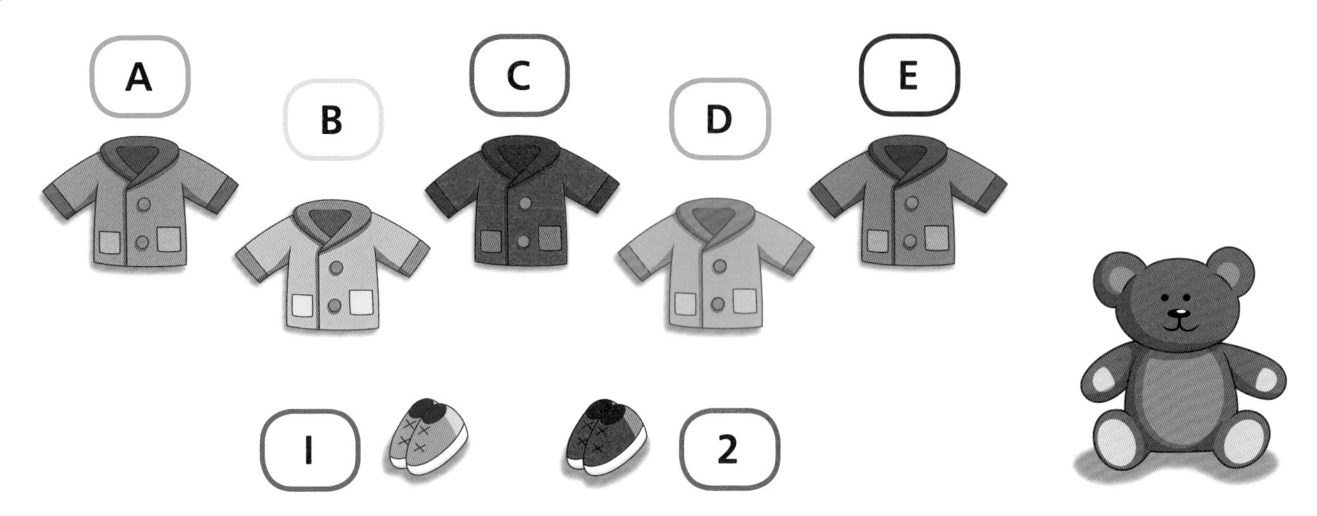

a) How many different ways are there of dressing the bear?

b) What are the possible ways to dress the bear?

2 Choose one item from each group.

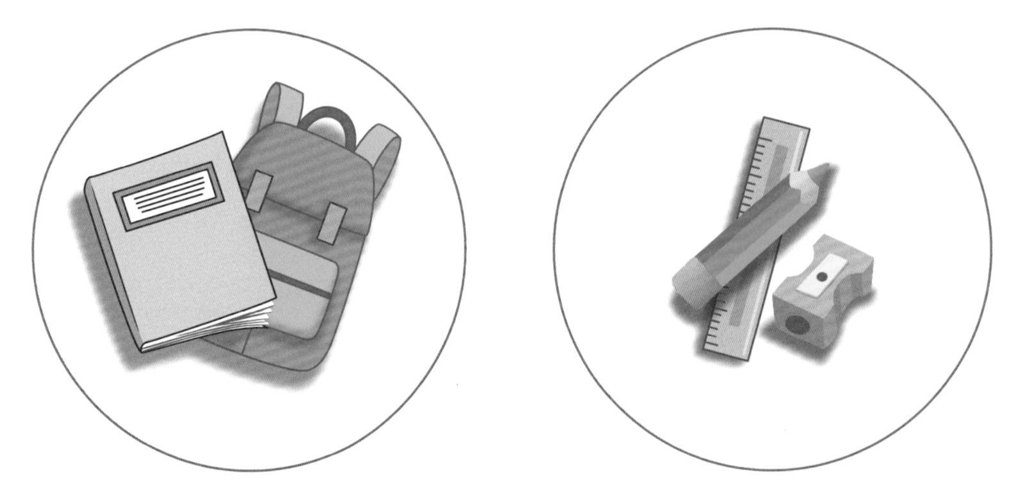

a) How many different pairs of items can you choose?

b) What are the possible pairs?

3 Reena and Luis each buy an item from the vending machine.

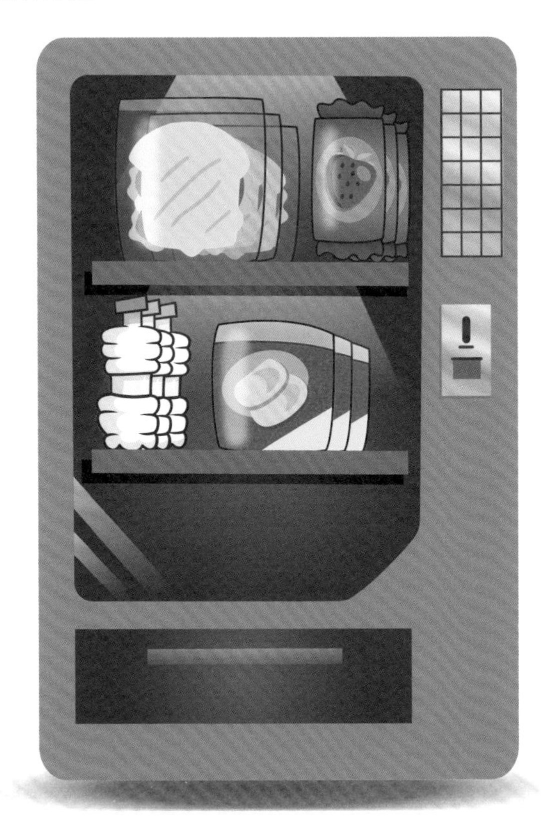

a) If they buy **different** items, how many different ways are there?

b) How does your answer change if they can buy the **same** item?

I am going to try to list all of the ways to work out the total number of options.

I am going to try to use multiplication to work out the number of options.

→ Practice book 3B p36

Problem solving – mixed problems 1

Discover

1 a) Amal makes 14 wooden horses a day.

How many does he make in 4 days?

b) Sofia makes 92 wooden giraffes in 4 days.

She makes the same amount each day.

How many does she make each day?

Share

a) Amal makes 14 wooden horses a day.

T	O

$4 \times 10 = 40$ $4 \times 4 = 16$

$40 + 16 = 56$ So $4 \times 14 = 56$

Amal makes 56 wooden horses in 4 days.

To work out how many for 4 days I need to multiply 14×4.

I multiplied the 10s first and then the 1s.

Then I added my answers.

b) Sofia makes 92 giraffes in 4 days.

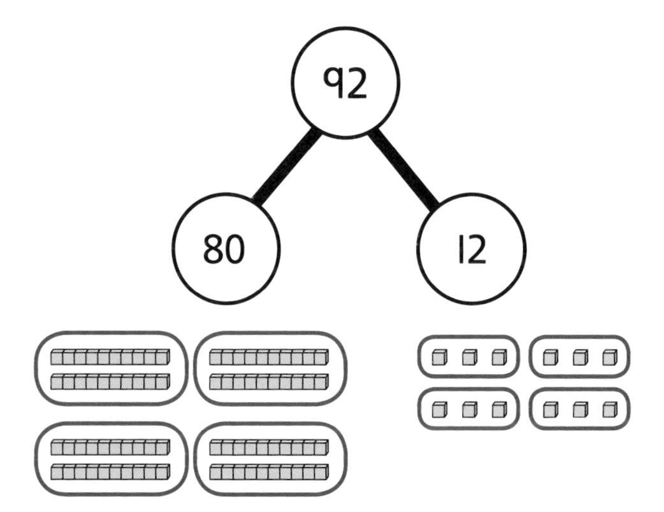

$80 \div 4 = 20$ and $12 \div 4 = 3$

$20 + 3 = 23$ so $92 \div 4 = 23$

Sofia makes 23 wooden giraffes each day.

I divided to find out how many Sofia made each day.

I used 2 numbers that divided by 4.

Think together

1 A wooden train has 12 wheels.

How many wheels are there on 6 trains?

Work out 6 ◯ 12.

T	O
10	1 1
10	1 1
10	1 1
10	1 1
10	1 1
10	1 1

6 ◯ 10 = □   6 ◯ 2 = □

□ + □ = □ so 6 ◯ 12 = □

There are □ wheels in total on 6 trains.

2 A wooden helicopter takes 3 hours to make.

How many helicopters can be made in 48 hours?

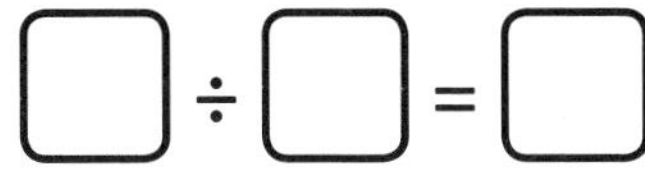

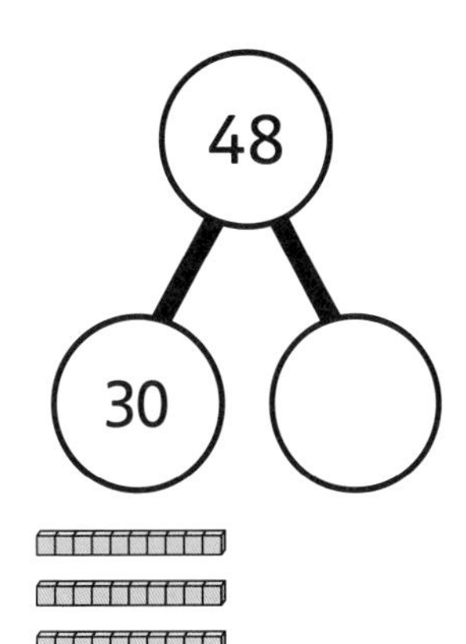

□ ÷ □ = □

□ + □ = □

48 ÷ 3 = □

□ helicopters can be made in 48 hours.

3 On Monday, Amal makes 39 toy people in 3 hours.

Sofia makes twice as many each hour.

How many does she make in 5 hours?

39

Amal

Sofia

?

→ Practice book 3B p39

Problem solving – mixed problems 2

Discover

1 **a)** Kate has 24 marbles in each bag.

How many marbles does Zac have?

b) Zac's marbles are in 2 bags.

There are 8 more marbles in one bag, compared to the other.

How many marbles are there in each bag?

Share

I used columns to multiply 3 by 24. I could have set it out in a different way to get the same answer.

a) Kate has 3 bags of marbles.

There are 24 marbles in each bag.

Kate has 72 marbles.

	T	O	
	2	4	
×		3	
	1	2	3 × 4
+	6	0	3 × 20
	7	2	

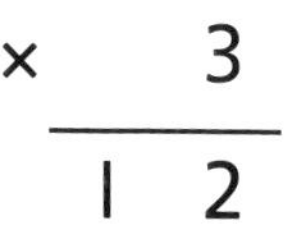

Zac has 10 fewer than Kate.

72 – 10 = 62

Zac has 62 marbles.

b) Zac has 2 bags. There are 8 fewer marbles in one of the bags.

62 – 8 = 54

I used a bar model to represent the problem.

Bag 1 | 27 | 8

Bag 2 | 27

62 → 54

62 – 8 = 54

54 ÷ 2 = 27

There are 35 marbles in Bag 1 and 27 marbles in Bag 2.

Think together

1 A bag contains 7 tiger marbles and 6 shooter marbles.

How much do the marbles weigh in total?

Tiger marble
5 grams

Shooter marble
8 grams

Tiger marbles	5	5	5	5	5	5	5
Shooter marbles	8	8	8	8	8	8	

Total: ?

☐ × 5 = ☐

☐ × 8 = ☐

☐ ◯ ☐ = ☐

The total weight of the marbles is ☐ grams.

2 How much more do 12 shooter marbles weigh than 12 tiger marbles?

Tiger marbles

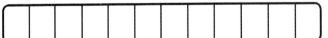

Shooter marbles

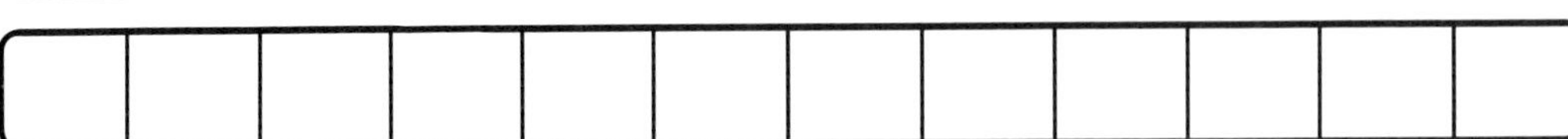

3 Zac buys 1 tiger and 2 shooter marbles for 71 pence.

Kate buys 1 tiger and 3 shooter marbles for 99 pence.

How much does a tiger marble cost?

71

Zac

Kate

99

The bar model will help you. Can you work out what each bar represents?

I wonder what Kate bought extra. Does this tell me something?

→ Practice book 3B p42

Problem solving – mixed problems 3

Discover

1 **a)** Box 3 contains 34 coins. Box 5 contains 48 coins.

Team A share the coins equally.

How many coins do they each receive?

b) If Team B had picked Box 3 and Box 5, could they have shared the coins equally? Explain your answer.

Share

a) Box 3 contains 34 coins.

Box 5 contains 48 coins.

3 5

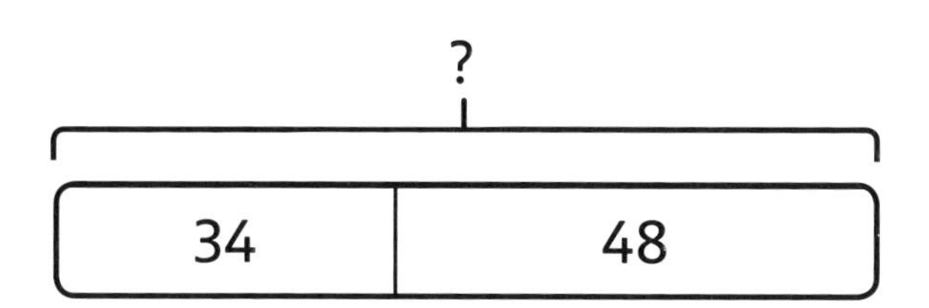

I drew a single bar model to represent the problem. I added the coins and then shared them equally between the 2 players.

34 + 48 = 82 and 82 ÷ 2 = 41

Each team member will receive 41 coins.

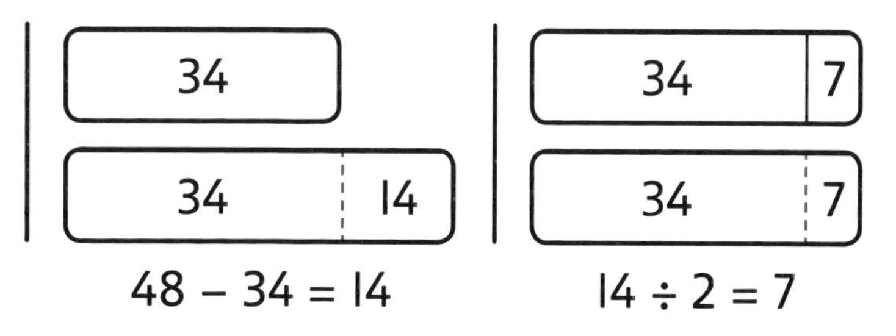

34 + 7 = 41 Each team member receives 41 coins.

I worked out how many more coins there were in Box 5 and shared this between the 2 players, in addition to the 34 coins each.

b) There are 82 coins in total.

60 ÷ 3 = 20   22 ÷ 3 = 7 r 1

82 ÷ 3 = 27 r 1

82
60 22

They could not have shared the coins equally because 82 does not divide equally among 3 people.

Think together

1 Box 2 contains 42 coins.

Box 10 contains the same amount.

How many coins does each person in Team B receive?

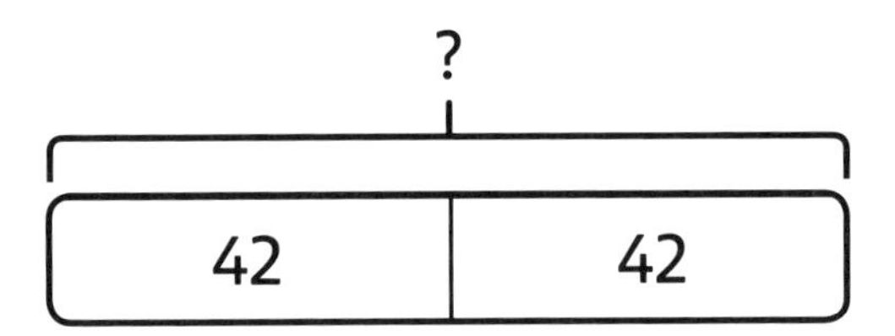

Choose your method to work out the calculations. Did you use the same method as your friends?

$42 \times 2 = \square$

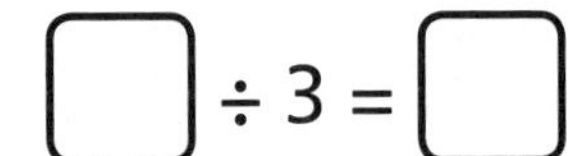

$\square \div 3 = \square$

Each person receives $\square$ coins.

2 In Box 4 there are 43 coins.

Box 6 contains twice as many coins.

How many coins are there in total?

Use the bar model to find the solution.

3 Here are 3 boxes.

Box 8 contains 10 more coins than Box 1.

Box 9 contains 10 more coins than Box 8.

There are 81 coins in total.

How many coins are there in each box?

Box 1 [ ]

Box 8 [ ]

Box 9 [ ]

81

I am going to work out how much longer each bar is than the bar for Box 1.

I need to get the bars equal. I need to subtract some numbers from 81.

→ Practice book 3B p45

End of unit check

1 Which of the following numbers could not complete the statement?

5 × 14 > 5 × ☐

A 14 **B** 12 **C** 10 **D** 0

2 What is 3 × 60?

A 18

B 36

C 180

D 240

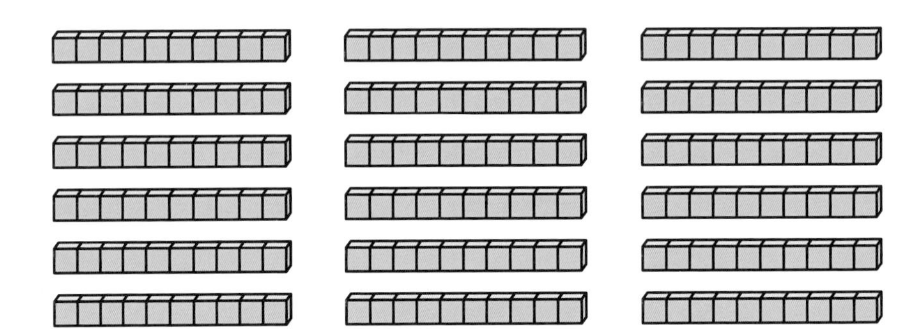

3 Work out 5 × 18.

A 23

B 40

C 50

D 90

T	O
●	●●●●●●●●
●	●●●●●●●●
●	●●●●●●●●
●	●●●●●●●●
●	●●●●●●●●

4 What is the value of the missing number?

16 × 3 = ☐ × 2

A 19 **B** 16 **C** 24 **D** 48

5 Which part-whole model does not help you solve $72 \div 3$?

A
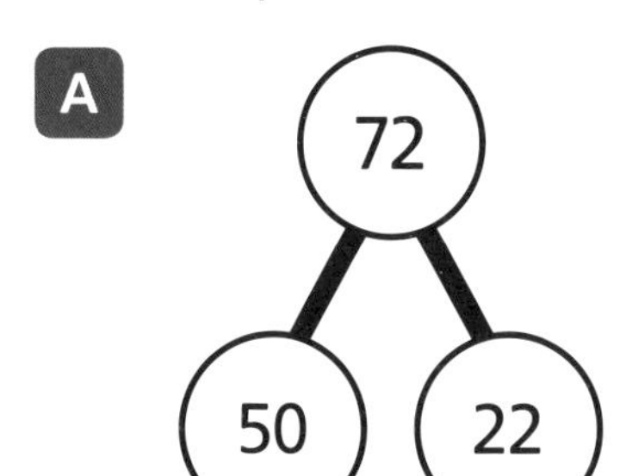

C
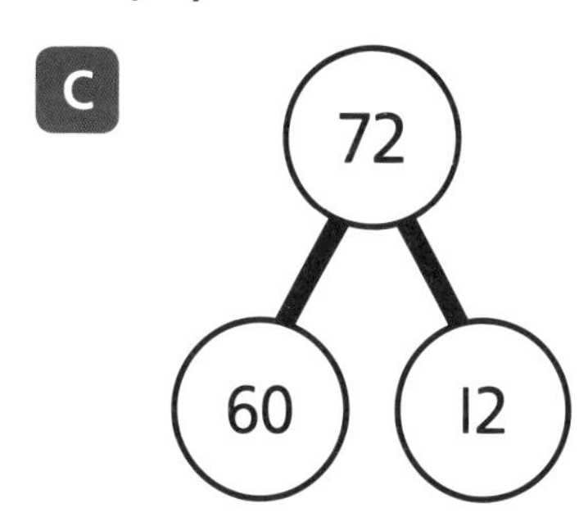

B
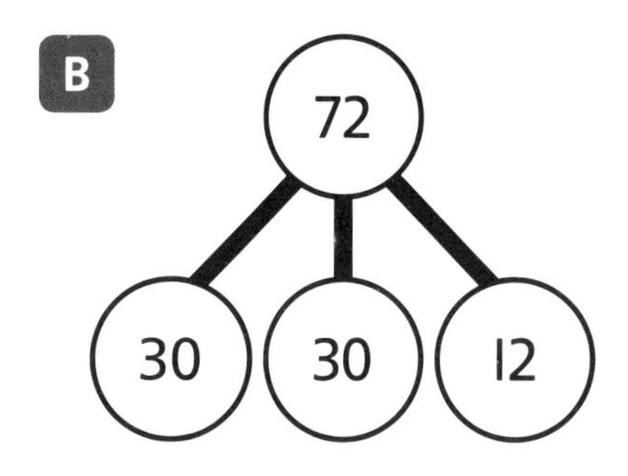

D
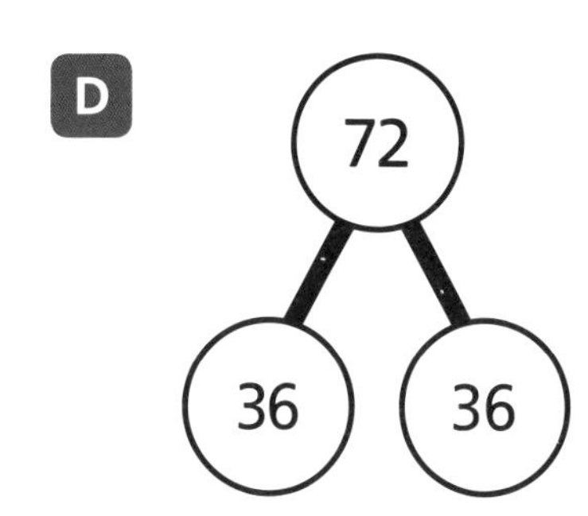

6 A sack of sugar weighs 20 kg.

A sack of oats weighs 15 kg.

Emma buys 8 sacks of each.

What is the total weight of sugar and oats she buys?

7 There are 2 boxes of counters.

There are 3 times as many counters in the second box as the first box.

There are 72 counters in total.

How many more counters are there in the second box than there are in the first box?

→ Practice book 3B p48

Unit 6
Money

In this unit we will ...

- Record money in £ and p
- Convert money
- Add and subtract amounts of money
- Solve problems including ones that involve finding change

In Year 2, we counted money in pounds and in pence. How much money is here?

We will need some maths words.
How many of these can you remember?

pounds (£) and pence (p)

convert **total**

difference **change**

We will also need to be able to add and subtract numbers. What calculations are shown here?

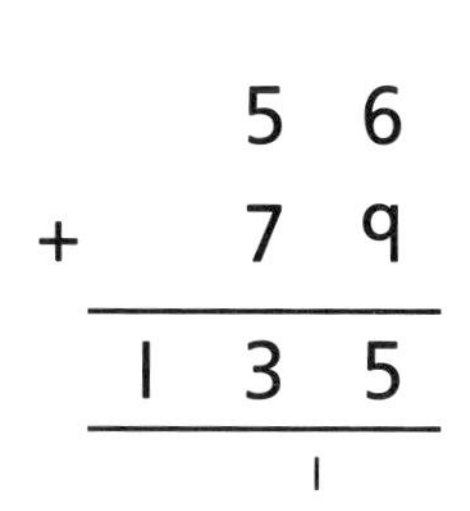

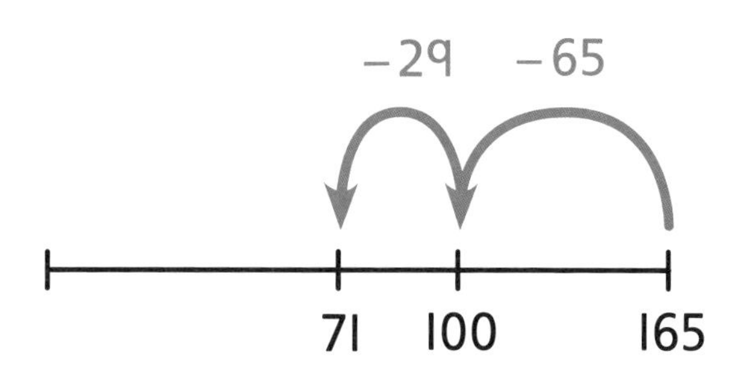

Pounds and pence

Discover

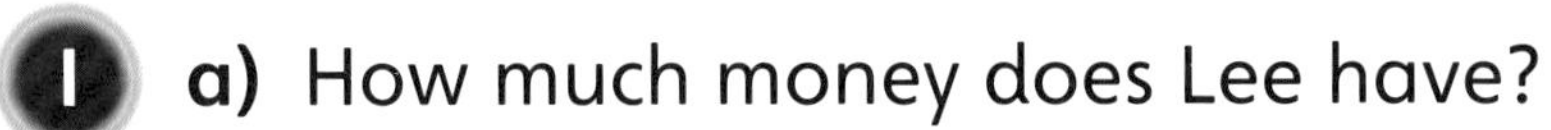

1 **a)** How much money does Lee have?

b) Sofia has these coins in her purse:

She gives Lee £2 and 28p.

Which coins did Sofia give Lee?

Key  1p  2p  5p  10p    20p  50p   £1  £2

Share

a) Sort the notes and coins into pounds (£) and pence (p).

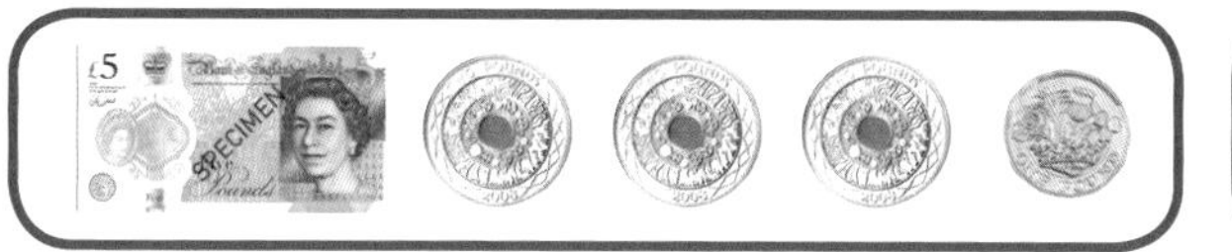

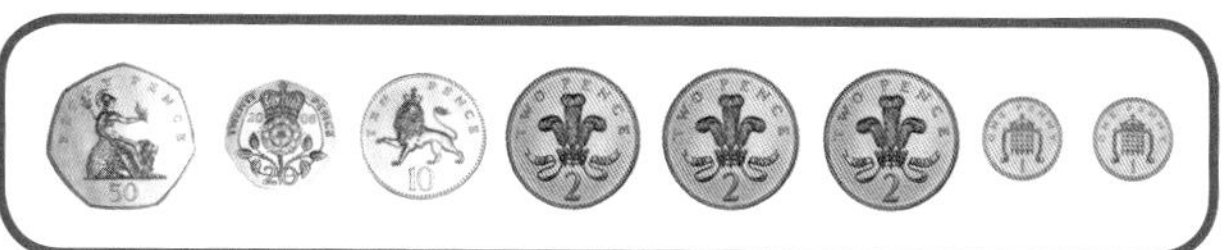

I counted the pounds first and then the pence.
I used a number line to find the total amount.
I started with the highest value.

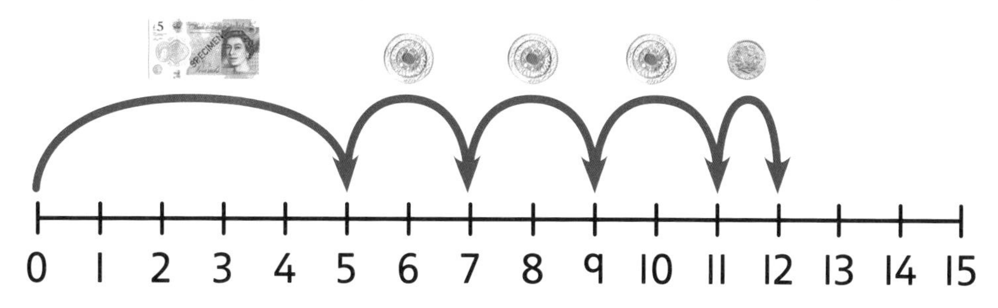

Lee has 12 pounds.

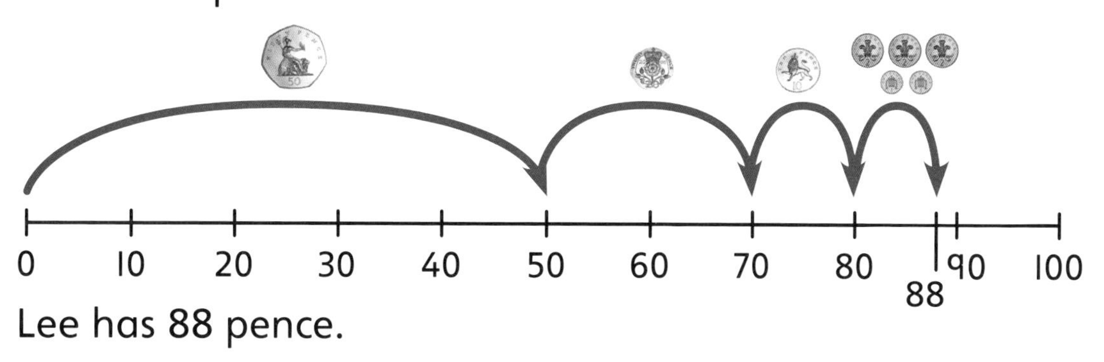

Lee has 88 pence.

Lee has 12 pounds and 88 pence in total, or £12 and 88p.

b) Sofia gave Lee a £2 coin and 20p, 5p, 2p and 1p coins.

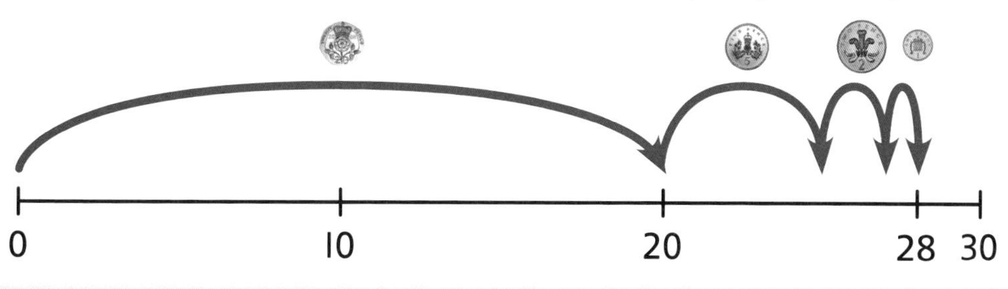

 £5   £10   £20  £50

Think together

1 How much money does Sofia have?

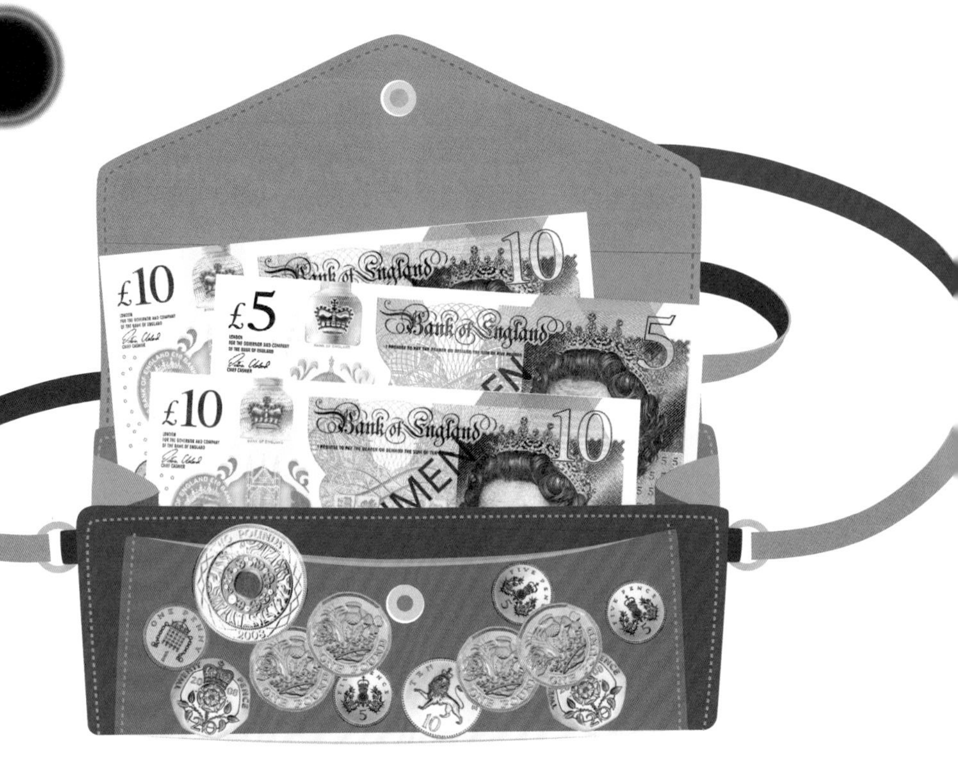

Sofia has [ ] pounds and [ ] pence.

Sofia has £ [ ] and [ ] p.

2 Lee took 25 pounds and 37 pence from his money box.

Choose some of the notes and coins to make this amount.

Key  1p  2p  5p  10p  20p 50p  £1  £2

3 Sofia is trying to make £1 with different numbers of coins. Complete the table using one more coin in each row.

I have £1 in total. I have fewer than 10 coins.

Number of coins	Possible
1	
2	
3	Not possible
4	
5	
6	
7	
8	
9	

I remember that 100 pence is equal to £1.

 £5  £10  £20 £50

→ Practice book 3B p51

Converting pounds and pence

Discover

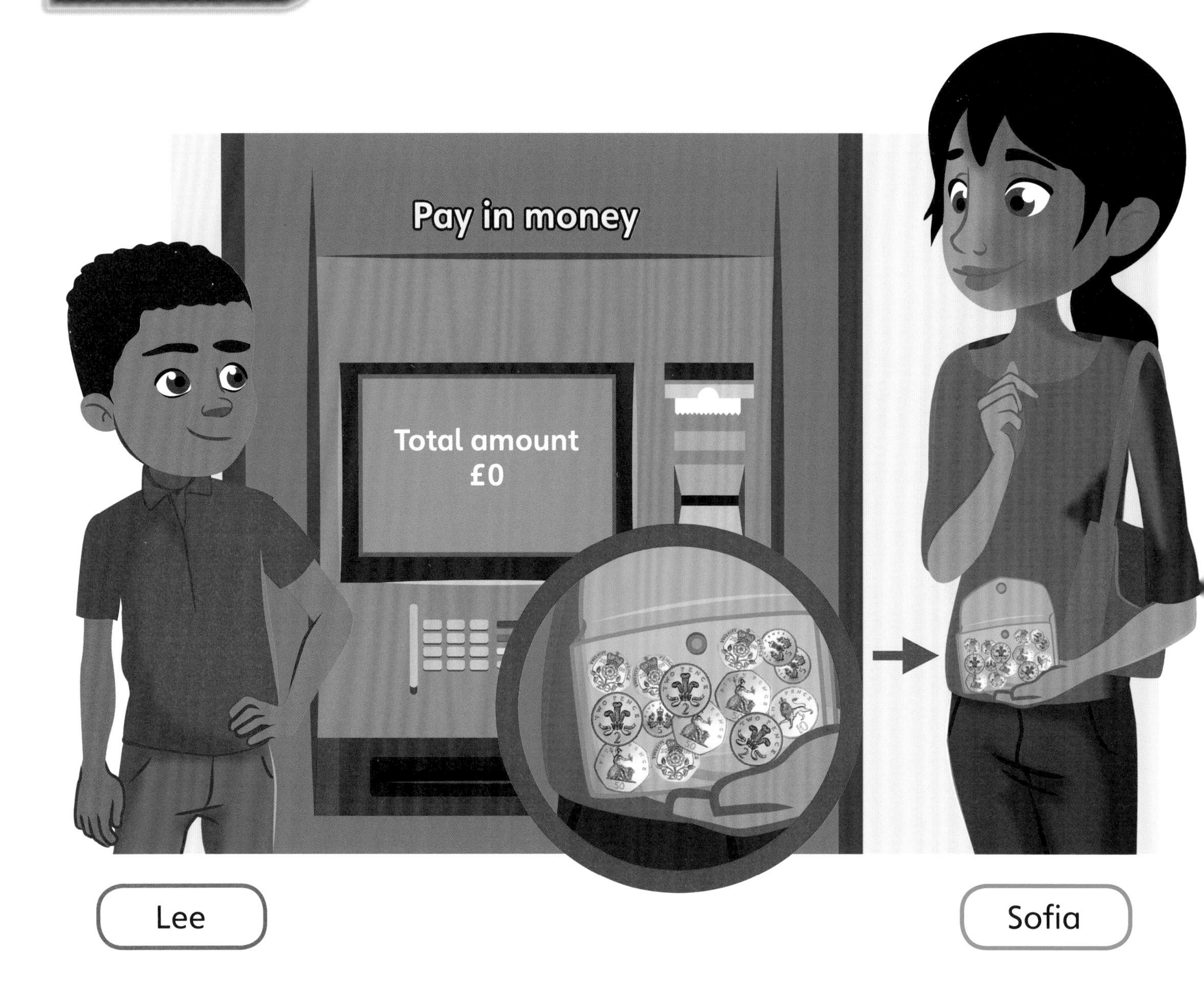

1 **a)** How much money does Sofia put into the machine?

b) Lee puts in £1 with some silver coins. They are all the same.

What could he have put in?

Key  1p  2p  5p  10p 20p  50p  £1  £2

Share

I put coins that make £1 together first. Then I counted the coins left over. There are different ways you can make £1.

a) There are 100 pence in a pound.

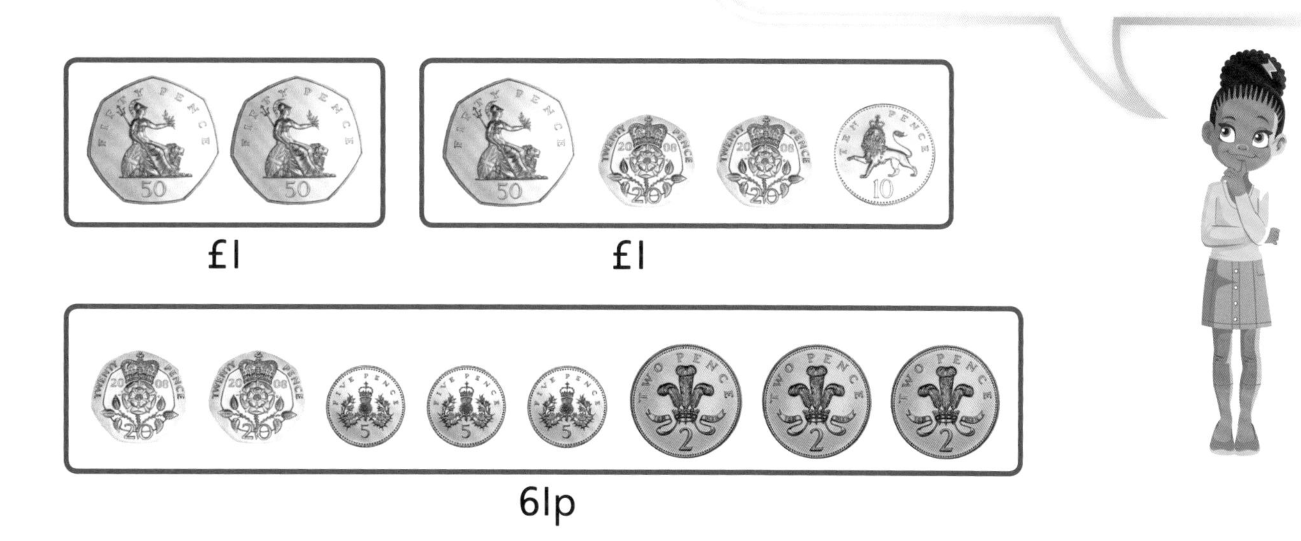
£1

£1

61p

Sofia puts £2 and 61p into the machine.

I worked out how many coins made £1 for each of the silver coins.

b) Lee could have put these coins in:

Two 50p coins

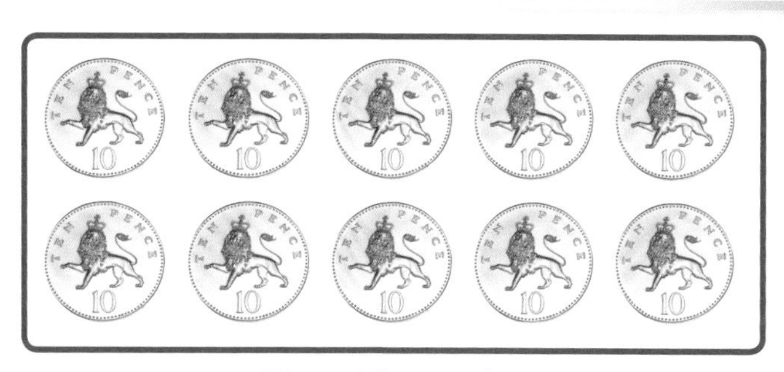
Ten 10p coins

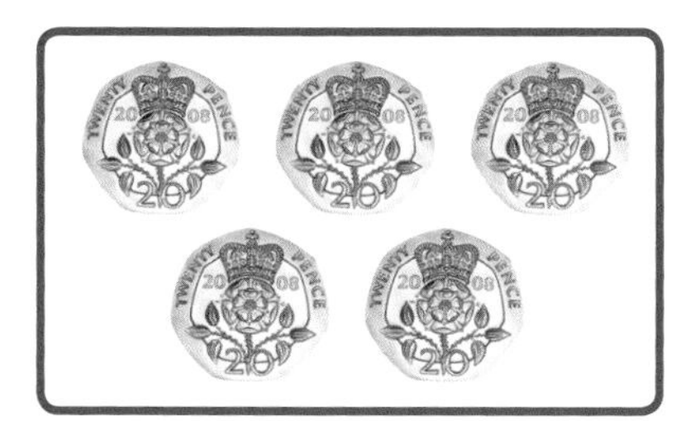
Five 20p coins

Twenty 5p coins

£5 £10 £20 £50

Think together

1 Which of these sets of coins make £1?

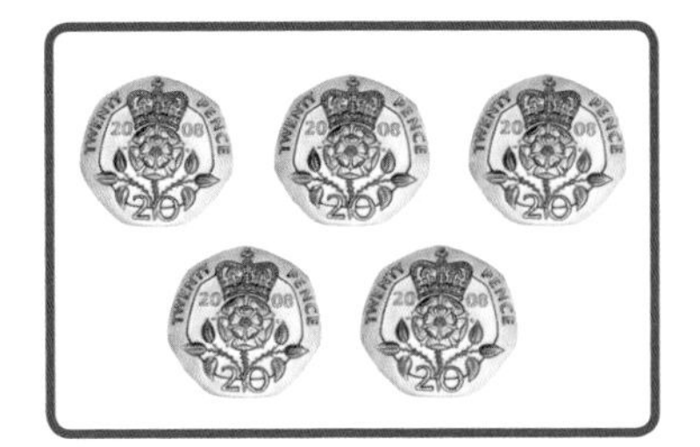

2 How much money does Holly have?

Holly has £ ☐ and ☐ p.

Key  1p  2p  5p  10p  20p  50p   £1  £2

 Mr Jones has some bags of coins from the bank.

How many coins are in each bag?

I used plastic coins and counted up in 2s, 5s, 10s and 20s until I made the amount in the bag.

I wonder if I can work out how many of each coin there are in £1 and then multiply.

→ Practice book 3B p54

Adding money

Discover

Can I have a cup of tea and a slice of cake, please?
Tea – £1 and 20p
Small coffee – £1 and 80p
Large coffee – £2 and 20p
Juice – £1 and 45p
Water – 79p
Toastie – £2 and 80p
Slice of cake – £2 and 32p
Strawberry tart – £3 and 58p
Sofia
Lee

1 **a)** How much do the tea and cake cost Sofia in total?

b) Lee wants juice and a toastie.

How much does this cost him in total?

Share

I made each amount with coins and added them together.

a) A cup of tea costs £1 and 20p.

A slice of cake costs £2 and 32p.

  + 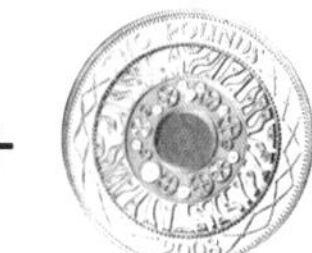    = 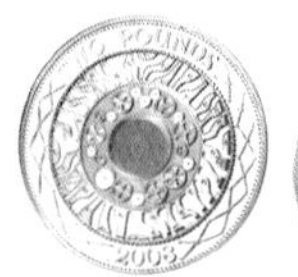   

£1 and 20p + £2 and 32p = £3 and 52p

Add the pounds first: £1 + £2 = £3

Then add the pence: 20p + 32p = 52p

The tea and cake cost Sophia £3 and 52p in total.

b) £1 and 45p = 145p

£2 and 80p = 280p

	H	T	O
	1	4	5
+	2	8	0
	4	2	5
	1		

I changed each amount to pence and then did a column addition.

425p is the same as £4 and 25p.

The juice and toastie cost Lee £4 and 25p in total.

  £5    £10  £20 £50

Think together

1 What is the total cost?

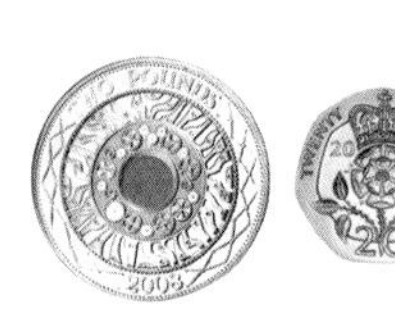

Add the pounds. £2 + £3 = £ ☐

Add the pence. 20p + 58p = ☐ p

The total cost is £ ☐ and ☐ p.

2 What is the total cost?

£1 and 80p = ☐ p

£1 and 45p = ☐ p

☐ p = £ ☐ and ☐ p

	H	T	O
	1	8	0
+	1	4	5

Key  1p  2p  5p  10p  20p  50p  £1   £2

3 The tills show the cost of some items from the café.

Tea – £1 and 20p
Small coffee – £1 and 80p
Large coffee – £2 and 20p
Juice – £1 and 45p
Water – 79p
Toastie – £2 and 80p
Slice of cake – £2 and 32p
Strawberry tart – £3 and 58p

Work out what items were bought at each till.

I used the end numbers to help me.

I wonder if anyone bought more than two items.

 £5  £10  £20   £50

→ Practice book 3B p57

Subtracting amounts of money

Discover

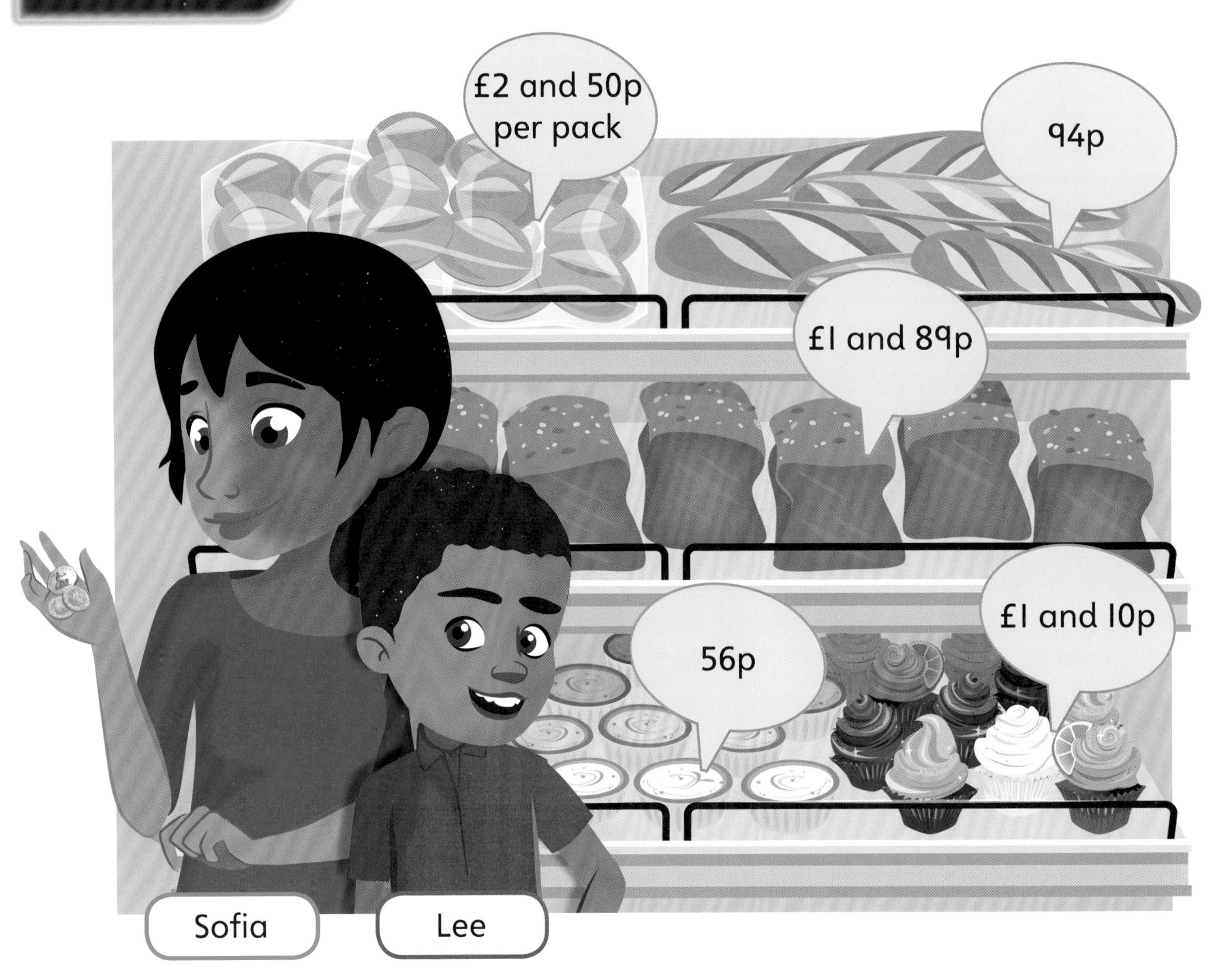

1 **a)** Sofia buys a cupcake.

How much money does she have left?

b) How much cheaper is the loaf of bread than the bread rolls?

Key  1p  2p  5p  10p  20p  50p  £1  £2

Share

a) Sofia has £2 and 50 pence.

She buys a cupcake for £1 and 10 pence.

I had to exchange the 50 pence for other coins.

Subtract £1 first.

Then subtract 10 pence.

Sofia has £1 and 40 pence left.

b) The loaf of bread costs £1 and 89 pence.

The bread rolls cost £2 and 50 pence.

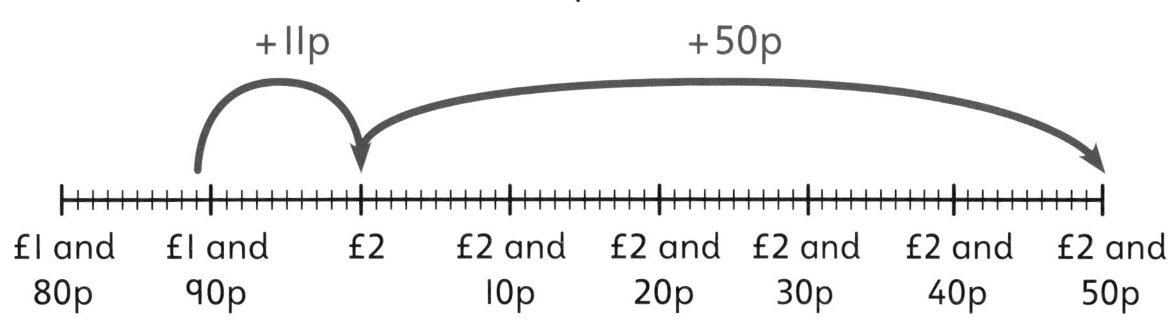

To find the difference between the costs, I counted on.

	H	T	O
	¹~~2~~	¹⁴~~5~~	¹0
−	1	8	9
		6	1

I changed the amounts to pence and used column subtraction.

11p + 50p = 61p

£2 and 50p − £1 and 89p = 61p

The loaf of bread is 61p cheaper than the bread rolls.

 £5   £10  £20 £50

Think together

1 How much more does the loaf of bread cost than the breadstick?

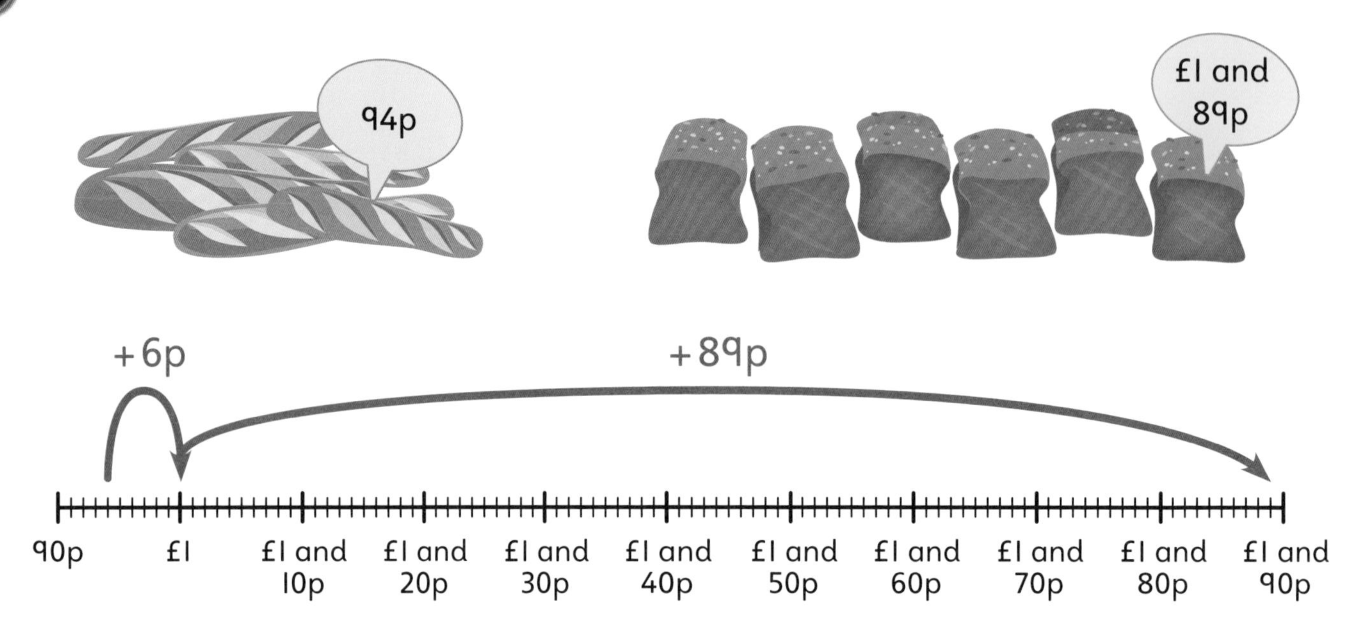

☐ p + ☐ p = ☐ p

189p – 94p = ☐ p

The loaf of bread costs ☐ p more than the breadstick.

2 Lee has some money.

Lee buys a custard tart.

How much money does Lee have left?

Lee has £ ☐ and ☐ pence left.

Key  1p  2p  5p  10p  20p   50p  £1 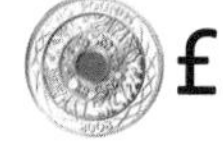 £2

3 **a)** Predict which of these subtractions will have an answer less than £1.

£1 and 95p – £1 and 42p

£5 and 30p – £1 and 50p

£2 and 18p – 64p

£4 and 45p – £3 and 88p

b) Work out the answers. Were your predictions correct?

I subtracted the pounds and pence separately.

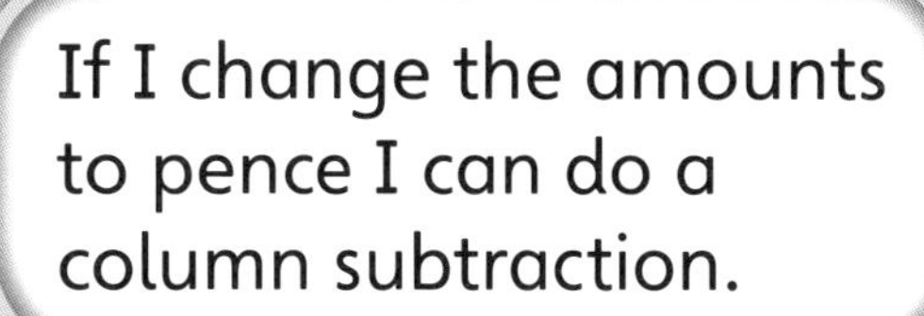

If I change the amounts to pence I can do a column subtraction.

 £5   £10  £20  £50

→ Practice book 3B p60

Problem solving – money

Discover

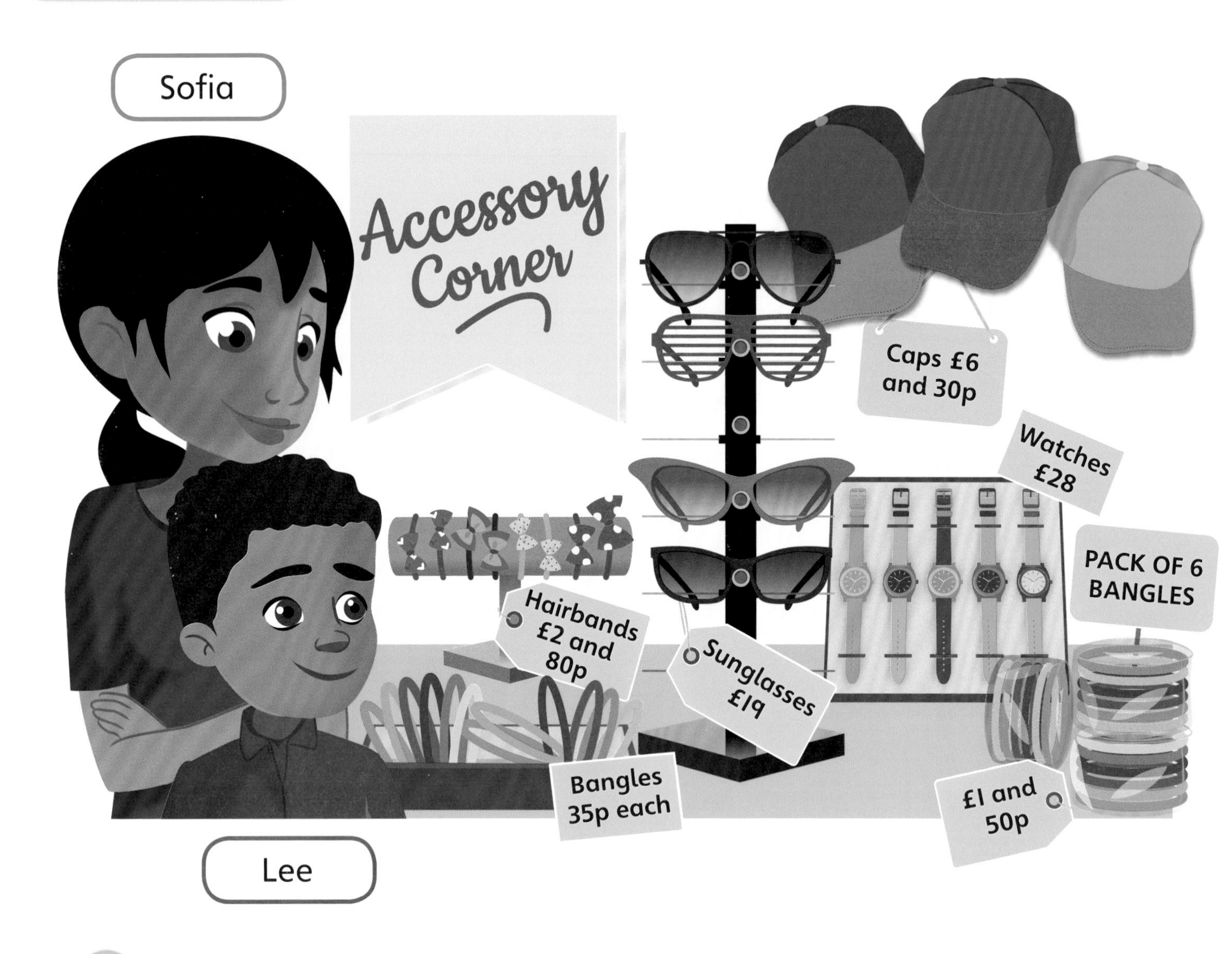

1 **a)** Sofia buys a pair of sunglasses and a watch.

How much **change** does she get from £50?

b) How much does Sofia save by buying a pack of 6 bangles rather than 6 single ones?

Key  1p  2p  5p  10p  20p   50p £1  £2

Share

a) Sunglasses cost £19 and a watch costs £28.

The total cost is:

£19 + £28 = £47

$$\begin{array}{rcc} & T & O \\ \hline & 1 & 9 \\ + & 2 & 8 \\ \hline & 4 & 7 \\ \hline & {}_1 & \end{array}$$

Subtract from £50 to work out the change.

£50 – £47 = £3

Sofia gets £3 change from £50.

I used column addition to find the total.

b) Single bangles cost 35p each.

6 × 35p = 210p

210p = £2 and 10p

$$\begin{array}{rccc} & & 3 & 5 \\ \times & & & 6 \\ \hline & & 3 & 0 \\ + & 1 & 8 & 0 \\ \hline & 2 & 1 & 0 \\ \hline & {}_1 & & \end{array}$$

I used column multiplication to find the cost of 6 bangles.
Then I found how much more using a number line.

The total cost of 6 single bangles is £2 and 10p.

You can buy bangles in a pack of 6. These cost £1 and 50p.

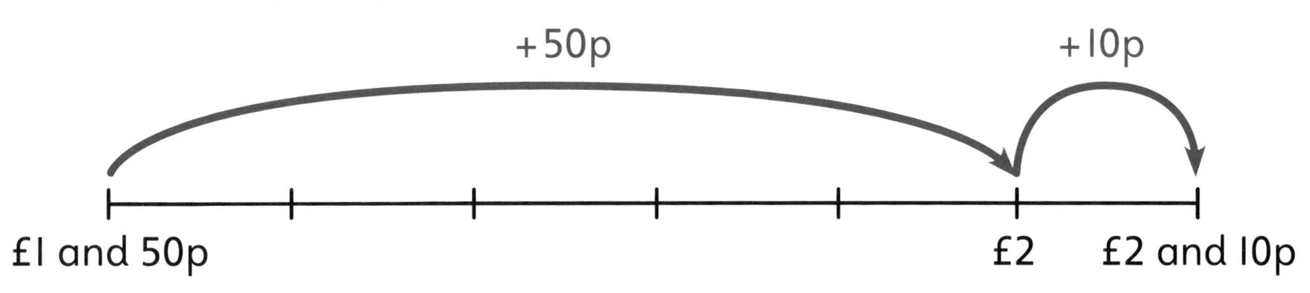

£2 and 10p – £1 and 50p = 60p

Sofia saves 60p by buying a pack of 6 bangles.

  £5 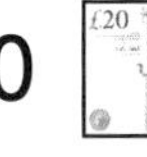  £10 £20  £50

Think together

1 Sofia buys 2 hairbands.

What is the total cost?

£2 + £2 = £☐

80p + 80p = ☐p = £☐ and ☐p

The total cost is £☐ and ☐p.

Lee buys a cap.

He pays with a £10 note.

How much change does he get?

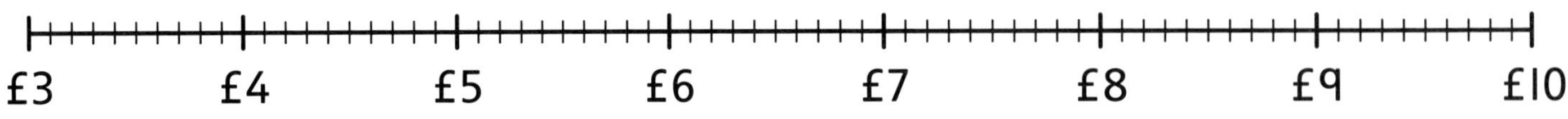

£10 – £6 and 30p = £☐ and ☐p

Lee gets £☐ and ☐p change.

Key  1p  2p  5p  10p  20p  50p  £1 £2

3 Find half of £2 and 90p.

Half of £2 and 90p is £☐ and ☐p.

4 Some items are on sale in the shop.

CHALLENGE

Sofia has £40 to spend in total.

Sofia buys 3 hairbands.

How many necklaces can she buy with the money she has left?

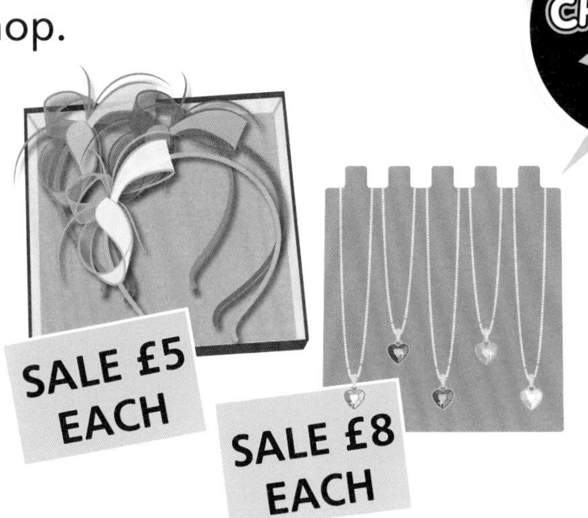

I used the bar model to help me.

£40			
£5	£5	£5	

Sophie can buy ☐ necklaces with the money she has left.

I wonder if it adds up to exactly £40. I think there might be some money left over.

 £5  £10  £20  £50

→ Practice book 3B p63

End of unit check

1 What is the total?

A £7 and 42p

B £742

C £6 and 42p

D £7 and 37p

2 What is 458p in pounds and pence?

A £4 and 58p

B £45 and 8p

C £458

D £4 and 85p

3 Which of the following sets of coins does not make £1?

A 

B 

C 

D 

Key  1p 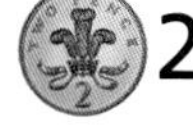 2p  5p 10p  20p  50p  £1  £2

4 How much money is shown here?

A £6 and 87p   B £7 and 87p   C £787   D £6 and 187p

5 A sandwich cost £3 and 65p. Kate pays with 

How much change does Kate get?

A £2 and 35p   B £1 and 45p   C £1 and 35p   D £2 and 45p

6 Olivia wants to buy a new sports cap.

She has £4 and 20p.

Her mum gives her £5 and 90p.

Does she have enough to buy the sports cap?

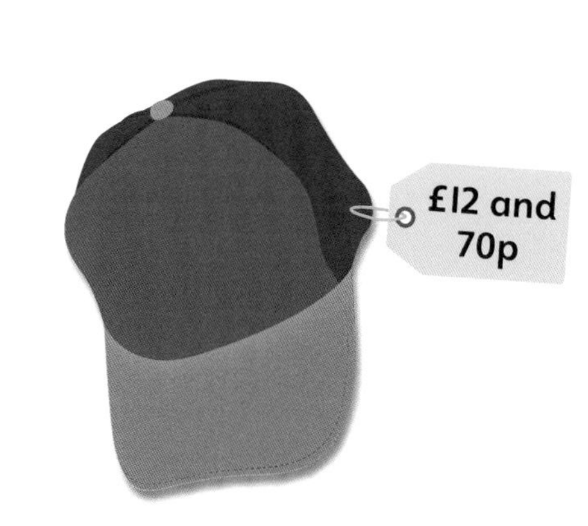

 £5  £10  £20  £50

→ Practice book 3B p66

Unit 7
Statistics

In this unit we will ...

- Present information in different ways
- Use pictograms, bar charts and tables
- Answer questions based on information that is presented in different ways

This looks like the block diagrams we used last year. I wonder what it is called.

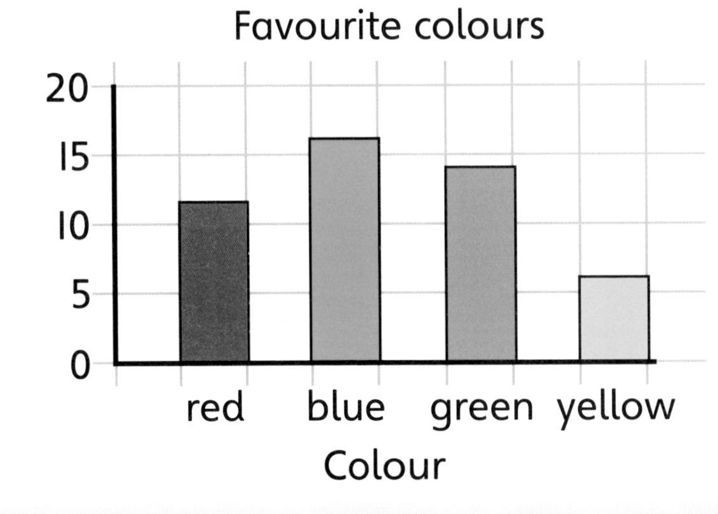

We will need some maths words. Which ones have you seen before?

pictogram **key** **bar chart**
scale **table** **row**
column **vertical axis**

We need pictograms too! Work out how many people like skiing.

Key: Each ☺ represents 2 people.

Sport	Number of people
skiing	☺☺☺☺☺
snowboarding	☺☺☺☺☺☺

Pictograms 1

Discover

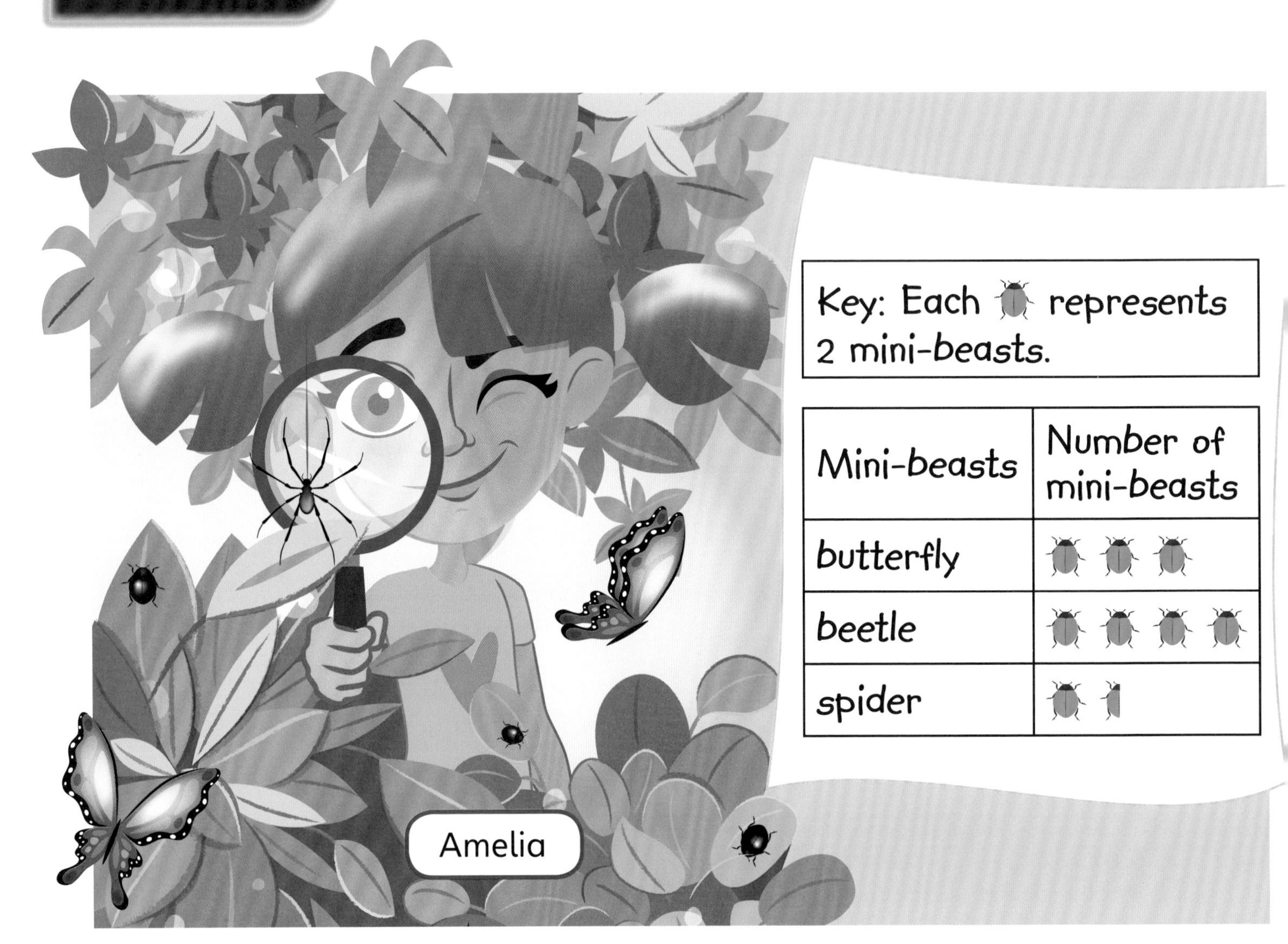

Key: Each represents 2 mini-beasts.

Mini-beasts	Number of mini-beasts
butterfly	
beetle	
spider	

1 Amelia is searching for mini-beasts. She records her results in a pictogram.

a) How many beetles did Amelia find?

b) How many spiders did Amelia find?

Did Amelia find more or fewer spiders than beetles?

Share

a) From the key we know that each symbol represents 2 mini-beasts.

There are 4 symbols for beetles.

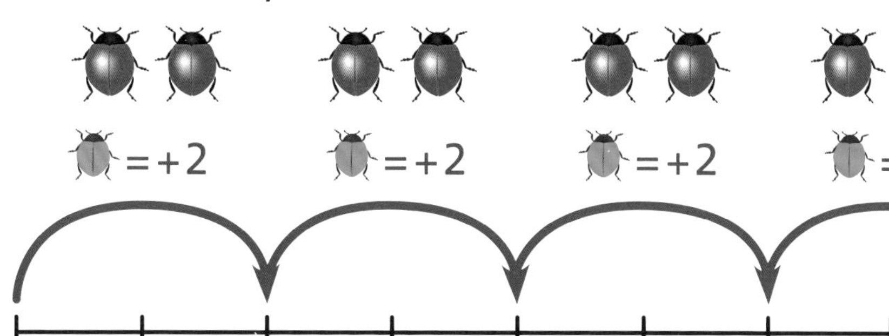

$4 \times 2 = 8$

$2 + 2 + 2 + 2 = 8$

Amelia found 8 beetles.

b) There are 1 and a half symbols for spiders.

spider	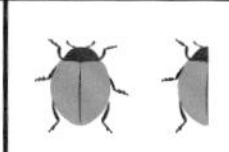

A whole symbol represents 2 spiders.

Half of 2 is 1.

So, represents 1 spider.

$2 + 1 = 3$

Amelia found 3 spiders.

$3 < 8$ so she found fewer spiders than beetles.

Think together

a) How many honeysuckles did Amelia find?

Flowers	Number of flowers
bluebell	
honeysuckle	
daffodil	
primrose	

Key: Each represents 10 flowers.

Each symbol represents ☐ flowers.

There are 3 symbols for honeysuckles.

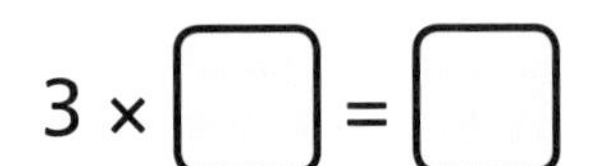

3 × ☐ = ☐

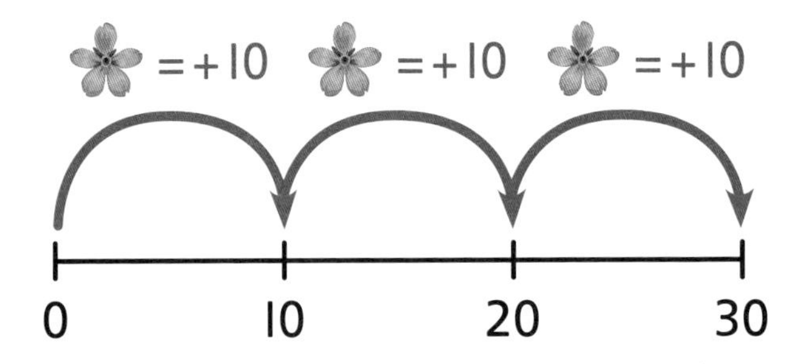

☐ + ☐ + ☐ = ☐

Amelia found ☐ honeysuckles.

b) How many daffodils did Amelia find?

= ☐ = ☐

There are ☐ whole symbols and ☐ half symbols for daffodils.

☐ + ☐ = ☐

Amelia found ☐ daffodils.

c) Amelia found 15 primroses. How should she show this on her pictogram?

2 Amelia created this pictogram showing the different trees she found.

She found 15 birch trees.

a) How much is each symbol worth?

b) How many conifer trees did she find?

Key: Each 🌳 represents ☐ trees.

Tree	Number of trees
birch	🌳 🌳 🌳
oak	🌳 🌳
conifer	🌳 🌳 🌳 🌳

CHALLENGE

3 Lee also searched for mini-beasts. He made this chart.

Mini-beasts	Number of mini-beasts
butterfly	🦋 🦋
beetle	🐞 🐞 🐞 🐞 🐞
spider	🕷 🕷 🕷 🕷

Each 🦋 represents 5 butterflies.
Each 🐞 represents 1 beetle.
Each 🕷 represents 2 spiders.

It is hard to compare. It looks like he found more beetles, but each symbol means a different amount. I am going to check if he found the most butterflies.

How could you improve the diagram so you can compare the results more easily?

→ Practice book 3B p68

Pictograms 2

Discover

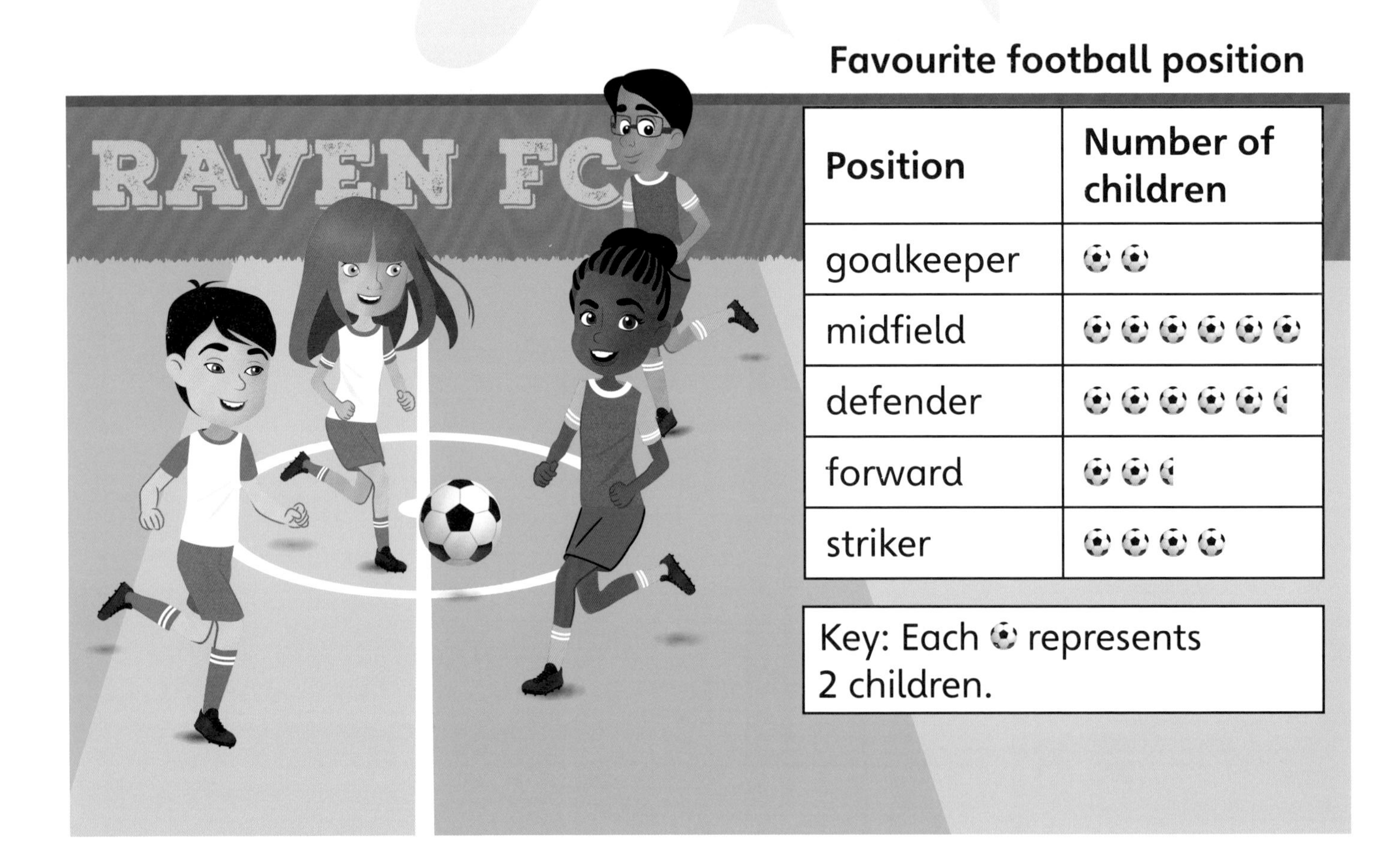

Favourite football position

Position	Number of children
goalkeeper	⚽ ⚽
midfield	⚽ ⚽ ⚽ ⚽ ⚽ ⚽
defender	⚽ ⚽ ⚽ ⚽ ⚽ ◐
forward	⚽ ⚽ ◐
striker	⚽ ⚽ ⚽ ⚽

Key: Each ⚽ represents 2 children.

1 **a)** How many more children prefer to play midfield compared to goalkeeper?

b) How many children chose defender or forward as their favourite position?

Share

Each symbol represents the same number of children. I am going to work out the difference in the number of symbols first.

a)

goalkeeper	⚽ ⚽
midfield	⚽ ⚽ ⚽ ⚽ ⚽ ⚽

There are 4 more ⚽ symbols for midfield.

Each symbol represents 2 children.
Half a symbol represents 1 child.

$4 \times 2 = 8$

Or $2 \times 2 = 4$ and $6 \times 2 = 12$

4 children prefer goalkeeper and 12 prefer midfield.

$12 - 4 = 8$

8 more children prefer to play in midfield than goalkeeper.

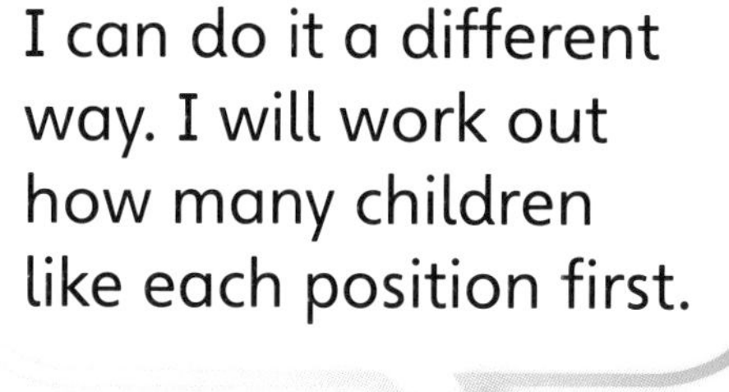

I can do it a different way. I will work out how many children like each position first.

b)

defender	⚽ ⚽ ⚽ ⚽ ⚽ ◐
forward	⚽ ⚽ ◐

For defender and forward there are 7 whole symbols and 2 half symbols altogether.

⚽ = 2 children, ◐ = 1 child

7 add 2 halves makes 8.

Each symbol represents 2 children.

$8 \times 2 = 16$

Or you could look at the amounts separately.

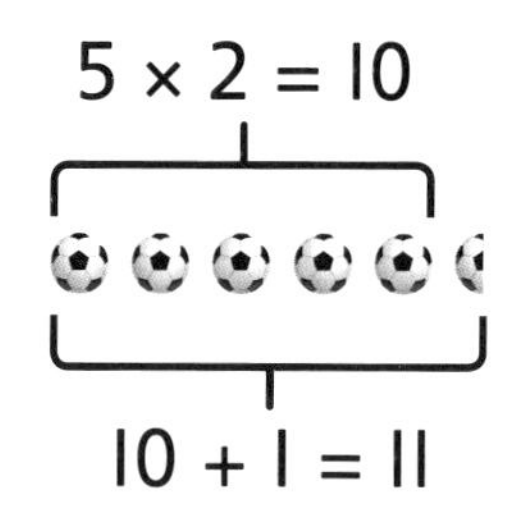

$11 + 5 = 16$

16 children chose defender or forward as their favourite position.

Think together

Age of children in Raven Football Club

Age	Number
age six	⚽ ⚽
age seven	⚽ ⚽ ⚽ ⚽
age eight	⚽ ⚽ ⚽ ⚽ ⚽ ◖
age nine	⚽ ⚽ ⚽ ⚽
age ten	⚽ ⚽ ⚽ ⚽ ◖

Key: Each ⚽ represents 2 children.

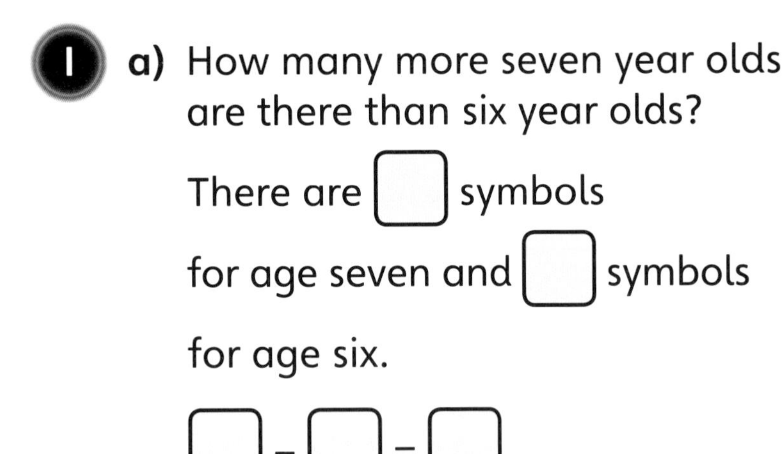

1 **a)** How many more seven year olds are there than six year olds?

There are ☐ symbols for age seven and ☐ symbols for age six.

☐ − ☐ = ☐

☐ × ☐ = ☐

There are ☐ more seven year olds than six year olds.

b) How many seven and eight year olds are there altogether?

For children aged seven and eight there are ☐ whole symbols and ☐ half symbols in total.

☐ × 2 = ☐

☐ × 1 = ☐

There are ☐ + ☐ = ☐ seven and eight year olds altogether.

I think there are two different ways I could work this out. I think one might be quicker.

I wonder if I need to work out each row separately or not?

2 How many players are in Raven FC altogether?

There are [ ] symbols altogether. Each symbol represents [ ].

[ ] × [ ] = [ ]

There are [ ] players altogether.

3 This pictogram shows the number of goals scored by the 4 top-scoring players.

How many more goals has the top player scored compared to the next best player?

Name	Number of goals
Jamilla	🏆 🏆 🏆 🏆 ½🏆
Lee	🏆 🏆
Luis	🏆 🏆 🏆
Olivia	🏆 ½🏆

Key: Each 🏆 represents 10 goals.

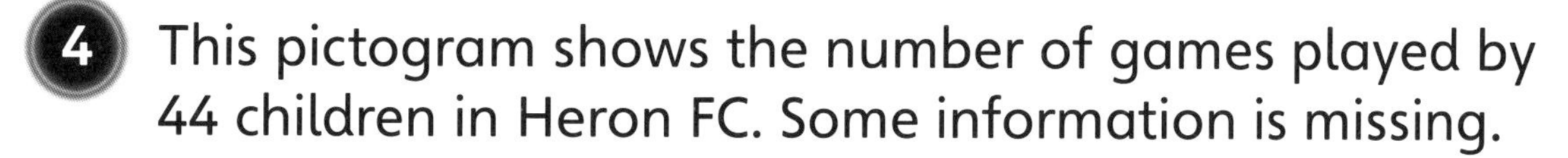

4 This pictogram shows the number of games played by 44 children in Heron FC. Some information is missing.

2 more children have played 6 games compared to 5 games.

a) How many children have played 5 or more games for Heron FC this season?

b) How many children have played 3 games?

Number of games	Number of children
3 games	
4 games	⚽ ⚽ ⚽ ⚽ ⚽
5 games	⚽ ⚽ ⚽ ½⚽
6 games	
7 games	⚽ ⚽ ⚽ ½⚽

Key: Each ⚽ represents 2 children.

You can use your answer from part a) to help you with b).

→ Practice book 3B p71

Bar charts 1

Discover

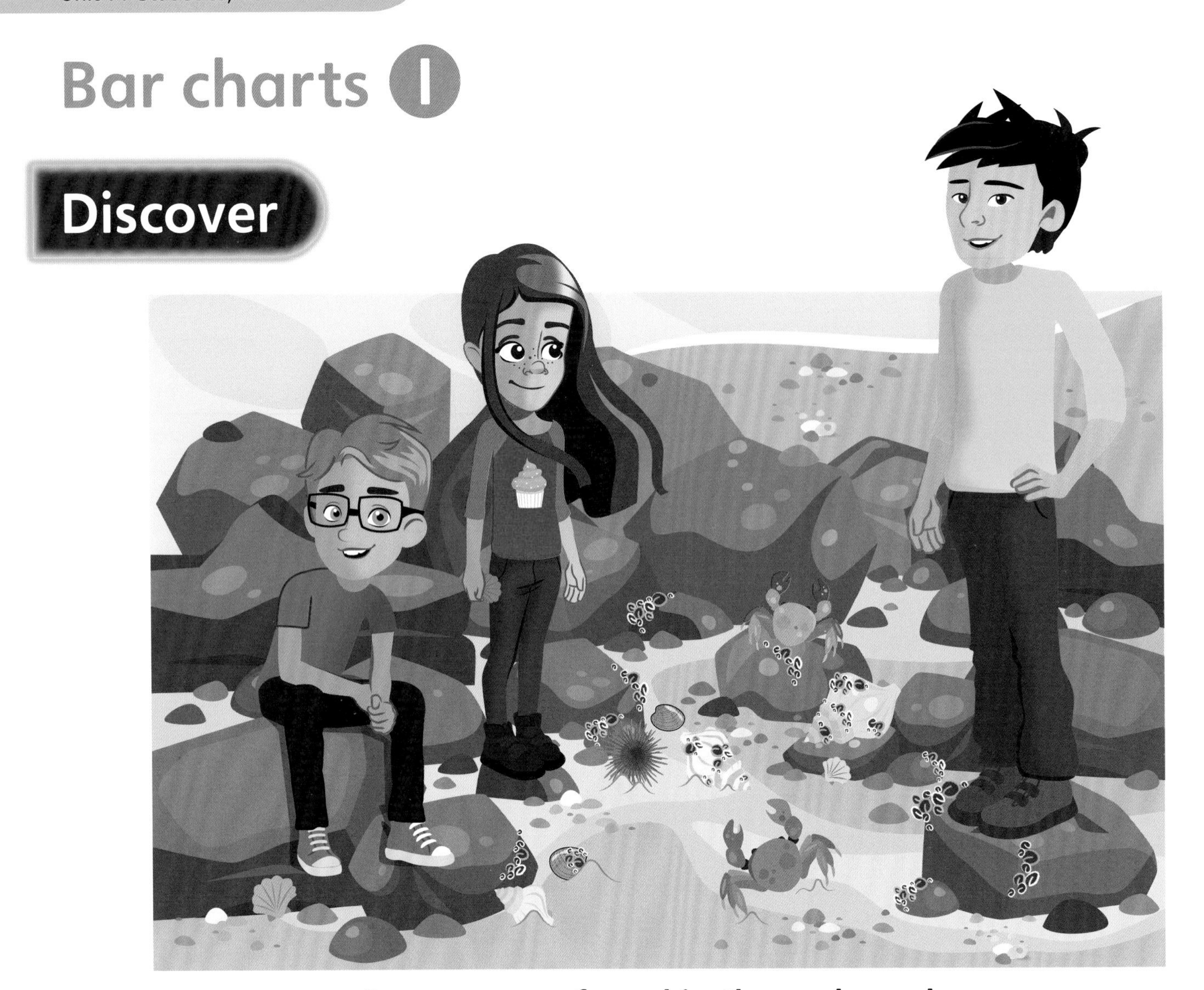

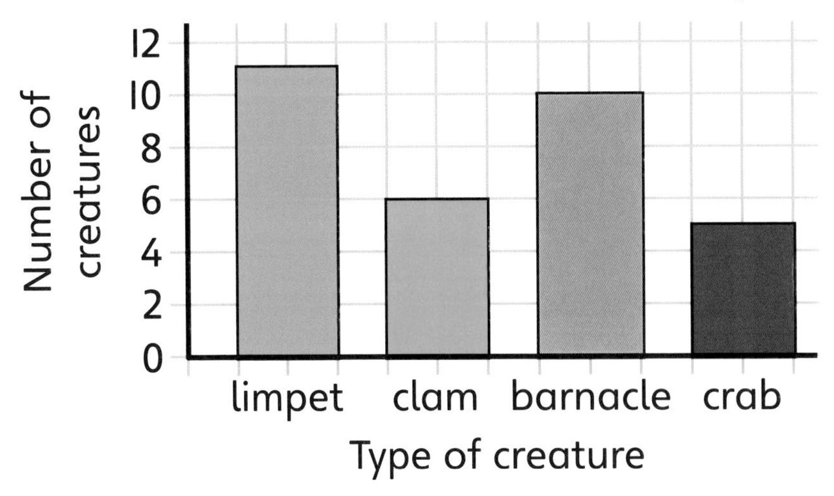

1 **a)** How many clams and barnacles did the children find?

b) How many limpets did the children find?

Share

The line that goes up the side of the bar chart is called the **vertical axis**. The numbers are called the **scale**.

a) This is a **bar chart**. Use the scale on the vertical axis to find the value of each bar.

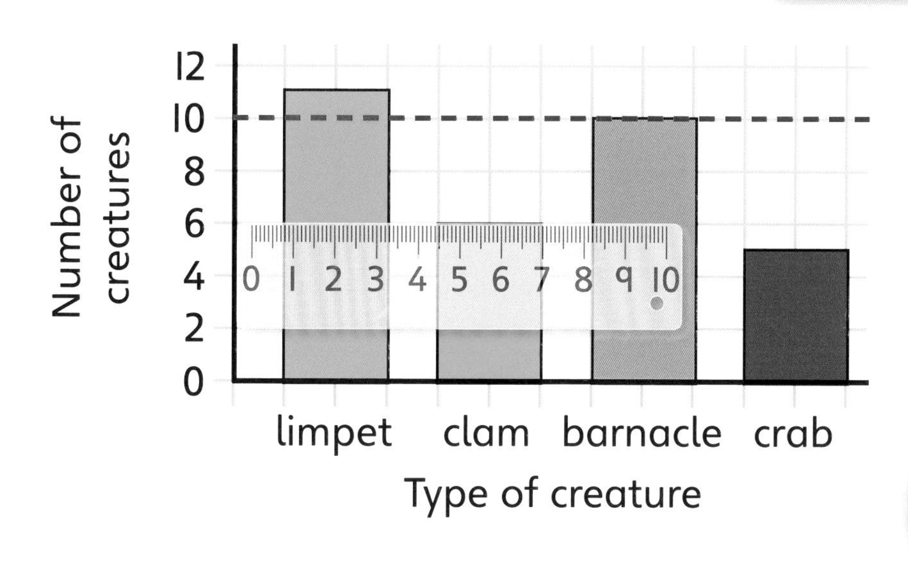

Use a ruler to help you.

The children found 6 clams and 10 barnacles.

The children found 16 clams and barnacles altogether.

b) The height of the bar for limpets is half-way between 10 and 12 on the vertical axis.

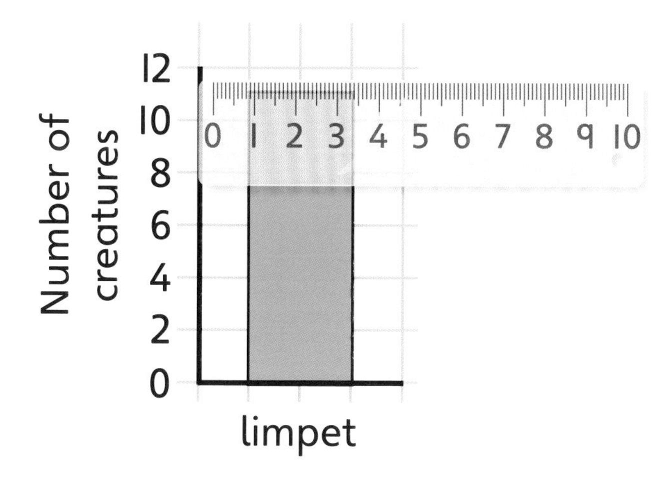

I read the scale like a number line.

The children found 11 limpets.

Think together

1 **a)** How many rockweeds did the children find?

The children found ☐ rockweeds.

b) How many sea lettuces did they find?

They found ☐ sea lettuces.

c) How many seaweeds and how many sea oaks did they find?

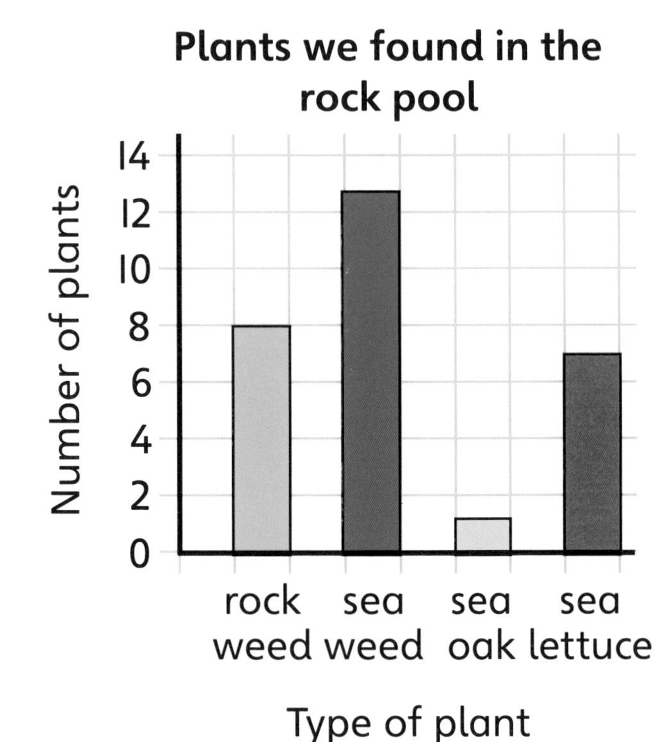

2 Complete the sentences.

a) ______________ found the most shells.

b) ______________ found the least shells

c) Toshi found ☐ shells.

Andy found ☐ shells.

Emma found ☐ shells.

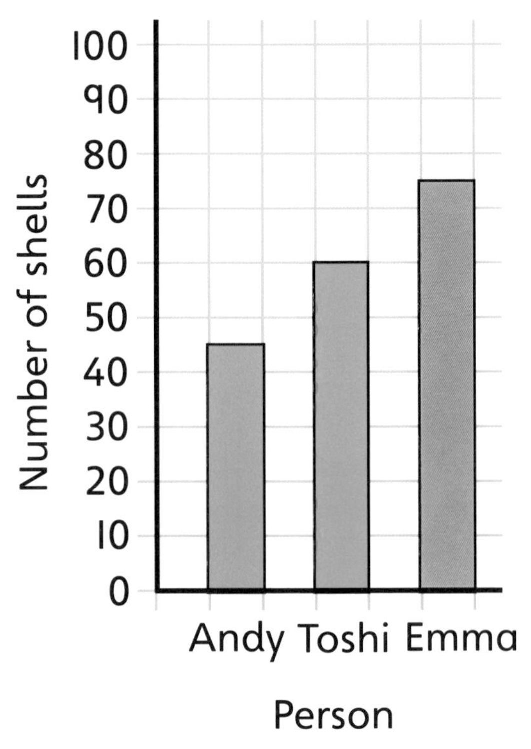

The scale goes up in 10s. I am going to work out what number is half-way.

3 Have a vote in your class to find out what your class's favourite sea animals are.

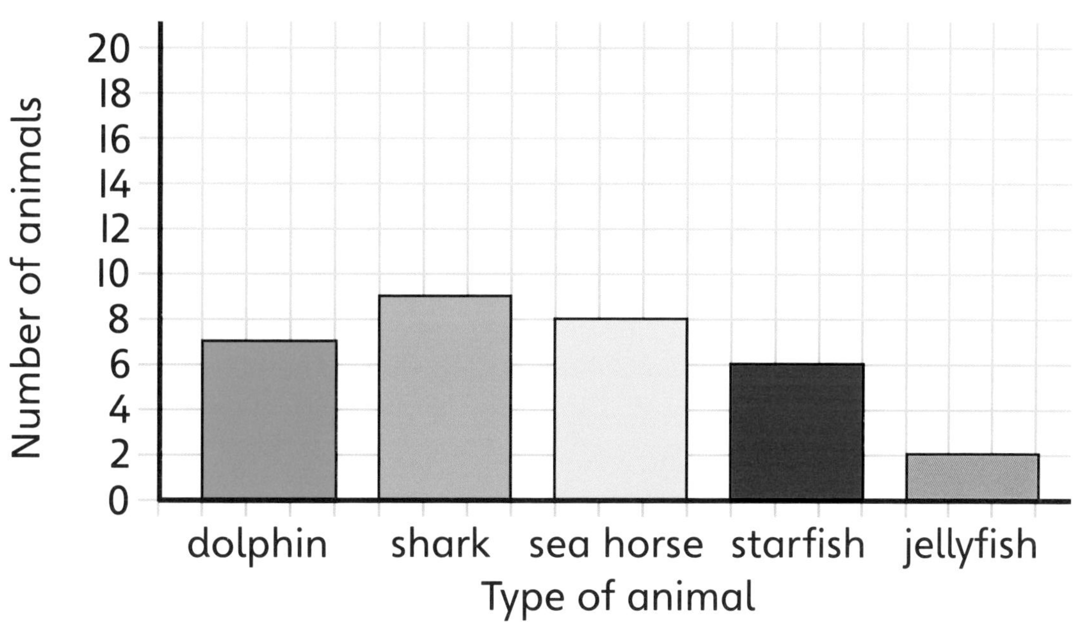

Favourite sea animal	Number of children
Dolphin	
Shark	
Sea horse	
Starfish	
Jellyfish	

Draw a chart to compare your class's results with Class 3A's.

a) Are Class 3A's most popular and least popular favourite animals the same as your class's?

b) Do more or less people like starfish best in Class 3A compared with your class?

c) How many more or less people like sharks best in Class 3A compared with your class?

→ Practice book 3B p74

Bar charts 2

Discover

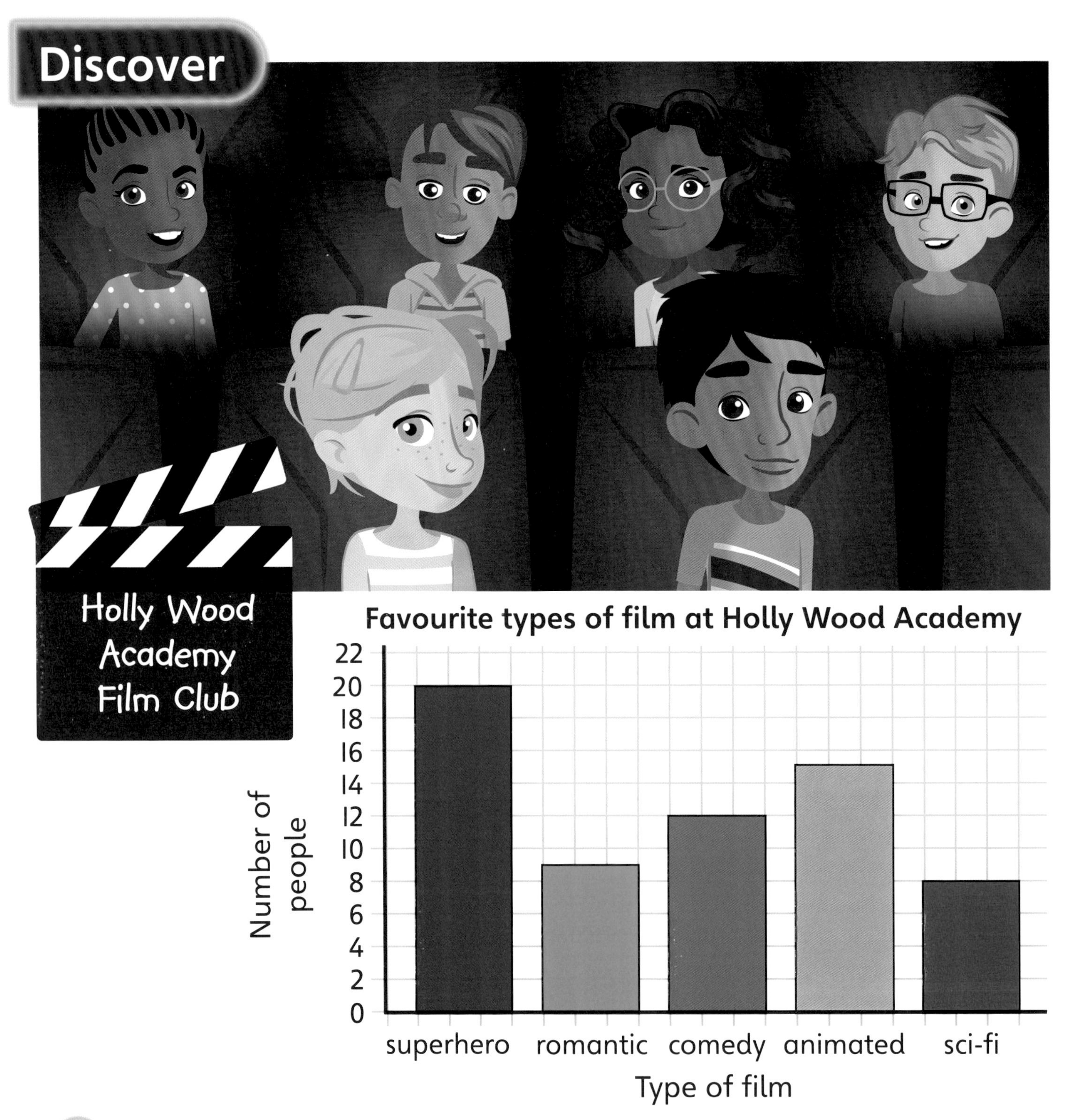

1 a) How many more people like superhero films than like comedy films?

b) How many people like comedy or animated films best?

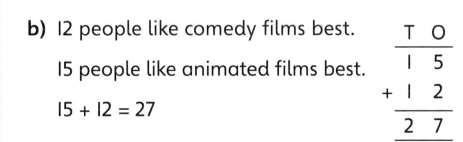

Share

a) You can draw lines or use a ruler to read off the number of people.

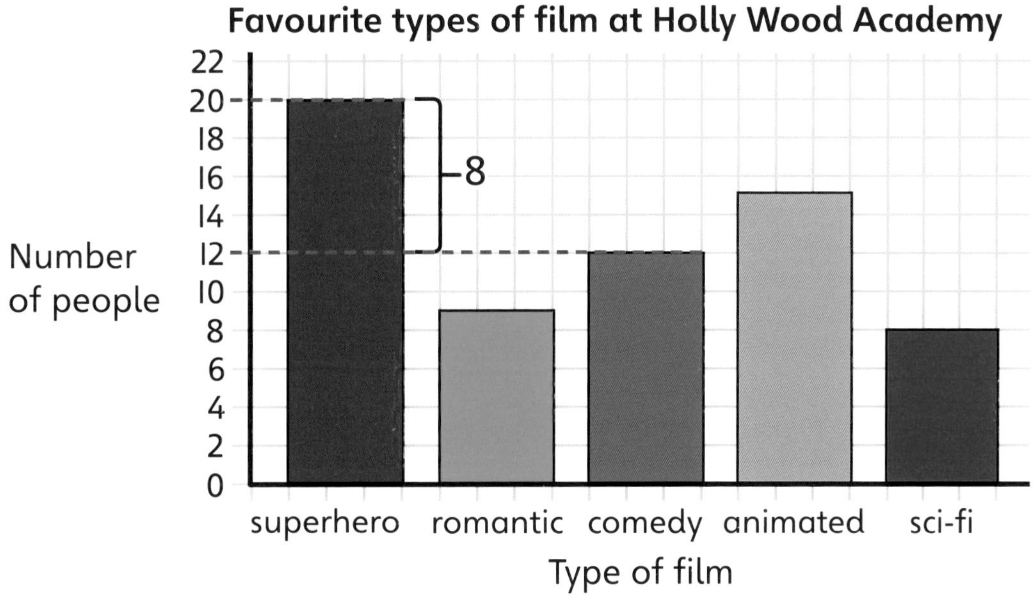
Favourite types of film at Holly Wood Academy
Number of people
22
20
18
16
14
12
10
8
6
4
2
0
8
superhero
romantic
comedy
animated
sci-fi
Type of film

20 people like superhero films best.

12 people like comedy films best.

20 – 12 = 8

8 more people like superhero films than comedy films.

I read the values off the chart and found the difference.

b) 12 people like comedy films best.

15 people like animated films best.

15 + 12 = 27

	T	O
	1	5
+	1	2
	2	7

I am going to work out how many people like comedy and animated films then add these numbers together.

27 people like comedy or animated films best.

Think together

1 **a)** How many more hot dogs were sold than nachos?

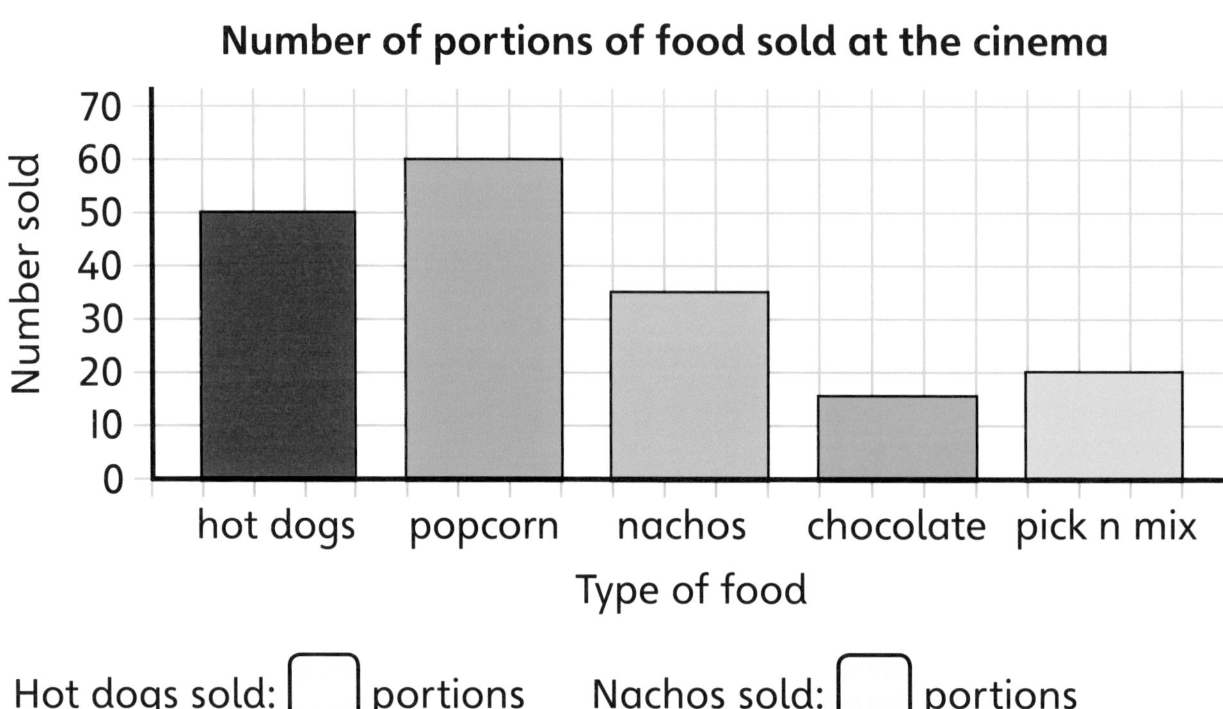

Hot dogs sold: ☐ portions Nachos sold: ☐ portions

☐ − ☐ = ☐

☐ more hot dogs were sold than nachos.

b) What is the difference between the most popular and the least popular food?

The most popular food was ______________ .

The least popular food was ______________ .

The difference between the most popular and least popular food is ☐ portions.

I am going to look at the tallest and shortest bars.

2 Class 3A drew a bar chart to represent the number of different tickets sold for a film.

Ticket type	Adult	Child	Student	Senior	Family
Number of people	20	25	40	15	20

Types of tickets sold for *Superheroes vs Turtles*

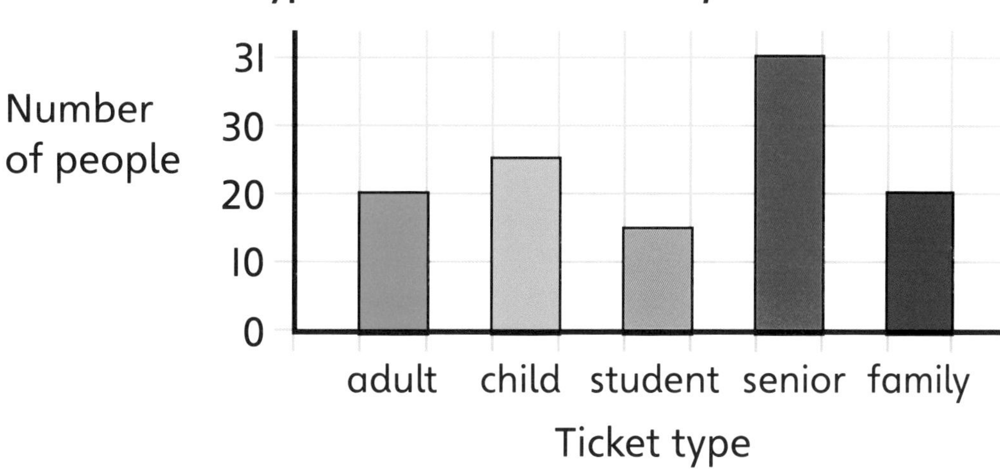

What mistakes did class 3A make?

3 Do more people prefer to go to the cinema during the week or at the weekend?

Favourite day to go to the cinema

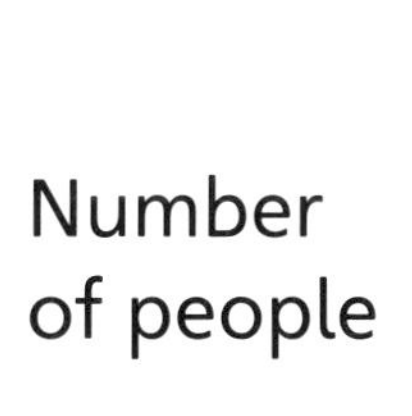

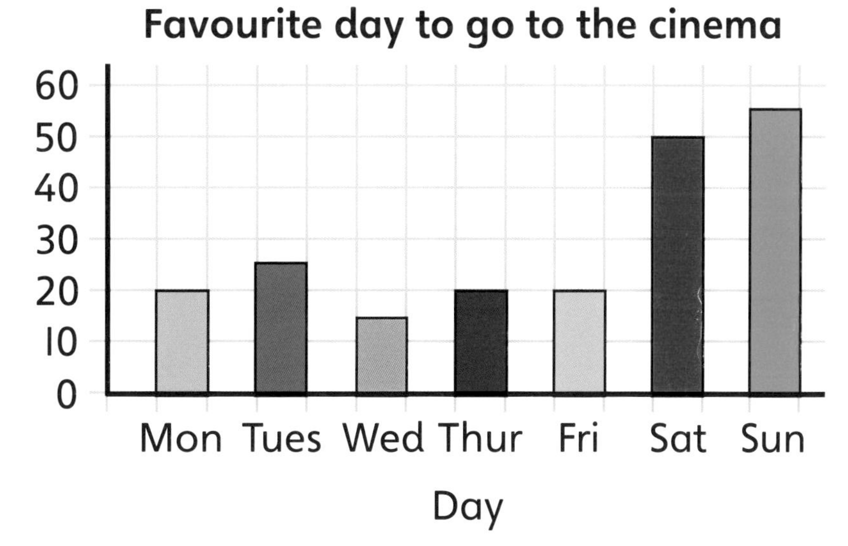

More people prefer to go to the cinema _______________ .

→ Practice book 3B p77

Tables

Discover

Field events			
	Javelin throw	Ball throw	Discus throw
Ambika	20 m	14 m	21 m
Ebo	18 m	23 m	18 m
Richard	25 m	21 m	16 m
Lexi	17 m	17 m	29 m

1 a) Who came in 1st, 2nd, 3rd and 4th place for the ball throw?

b) How much further did Lexi throw the discus compared to Ambika?

Share

a) Look at the column for the ball throw.

Field events			
	Javelin throw	Ball throw	Discus throw
Ambika	20 m	14 m	21 m
Ebo	18 m	23 m	18 m
Richard	25 m	21 m	16 m
Lexi	17 m	17 m	29 m

Rows in a table go across the page. **Columns** in a table go down the page.

Look along the row to find out who got each distance.

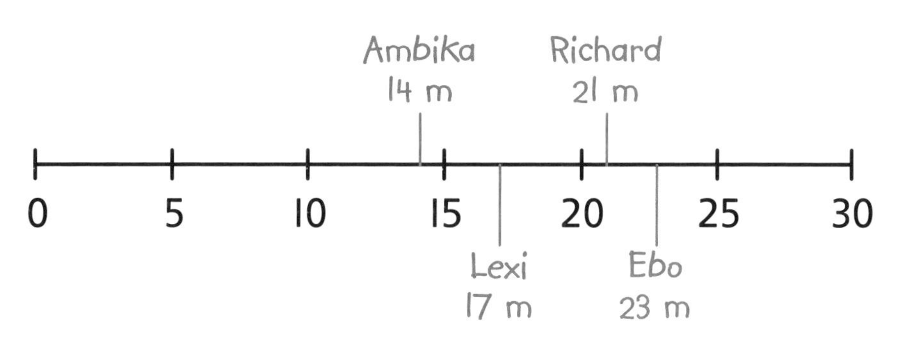

I put the numbers on a number line.

14 < 17 < 21 < 23

Ebo came in 1st place, Richard came in 2nd place, Lexi came in 3rd place and Ambika came in 4th place for the ball throw.

b) Look at the distances for Ambika and Lexi in the discus throw column.

	Discus throw
Ambika	21 m
Lexi	29 m

Ambika threw the discus 21 m.

Lexi threw the discus 29 m.

29 m – 21 m = 8 m

Lexi threw the discus 8 m further than Ambika.

Think together

1 These are the results from the running event.

Running event times		
	100 m race	**200 m race**
Ambika	22 seconds	49 seconds
Ebo	31 seconds	45 seconds
Richard	27 seconds	41 seconds
Lexi	26 seconds	53 seconds

a) Who came 1st, 2nd, 3rd and 4th in the 100 m race?

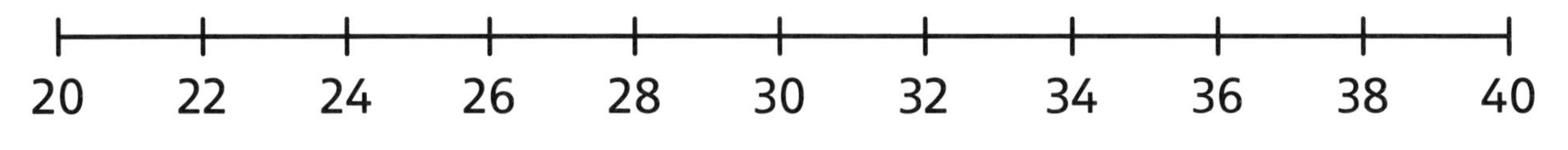

☐ < ☐ < ☐ < ☐

The order starting with the fastest is:

1st: ___________

2nd: ___________

3rd: ___________

4th: ___________

I think the fastest time will be the lowest number and the slowest time will be the highest number.

b) How much faster did Richard run the 200 m race compared to Ambika?

Richard took ☐ seconds. Ambika took ☐ seconds.

☐ – ☐ = ☐

Richard was ☐ seconds faster than Ambika.

2 This table shows how many points each house won on sports day. Complete the table.

House	Running	Field	Total
Ash House	30		80
Oak House	45		80
Maple House	40		85

3 This table shows the number of medals won by each year group.

Year	1st, 2nd or 3rd	Commended	Total
Year 3	21	15	
Year 4		9	42
Year 5	20		37
Year 6		26	48

a) Use the information to complete the table.

b) Write three sentences about the information in the table.

I think I can work out this question based on the information I know.

→ Practice book 3B p80

End of unit check

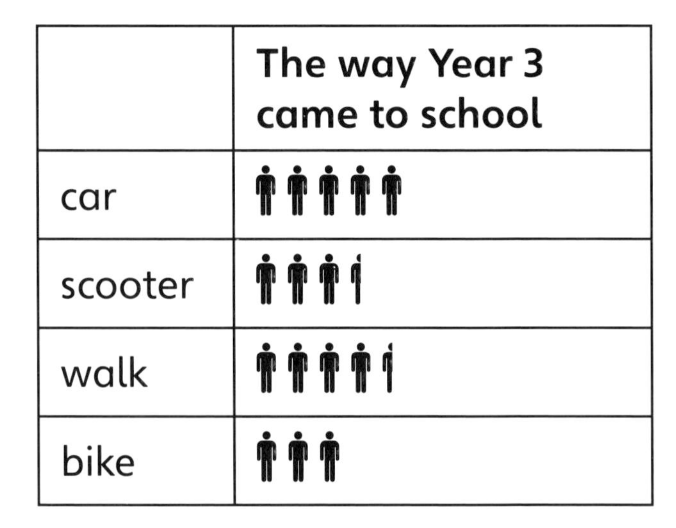

The way Year 3 came to school
car
scooter
walk
bike

Key: Each represents 2 people.

1 How many children came to school by scooter?

A $3\frac{1}{2}$

B 3

C 7

D 4

2 Based on the pictogram, which statement is true?

A The same number of children walked to school as came by car.

B Walking is the most popular way for children to come to school.

C 3 children came to school by bike.

D 2 more children walked to school than came to school by scooter.

3 This table shows the scores of three children in their English and Maths tests.

	Maths	**English**
Jamie	30	25
Mo	15	32
Danny	28	20

How many more marks did Mo get than Jamie in English?

A 7 marks

B 15 marks

C 12 marks

D 17 marks

4 Lee asked some children in Year 3 how many pets they had.

He put his results in a bar chart.

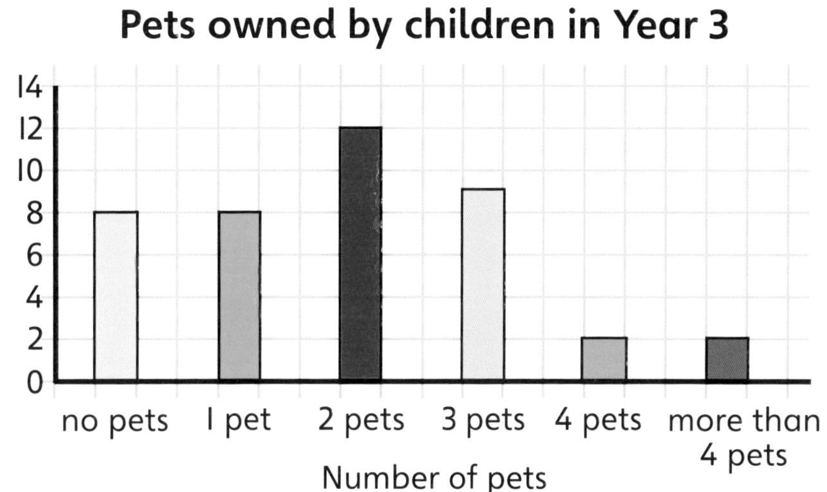

How many children have 3 pets?

A 9 **B** $4\frac{1}{2}$ **C** 12 **D** 2

5 How many children altogether did Lee ask?

A 37 **B** 12 **C** 41 **D** 20

6 This table shows the highest and lowest temperatures in Norwich on four days in September.

	Highest temperature	**Lowest temperature**
Friday	13	8
Saturday	16	10
Sunday	18	9
Monday	15	8

a) Which day had the highest temperature? ______________

b) Which day had the greatest difference between the highest and lowest temperature? ______________

c) What is the difference between the highest temperature on Friday and the highest temperature on Sunday? ☐ °C

→ Practice book 3B p83

Unit 8
Length

In this unit we will ...

- Measure lengths in millimetres, centimetres and metres
- Compare lengths
- Add and subtract lengths
- Measure the perimeter of a shape
- Learn about equivalent lengths

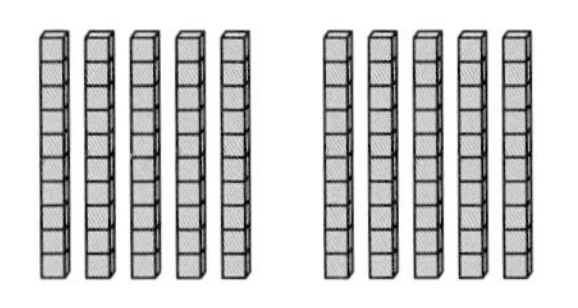

How many 10s go into 100? We could use base 10 equipment or counters to show this.

We will need some maths words.
Which ones do you recognise?

length **height** **width** **perimeter**

distance **centimetres (cm)** **millimetres (mm)**

metres (m) **unit of measurement** **measure**

add **subtract** **multiply** **equivalent**

convert **greater than (>)** **less than (<)**

ruler **metre stick**

Number lines can be useful. Can
you find 10 more than 17 on here?

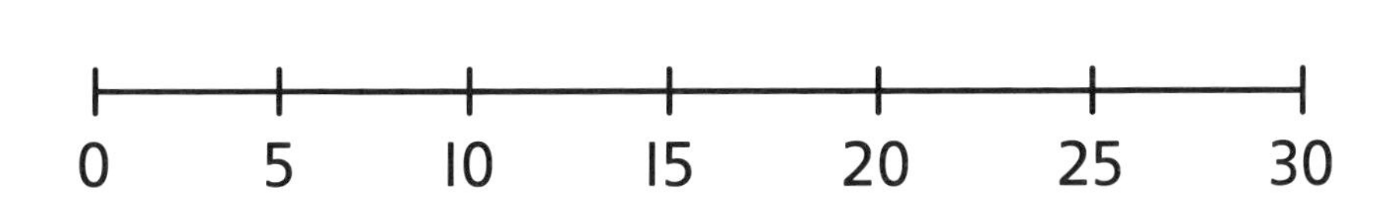

Measuring length 1

Discover

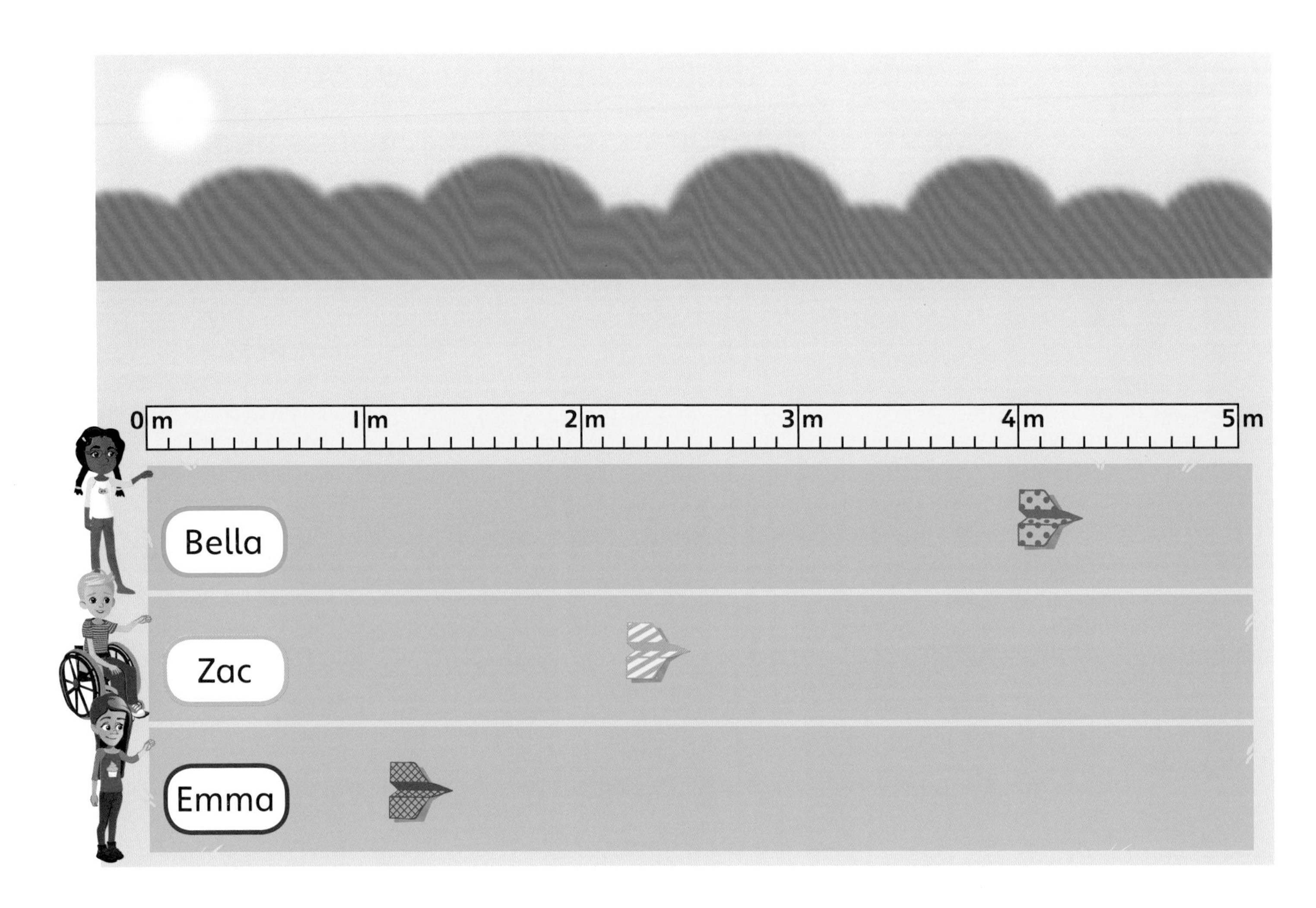

1 a) How far has Zac's paper aeroplane travelled?

b) Whose paper aeroplane has travelled 4 m 30 cm?

m is short for metre.

cm is short for centimetre.

Share

a) 0 I m

0 | 10 cm | 20 cm | 30 cm | 40 cm | 50 cm | 60 cm | 70 cm | 80 cm | 90 cm | 100 cm

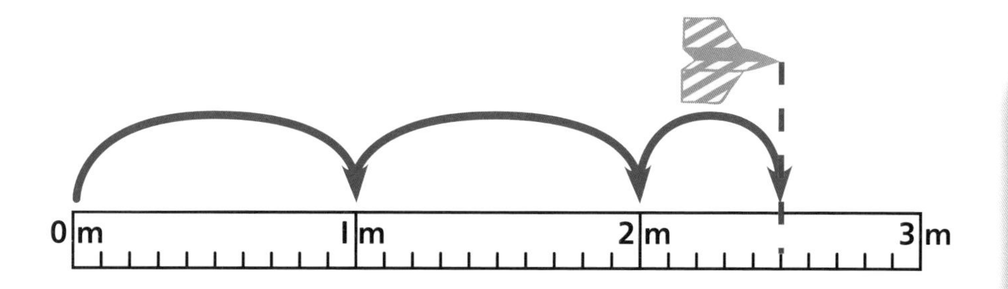

There are 100 cm in one metre. The metre stick has a mark for every 10 cm.

I can see Zac's paper aeroplane has travelled 2 whole metres and half a metre.

Zac's paper aeroplane has travelled 2 m 50 cm.

b)

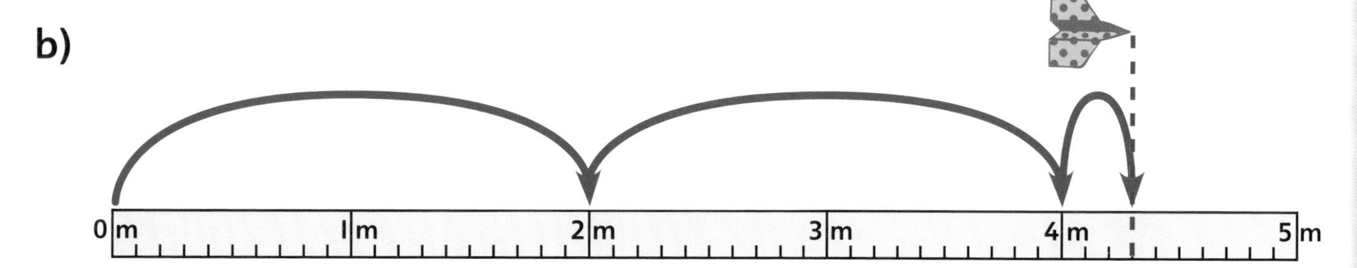

Bella's paper aeroplane has travelled 4 m 30 cm.

4 m 30 cm is greater than 2 m 50 cm, so Bella's aeroplane has travelled the furthest.

Think together

1 How far has each ball rolled?

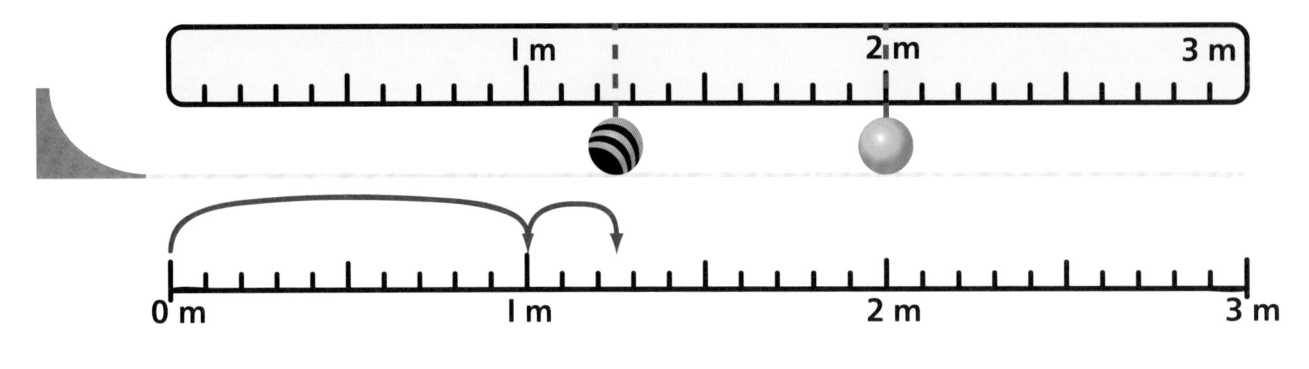

The stripy ball has rolled ☐ m ☐ cm.

The blue ball has rolled ☐ m.

The blue ball has rolled ☐ cm more than the stripy ball.

2 How tall is Max?

It looks to me like working out height is a lot like measuring length.

Max is ☐ m ☐ cm tall.

3 Work with a partner. Use metre sticks to measure a table in your classroom. What is the height, length and width?

a) The height of the table

is ☐ m ☐ cm.

b) The length of the table

is ☐ m ☐ cm.

c) The width of the table

is ☐ m ☐ cm.

length ☐ cm

width ☐ cm

height ☐ cm

CHALLENGE

4 How could you cut a 3 m 7 cm piece of string off a ball of string?

I could cut a 3 m 7 cm piece of string off a ball of string

by ________________________________ .

I am sure there is a way of doing this with just one metre stick.

What does 3 m 7 cm actually mean?

→ Practice book 3B p86

Measuring length 2

Discover

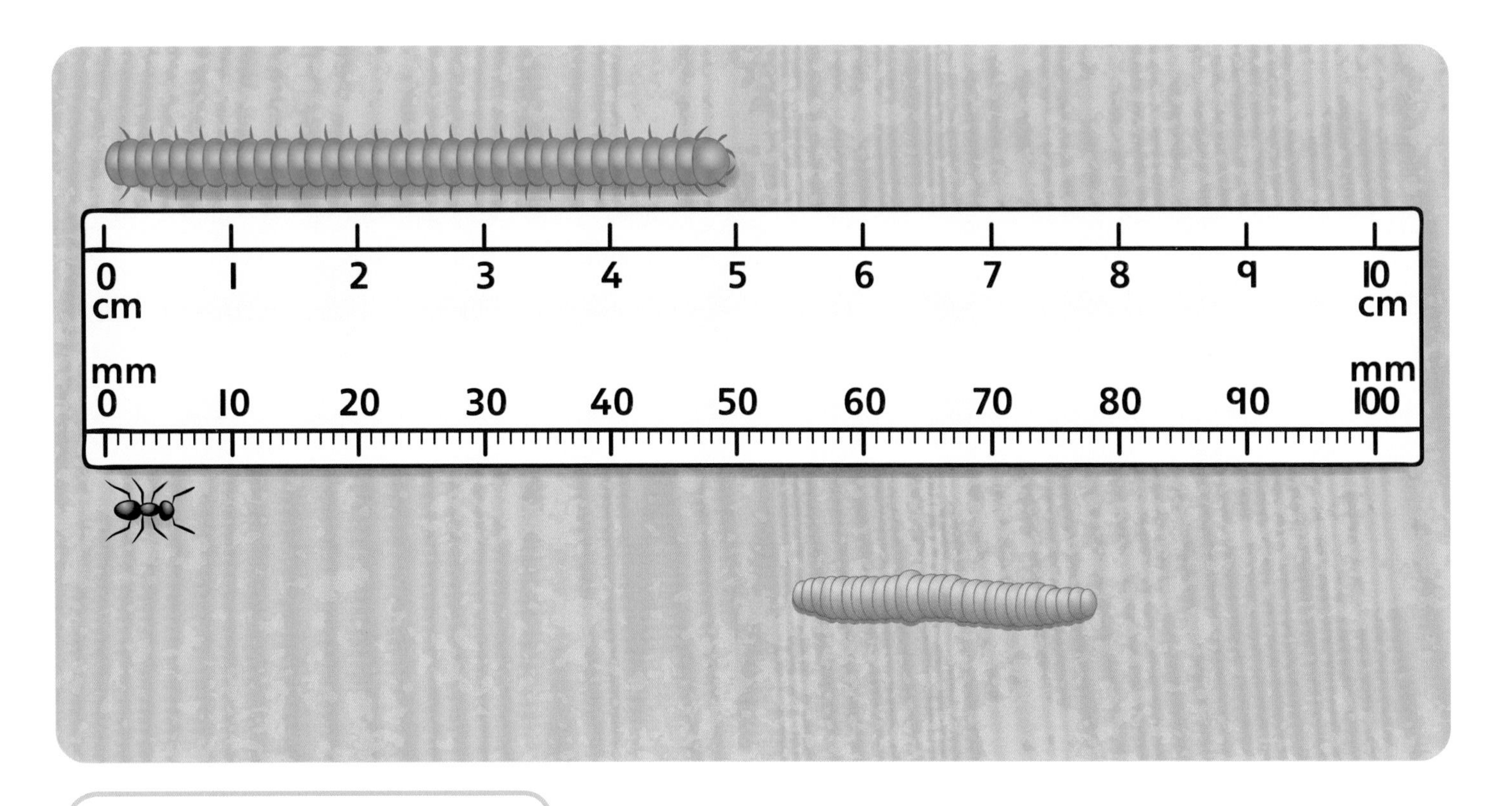

Larger than actual size

1 **a)** How long are the centipede and the ant?

b) The worm is 27 mm. Show this on a ruler.

Share

a)

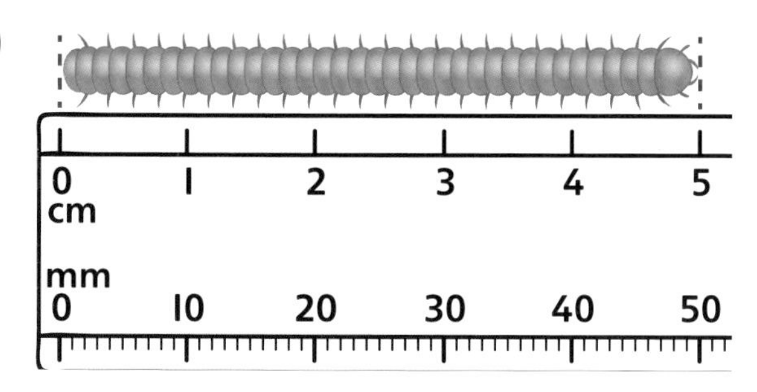

Larger than actual size

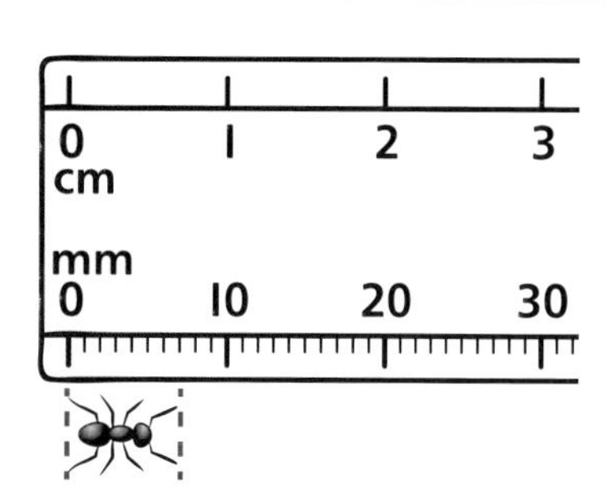

The centipede is exactly 5 cm long.

The ant is shorter than 1 cm. I wonder how I could measure it more accurately.

0 cm 1 2 3 4 5

Actual size

mm 0 10 20 30 40 50

These are centimetre (cm) marks. 1 cm is roughly the width of one of your fingers.

These are **millimetre (mm)** marks. 1 mm is very small. It is about the thickness of a 5p coin.

The ant is 7 mm long.

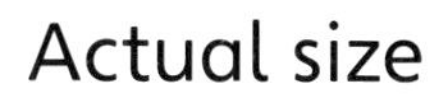

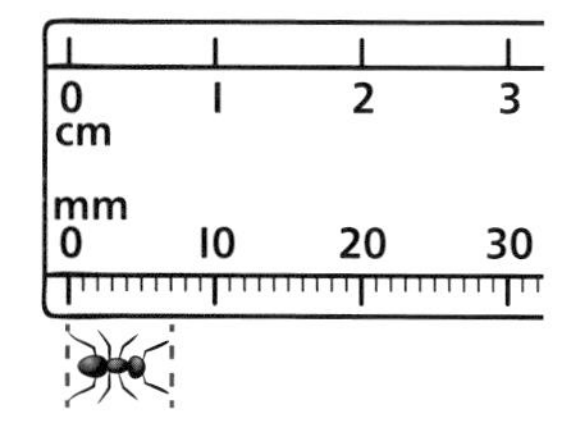

There are 10 mm in 1 cm.

b) The worm is 27 mm.

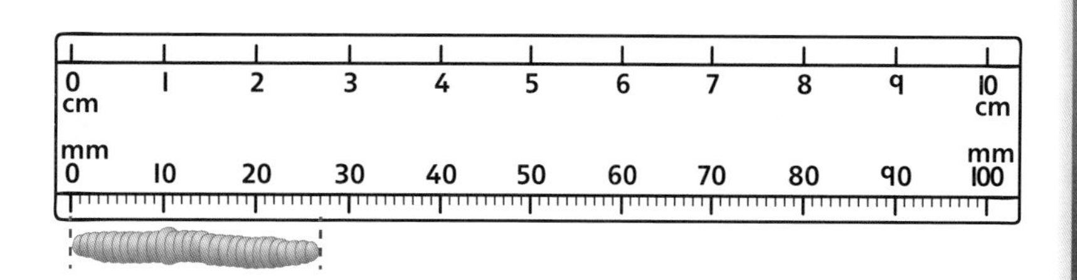

Think together

1 How long is the snail in mm?

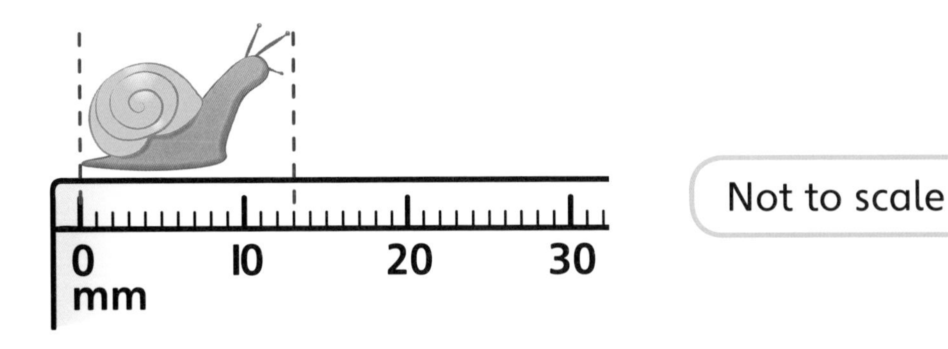

The snail is [ ] mm long.

2 **a)** Measure these insects using the ruler provided.

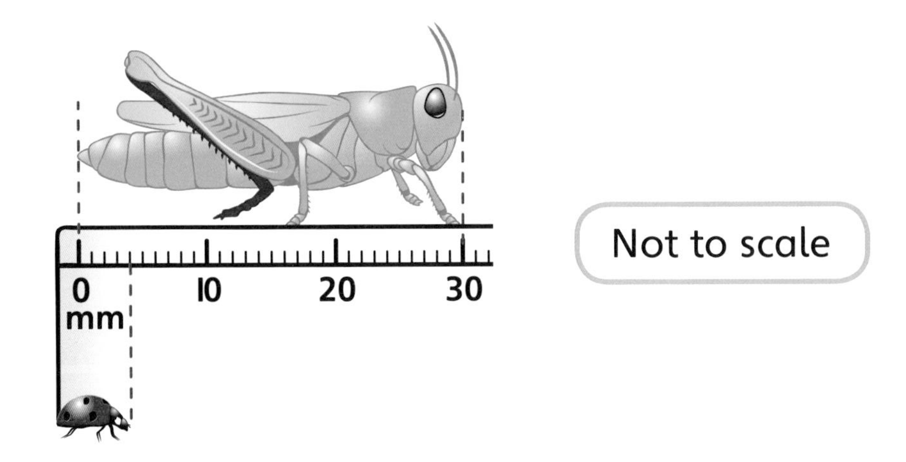

The grasshopper is [ ] cm long.

The ladybird is [ ] mm long.

b) Use a ruler to draw a line the same length as each of the insects.

3 Max has measured the blue line.

He says it is 27 mm long. Do you agree?

Explain how you could work out the length.

I can work out the length without needing to measure again!

0 mm 10 20 30 40 50

Larger than actual size

4 Measure these lines using a ruler.

a)

Line **a)** is ☐ mm.

b)

Line **b)** is ☐ cm.

c)

Line **c)** is ☐ cm and ☐ mm.

Line b) is 40 mm.

I need to answer in cm.
How many mm make up 1 cm?

→ Practice book 3B p89

Equivalent lengths – metres and centimetres

Discover

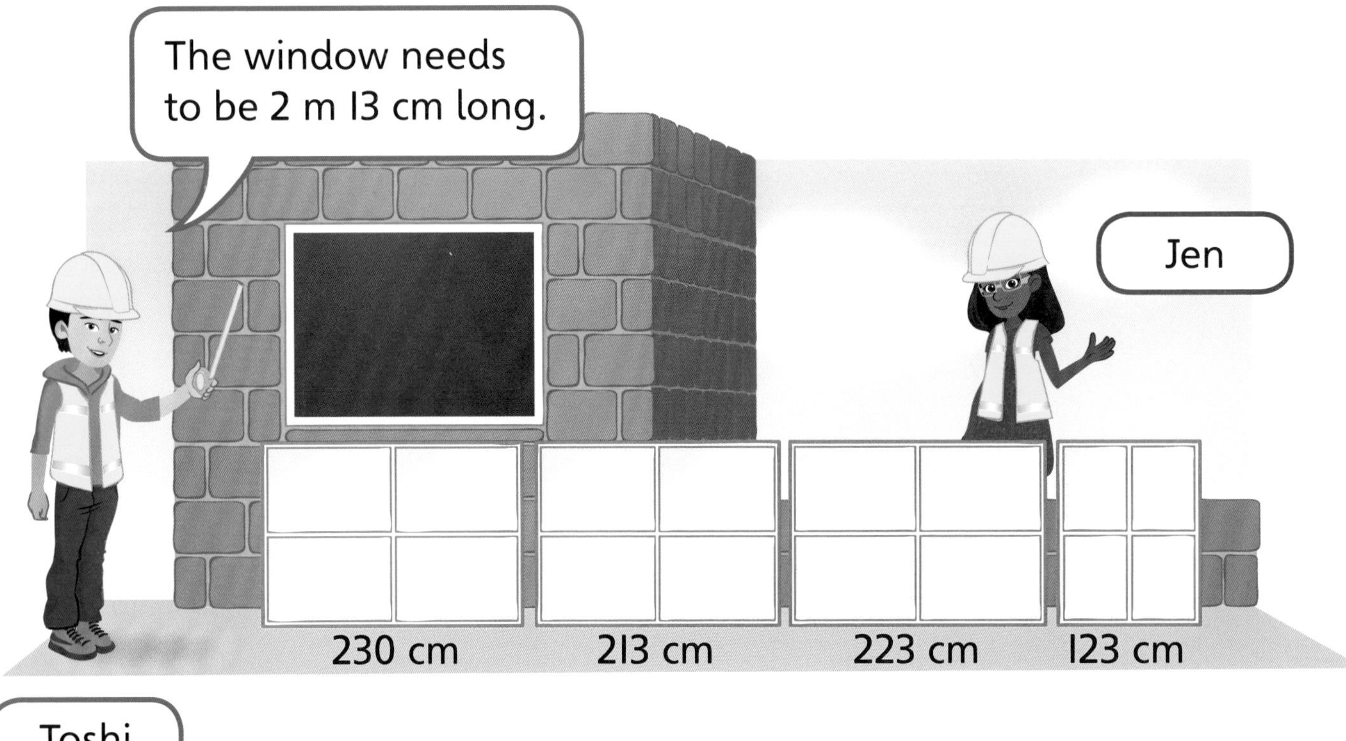

1 **a)** Which window will fit?

b) Toshi says the window needs to be 1 m 21 cm high.

What will this be in centimetres?

Share

a) 200 cm is the same as 2 m.

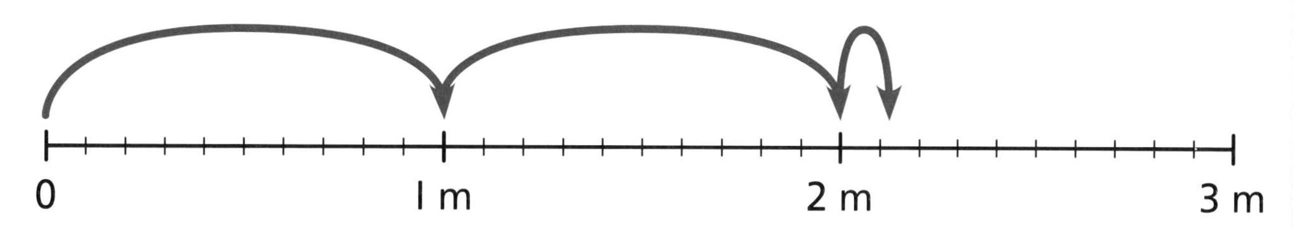

There are 13 more centimetres.

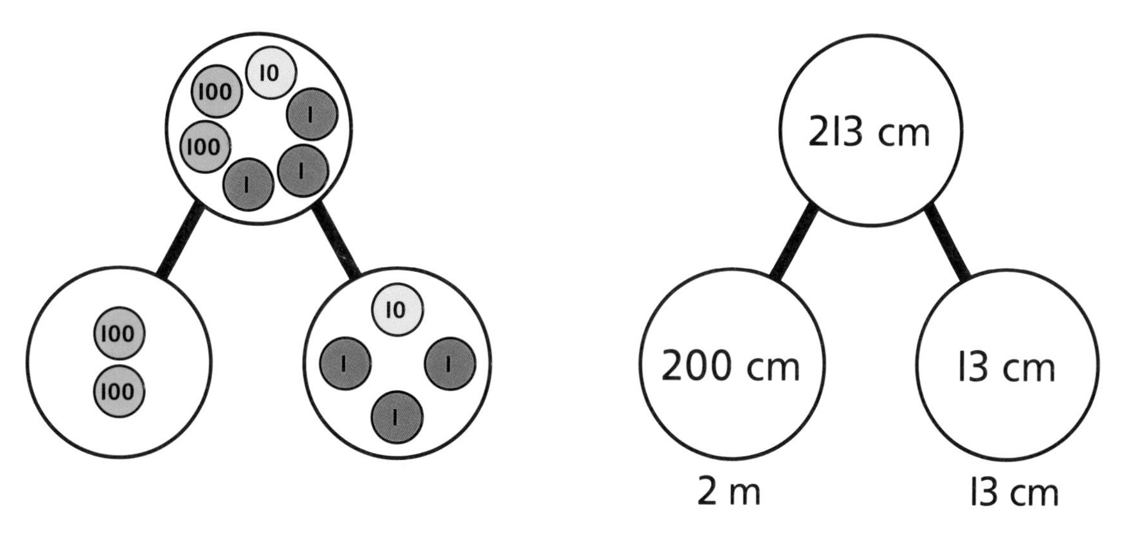

213 cm is the same as 2 m and 13 cm, so the 213 cm window will fit.

b) There are 100 cm in 1 m.

100 cm and 21 cm totals 121 cm.

1 m 21 cm will be 121 cm.

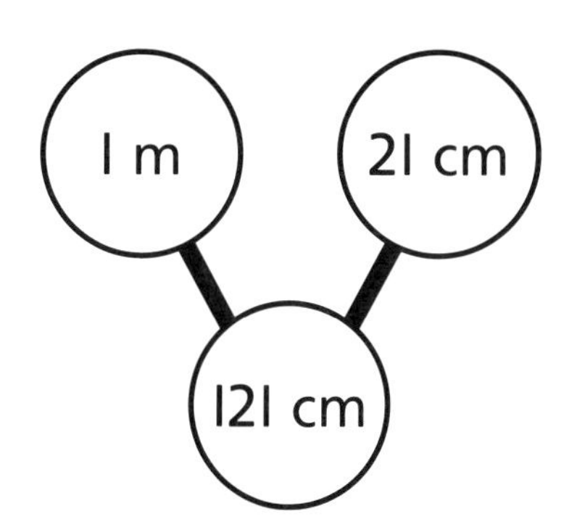

Remember that 1 m is the same as 100 cm.

What is another word for 'the same as'?

Think together

1 What are the missing measurements in these sentences?

a) The window is ☐ m and ☐ cm wide.

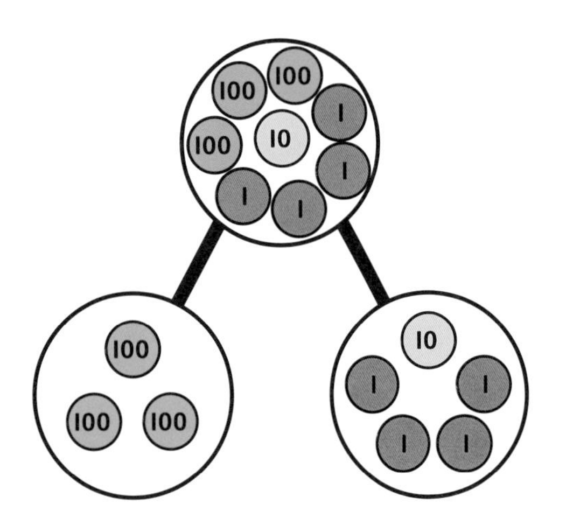

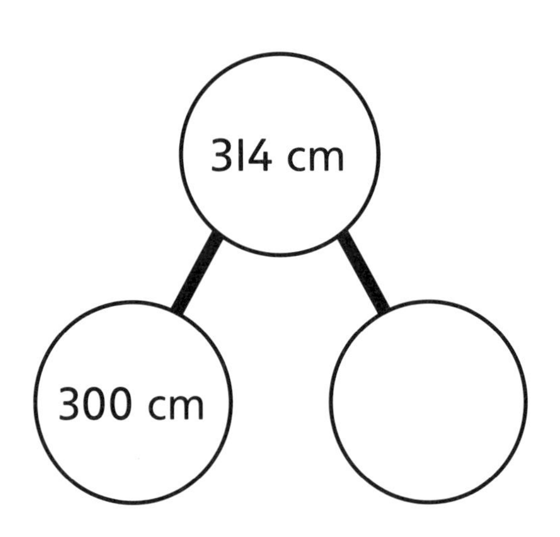

b) The window is ☐ cm high.

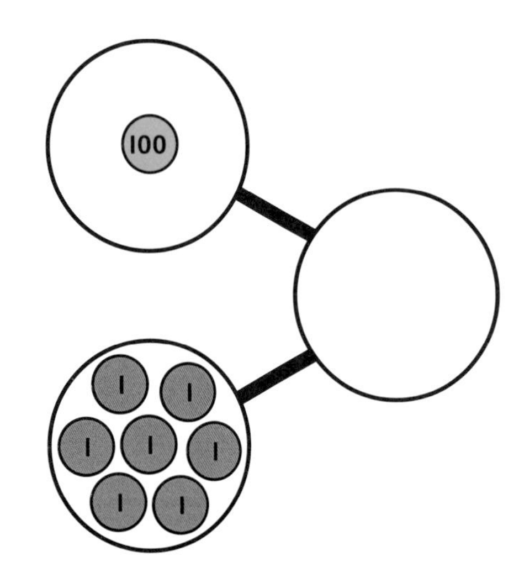

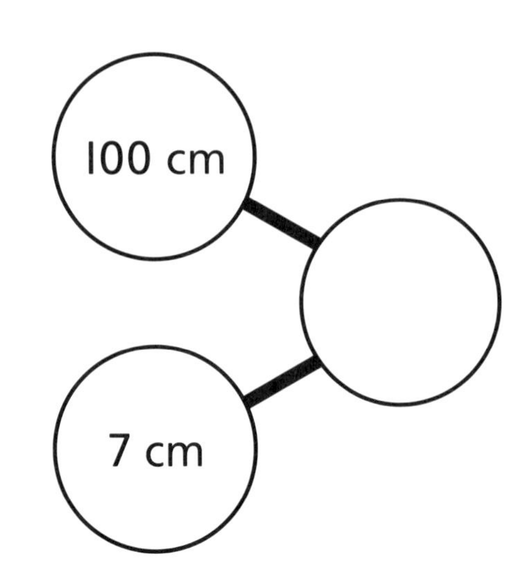

2 Work out the missing measurements.

2 m 34 cm	234 cm
3 m 17 cm	☐ cm
☐ m ☐ cm	463 cm
☐ m ☐ cm	93 cm

3 Match each crocodile to the egg that shows its length in centimetres.

a)
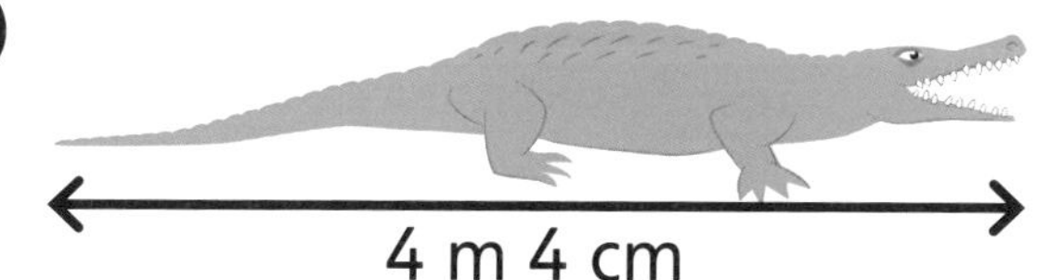
4 m 4 cm

440 cm

b)
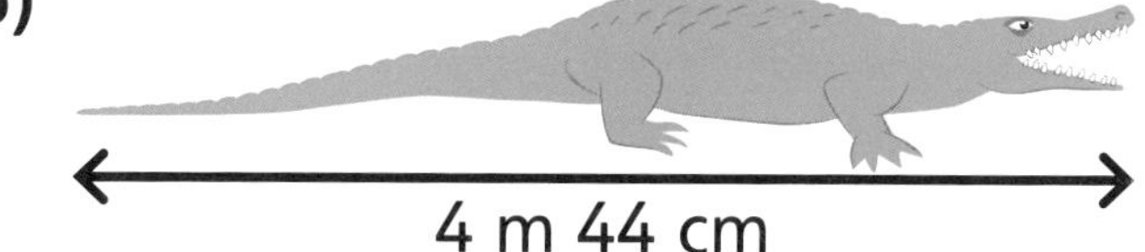
4 m 44 cm

444 cm

c)
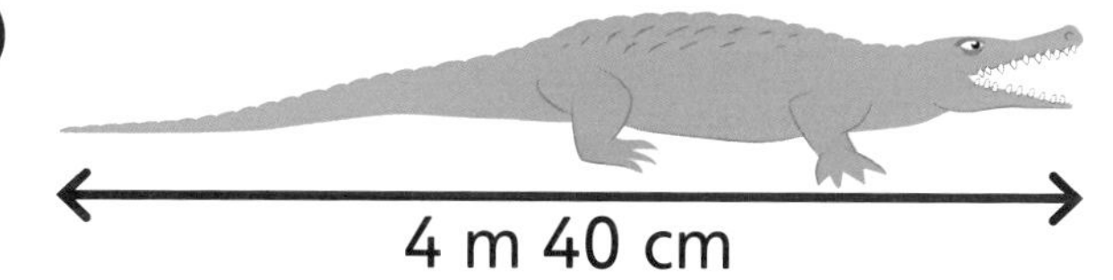
4 m 40 cm

400 cm

d)
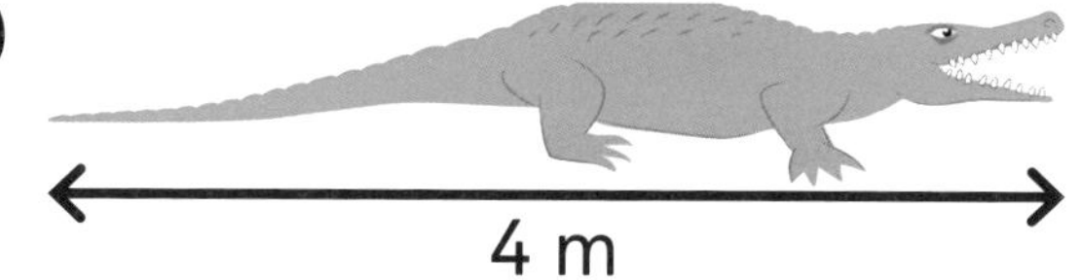
4 m

404 cm

I will think carefully about place value of 100s, 10s and 1s.

I will use part-whole models to help.

→ Practice book 3B p92

Equivalent lengths – centimetres and millimetres

Discover

1 Luis has finished sewing and has some thread left.

a) Which ruler should Luis use to measure the length of the thread?

b) How long is the piece of thread?

Share

a) You can measure smaller objects using millimetres **or** centimetres and millimetres.

1 cm

0 mm 10

10 mm is equivalent to 1 cm.

Luis could use either ruler to measure the thread.

Larger than actual size

b) The thread measures 24 mm or 2 cm 4 mm.

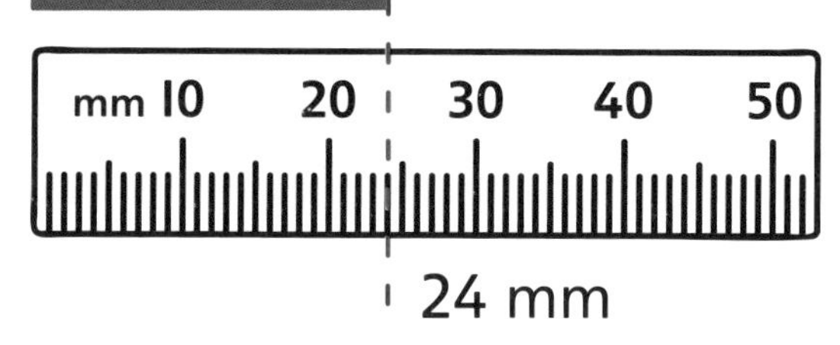

Larger than actual size

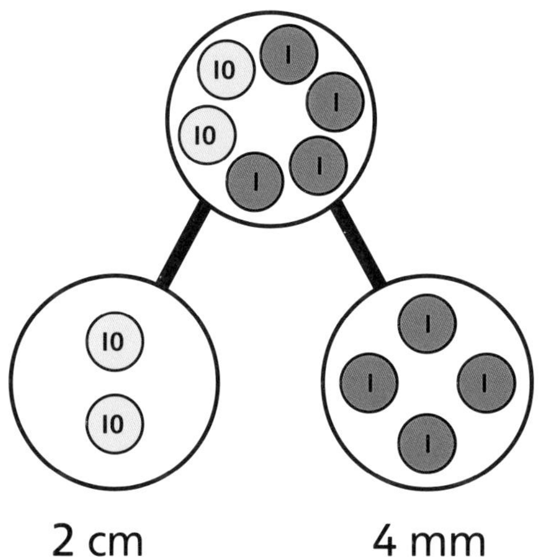

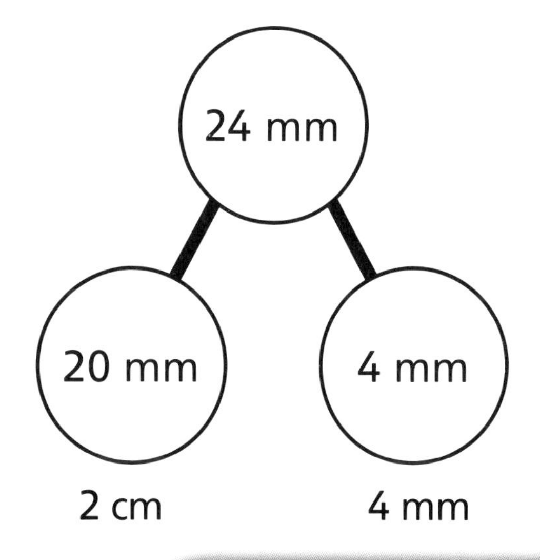

There are 10 mm in 1 cm.

20 mm is equal to 2 cm.

The string is 20 mm and 4 mm more.

It is 24 mm, the same as 2 cm 4 mm.

I wonder what other things I could measure in millimetres.

Think together

1 What are the missing measurements in these sentences?

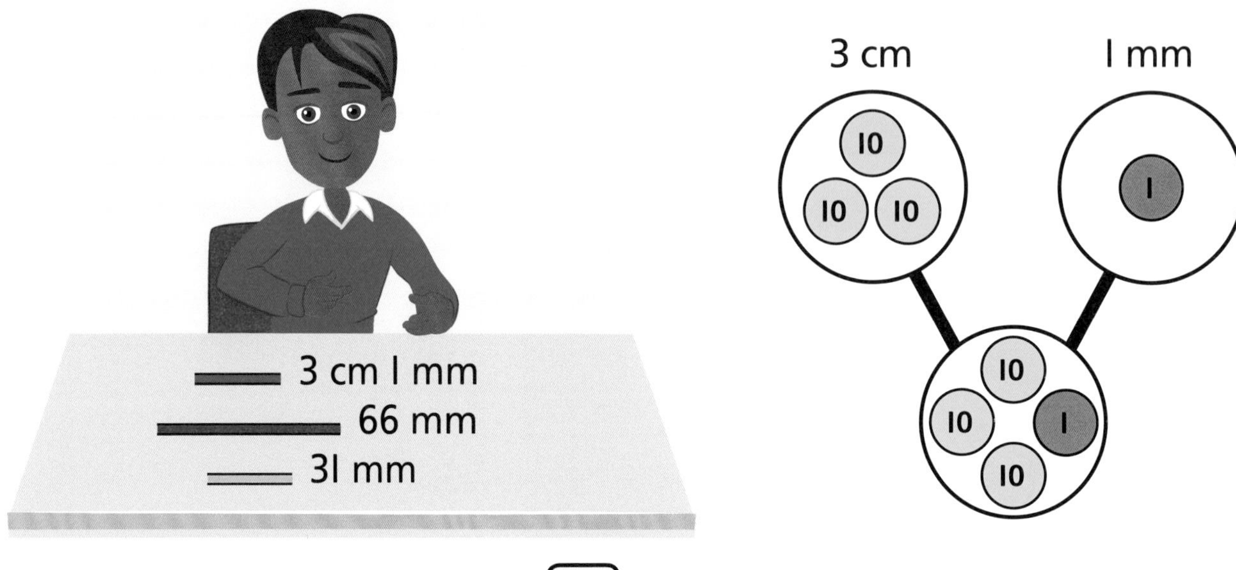

a) The blue piece of string is ☐ mm long.

b) The red piece of string is ☐ cm ☐ mm long.

c) The ______ and ______ pieces of string are equal in length.

2 Work out the missing measurements.

2 cm 9 mm	29 mm
8 cm 4 mm	☐ mm
☐ cm ☐ mm	60 mm
☐ cm ☐ mm	9 mm

3 Draw lines of these lengths.

a) 5 cm 8 mm

b) 102 mm

c) 10 cm 3 mm

d) 13 mm

Be sure to use your ruler accurately.

4 Look at the wavy lines. Can you find a way to measure them?

Write your answers in mm and in cm and mm.

a)

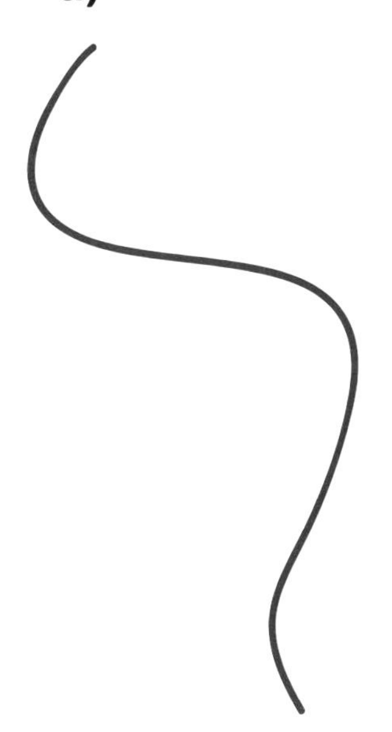

b)

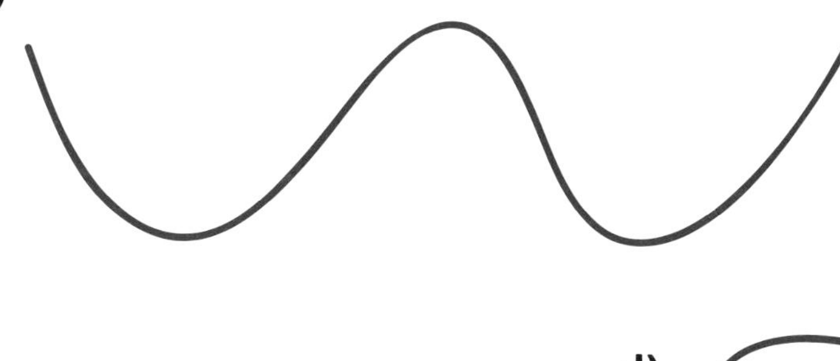

c)

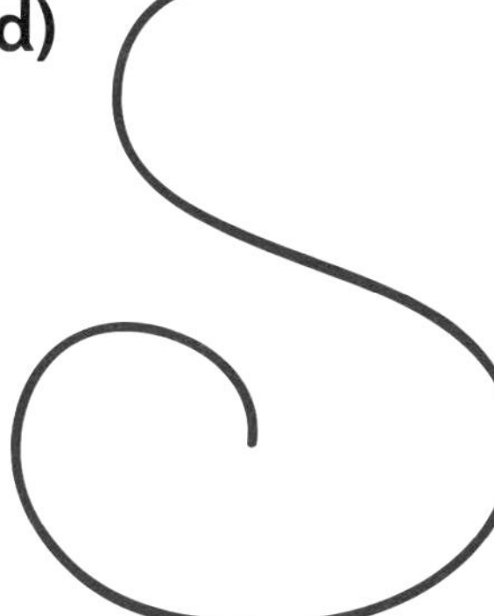

→ Practice book 3B p95

Comparing lengths

Discover

I am 125 cm.
I am 39 cm more than a metre.
I am 1 m 33 cm.
Minimum height 1 m 30 cm
Ambika
Olivia
Lee

1. Ambika, Olivia and Lee are waiting to go on the ride.

   a) Who is tall enough to go on the ride?

   b) Whose height is closest to 1 m 30 cm?

Share

a)

I think heights that are 3-digit numbers must be tall enough to use the ride.

I am going to think about equivalent measurements so I can compare their heights to 1 m 30 cm.

125 cm = 1 m 25 cm

1 m 25 cm < 1 m 30 cm

Ambika cannot go on the ride.

39 cm more than 1 m = 1 m 39 cm.

1 m 39 cm > 1 m 30 cm

Olivia can go on the ride.

1 m 33 cm = 1 m 33 cm

1 m 33 cm > 1 m 30 cm

Lee can go on the ride.

< means less than

> means greater than

b) Lee's height is closest to 1 m 30 cm.

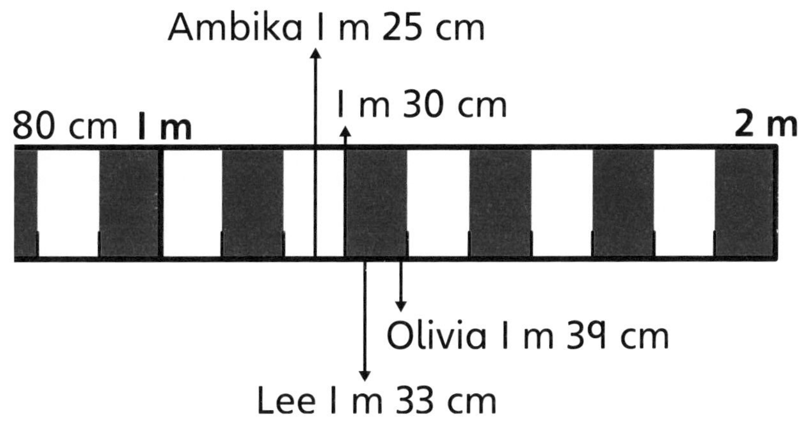

Think together

1

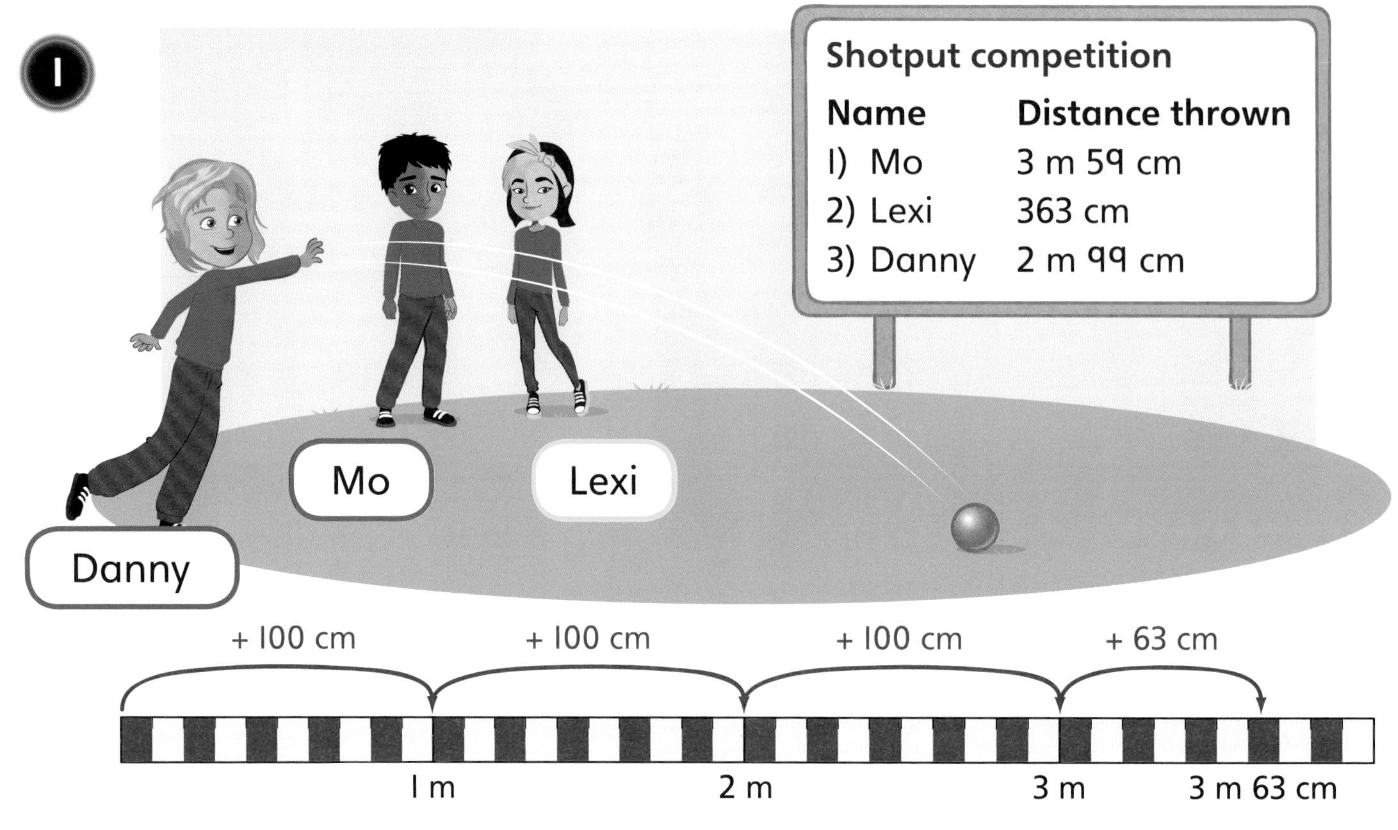

Who is in first, second and third place?

______________ is in first place.

______________ is in second place.

______________ is in third place.

2 Which box has the shortest ribbons?

Box ☐ has the shortest ribbons.

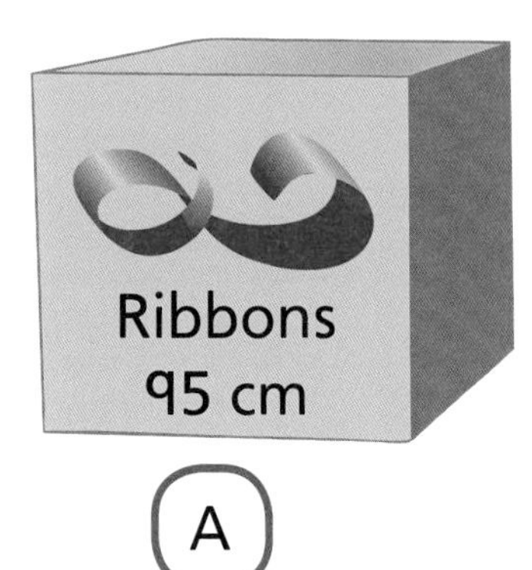

A

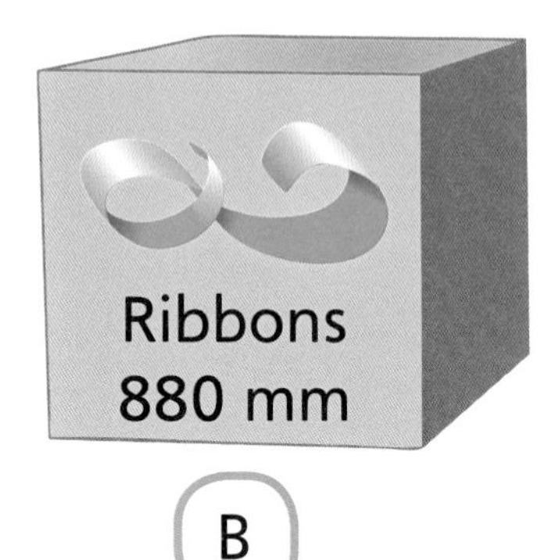

B

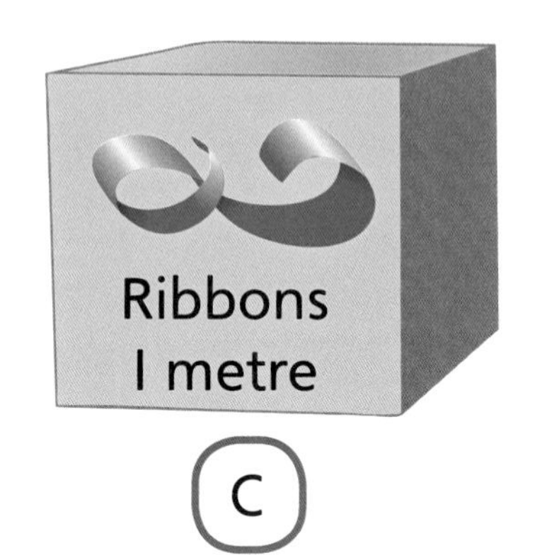

C

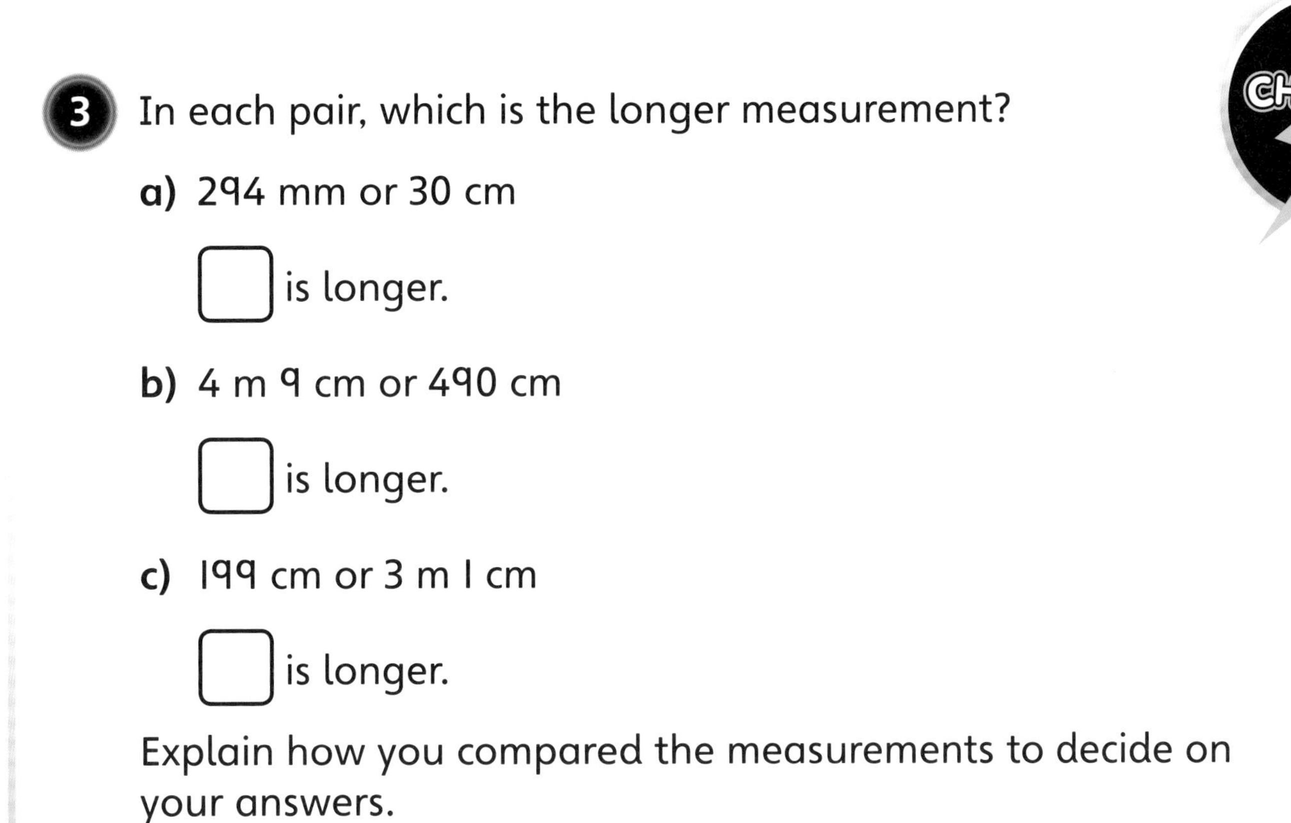

3 In each pair, which is the longer measurement?

CHALLENGE

a) 294 mm or 30 cm

☐ is longer.

b) 4 m 9 cm or 490 cm

☐ is longer.

c) 199 cm or 3 m 1 cm

☐ is longer.

Explain how you compared the measurements to decide on your answers.

294 is a much larger number than 30 but I think I must look at the units of measure.

For part b) I will compare the metres, then the centimetres.

→ Practice book 3B p98

Adding lengths

Discover

We have three pieces of bunting left.
Let's join them together to make a longer piece.
Kate
Ebo
25 cm
450 cm
3 m

1 **a)** Kate and Ebo join the three pieces of bunting together to make one piece. How long is the new piece?

b) If Kate and Ebo had joined the 3 m piece to the 450 cm piece, what total length would they have?

Share

a) Once converted, add the metres and centimetres separately.

First the metres:
4 m + 3 m = 7 m

Then the centimetres:
25 cm + 50 cm = 75 cm

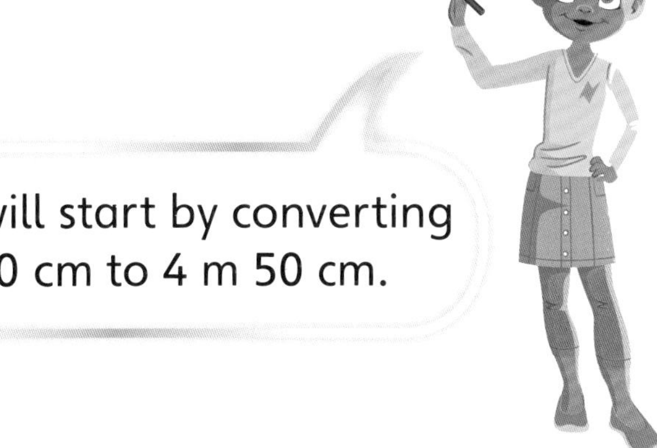

I will start by converting 450 cm to 4 m 50 cm.

Then add the total metres and centimetres together.

7 m + 75 cm = 7 m 75 cm

I would change all the lengths to centimetres and then add them up.

	H	T	O	
		2	5	
	4	5	0	
+	3	0	0	
	7	7	5	cm

The new piece of bunting is 7 m 75 cm.

I wonder if both these methods give the same answer.

b) One piece is 3 m.

450 cm is the same as 4 m 50 cm.

Kate and Ebo would have a total length of 7 m 50 cm (or 750 cm).

Think together

1 Use both Flo's method and Dexter's method to find the total length of these three pieces of bunting. Check that both methods give the same answer.

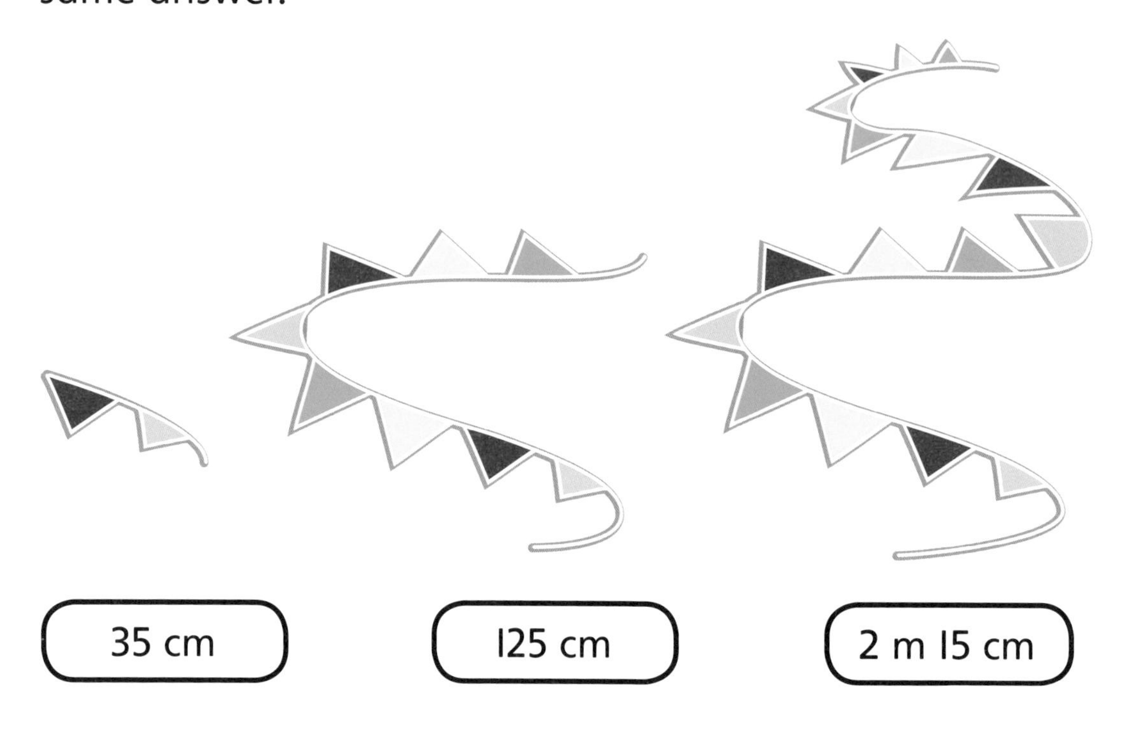

2 These three pieces will be joined together to make a plastic model. Use both Flo and Dexter's methods to work out the total height of the model.

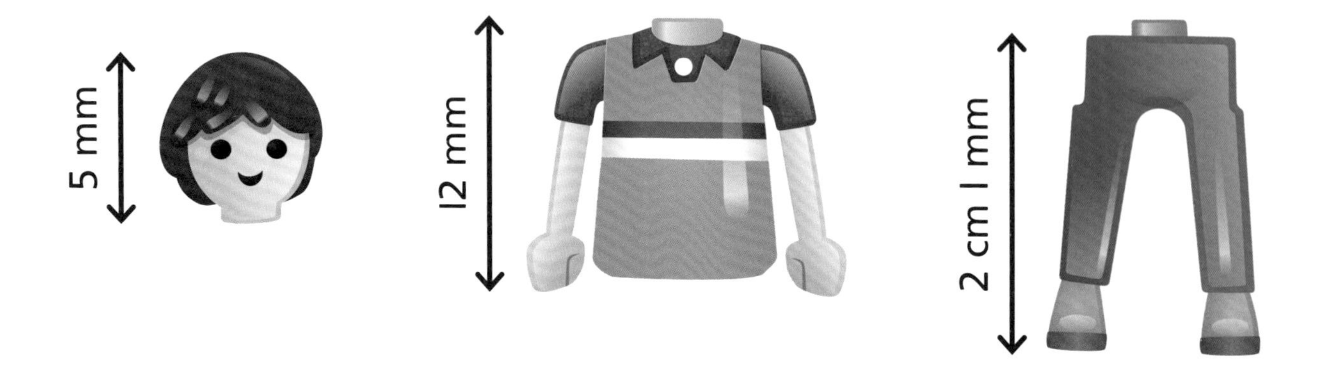

3 Work out the missing numbers.

a) 50 cm + 50 cm = ☐ m

b) 4 cm + 60 mm = ☐ cm

c) 12 mm + ☐ mm = 2 cm

d) 1 m 40 cm + ☐ cm = 3 m

4 There are 3 pieces of wool. What lengths can you make by joining different combinations of the pieces together?

Which is the best way of doing the calculations?

1 m 85 cm

50 cm

60 cm

I am adding something on to 1 m 85 cm, so I will first add until I make 2 m and then add on whatever is left.

I think it is quicker to convert everything into centimetres and then add them together.

→ Practice book 3B p101

Subtracting lengths

Discover

1 Holly is making a guinea pig run. She is going to cut a piece of wood 1 m long from a board that is 2 m 50 cm long.

a) What length of board will be left after Holly has cut off the 1 m piece?

b) Will there be enough left to cut another 1 m piece? Explain your answer.

Share

a)

The board is 2 m and 50 cm. Holly could mark the board with two parts that are each 1 m long, and one part that is 50 cm long. When Holly has cut off 1 m, she will have a 1 m 50 cm length of board left.

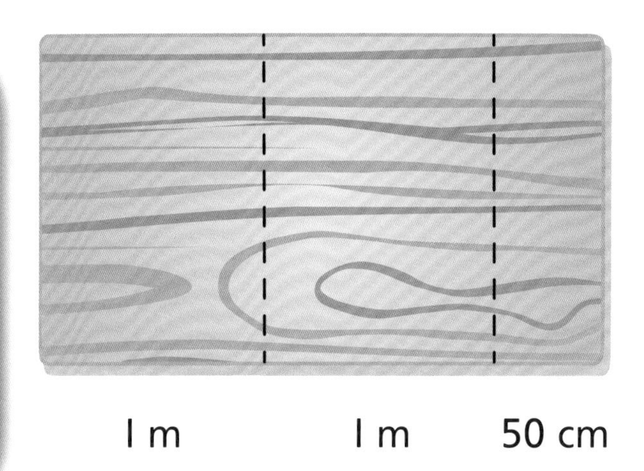

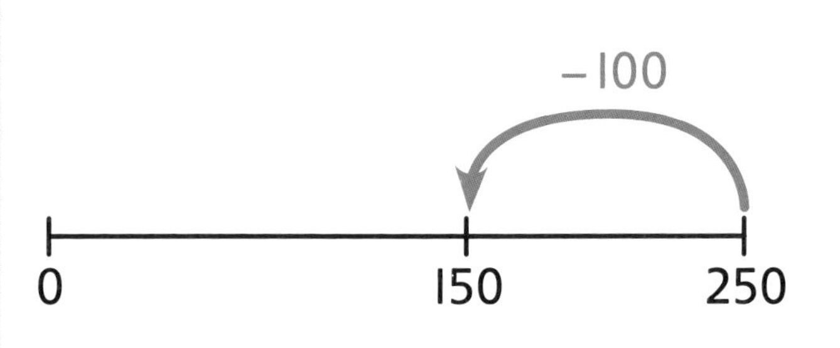

I know another way to do it. 2 m 50 cm is the same as 250 cm. A 100 cm piece is being cut off, so I will do a subtraction:
250 – 100 = 150 cm.

b)

There is 150 cm left. That is enough to cut another 1 m piece.

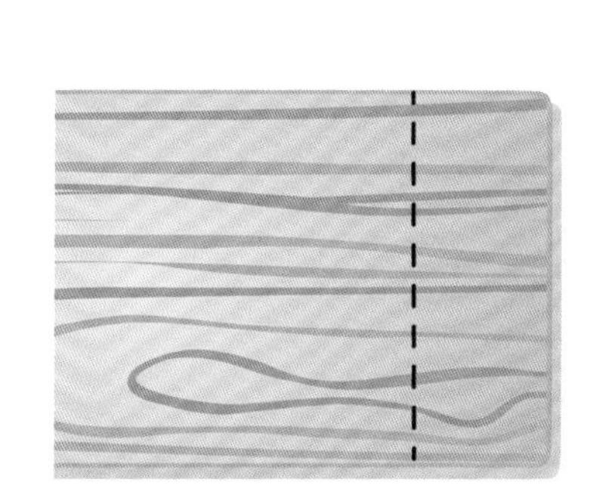

There may also be times when it is best to use column subtraction.

Think together

1 A plank is 3 metres long. Amal cuts off a piece that is 50 cm long.

How much is left?

[ ] cm – 50 cm = [ ] cm.

2 Emma's picture is 1 m 10 cm long. She trims a 35 cm piece off the end.

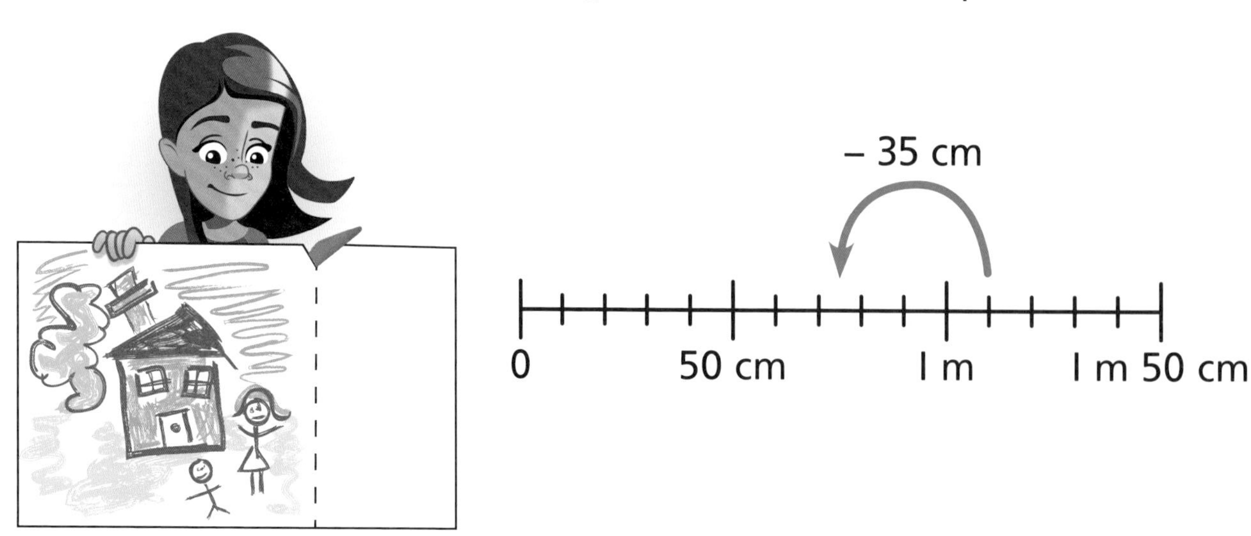

How long is the picture now?

It is [ ] cm.

3 Lee has a piece of string that is 8 cm 5 mm long. He cuts some off so that now the string is 65 mm long. How much has he cut off?

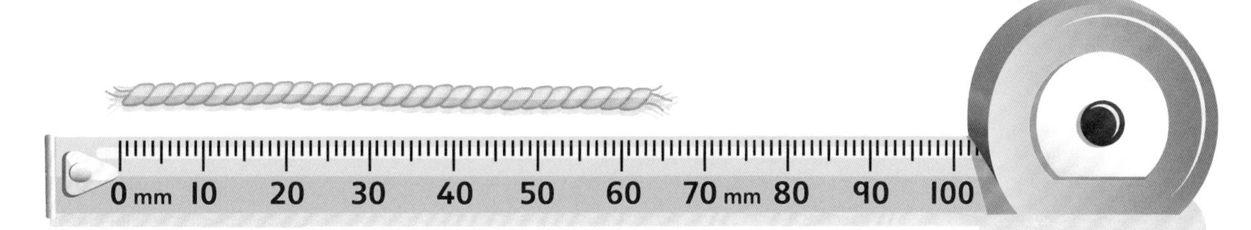

4 There are 10 metres of ribbon on a reel. Danny cuts off 1 m 50 cm and Bella cuts off 77 cm.

How much ribbon is left on the reel?

Suggest different ways of finding the answer.

You could change all of the lengths to centimetres … or there might be a better way!

→ Practice book 3B p104

Measuring the perimeter 1

Discover

1 a) Alex is making shapes out of wool to stick on her card.

How much wool has Alex used to make the red triangle?

b) Has Alex used more or less wool to make the blue polygon than the red triangle?

Share

a)

We call the distance around the sides of a shape the **perimeter** of the shape.

I am going to work out the length of wool used by measuring the length of each of the sides.

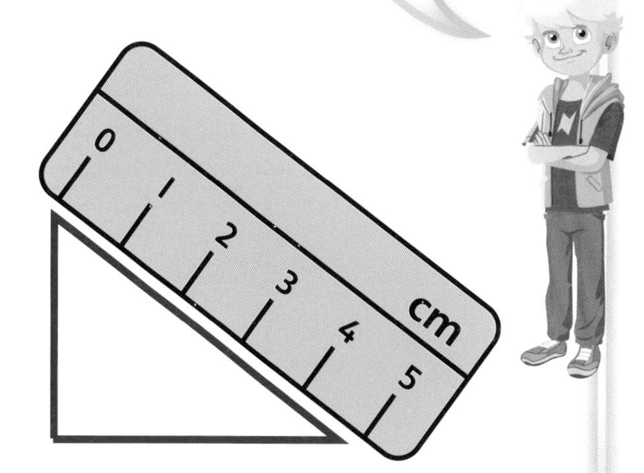

First use a ruler to measure the length of each side.

The diagonal side of the triangle is 5 cm long.

The other two sides of the triangle measure 4 cm and 3 cm.

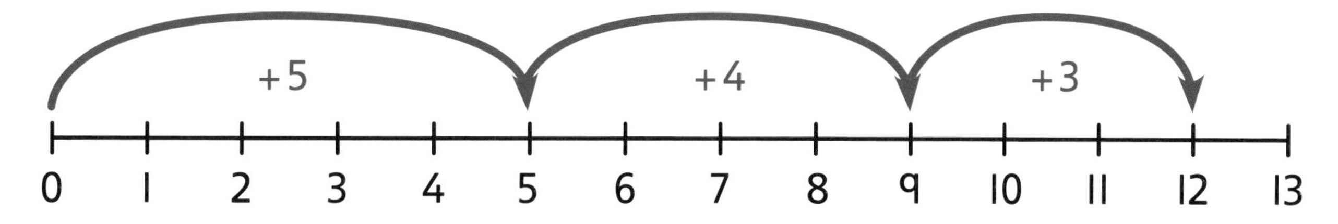

5 cm + 4 cm + 3 cm = 12 cm

Alex has used 12 cm of wool to make the red triangle.

b) First use a ruler to measure each side of the blue polygon.

The sides are 3 cm + 2 cm + 2 cm + 1 cm + 1 cm + 1 cm = 10 cm.

Alex used 10 cm of wool to make the blue polygon.

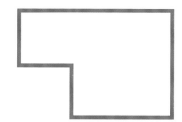

12 cm > 10 cm

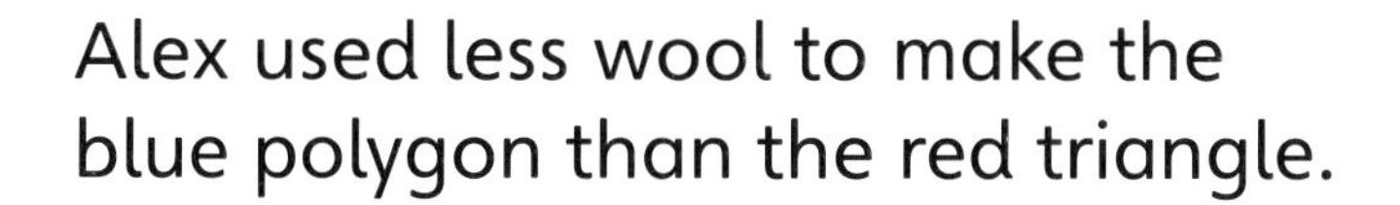

Alex used less wool to make the blue polygon than the red triangle.

Think together

1. Work out the length of wool you would need to make each of these shapes.

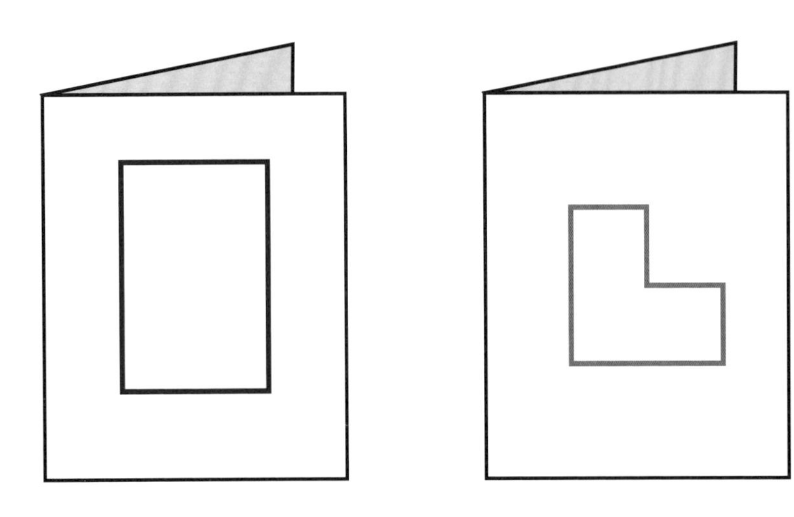

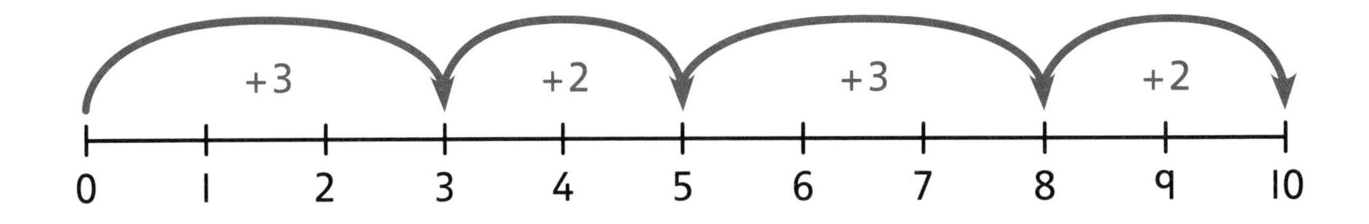

The blue rectangle would need ☐ cm of wool.

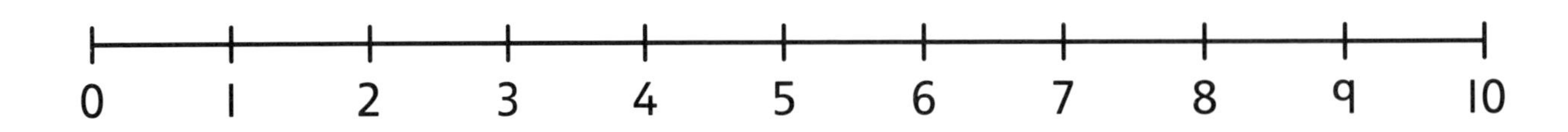

The orange polygon would need ☐ cm of wool.

2 Find the perimeters of these shapes.

You will need to measure some of the sides.

I will need to convert some of these measurements.

If some of the sides are the same length, do I still need to measure all of them?

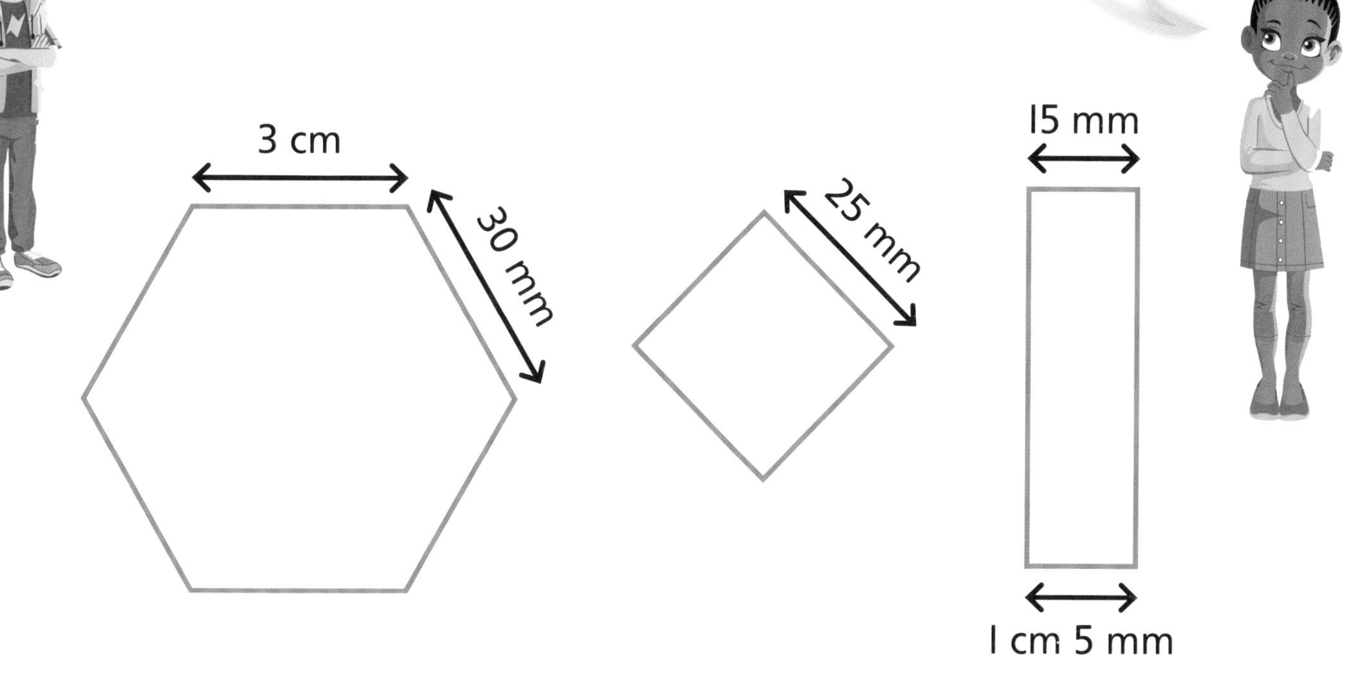

3 Leo is making shapes out of string.

He says that his shape has a perimeter of 14 cm.

Draw one possible shape that Leo might have made.

I think I can draw more than one shape that has a perimeter of 14 cm.

→ Practice book 3B p107

Measuring the perimeter 2

Discover

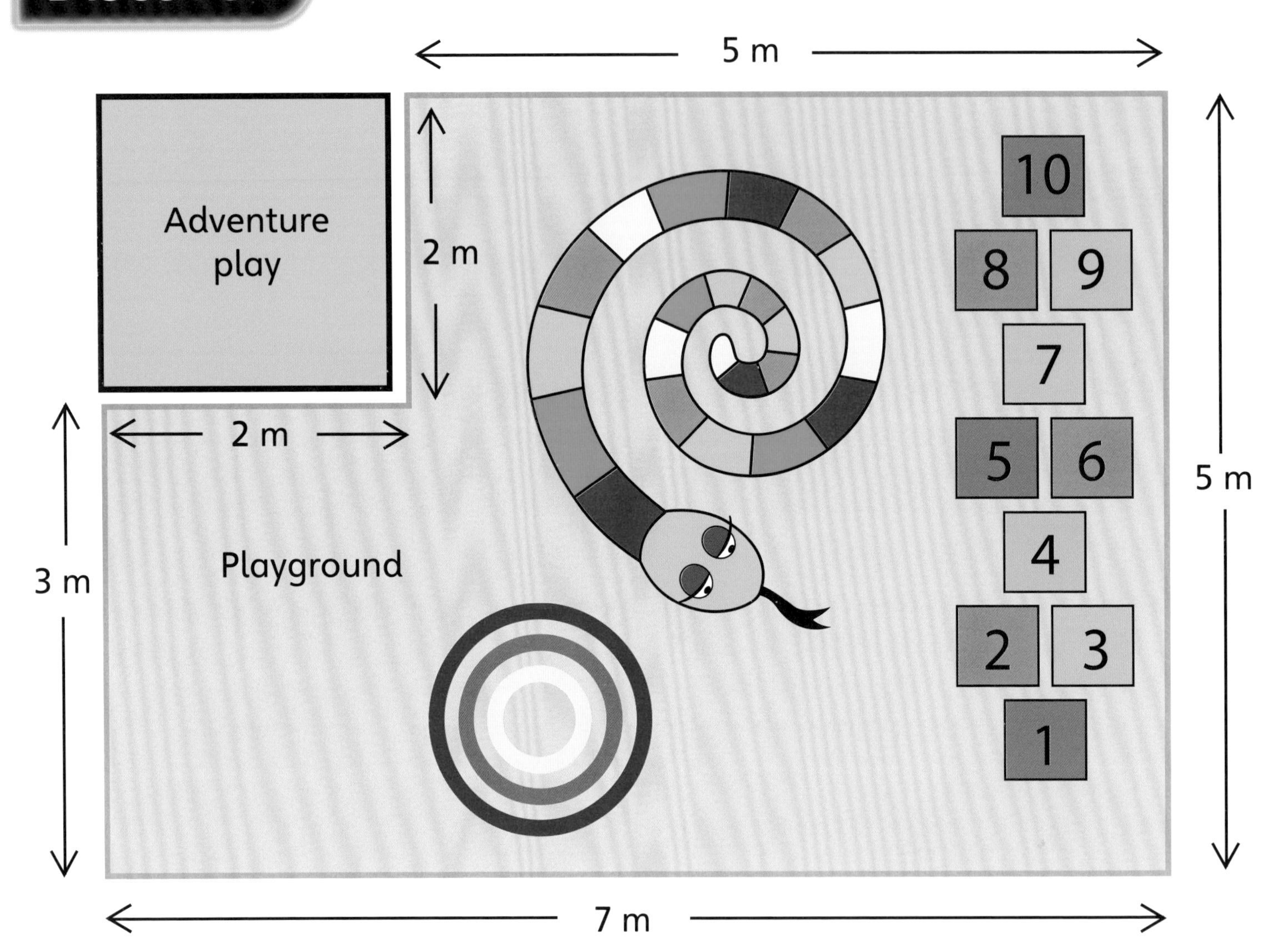

1 **a)** The school is putting a new fence around the playground.

How much fence does the school need to buy?

b) Amelia runs twice around the outside of the playground.

How many metres does she run?

Share

There must be a way to work out the perimeter without measuring.

a) To work out how much fence is needed, first work out the perimeter.

I remember! If I add the sides together I will find the perimeter. The playground has side lengths of 5 m, 5 m, 7 m, 3 m, 2 m and 2 m.

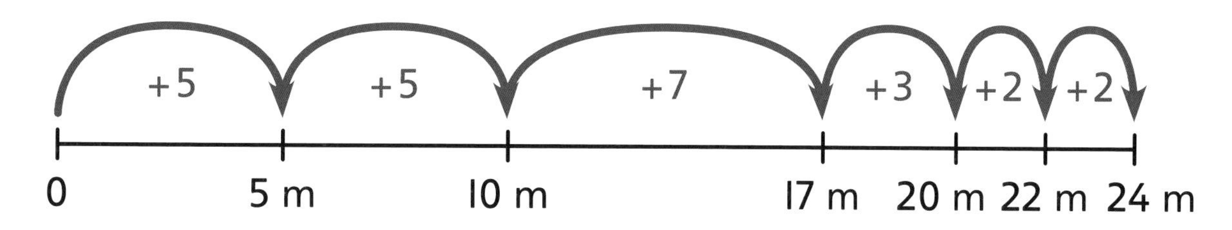

5 m + 5 m + 7 m + 3 m + 2 m + 2 m = 24 m

I wonder if there is a quicker way to add these numbers up.

The perimeter of the playground is 24 metres.

The school will need to buy 24 metres of fence.

b) Amelia runs around the perimeter of the playground twice.

	T	O
	2	4
+	2	4
	4	8

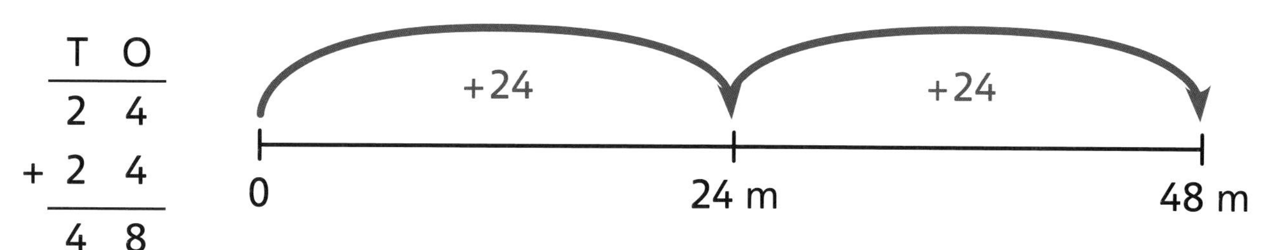

Amelia runs 48 metres.

Think together

1 What is the perimeter of the school's adventure play area?

The adventure play area has four sides that are each 2 m long.

2 m + 2 m + 2 m + 2 m = ☐ m

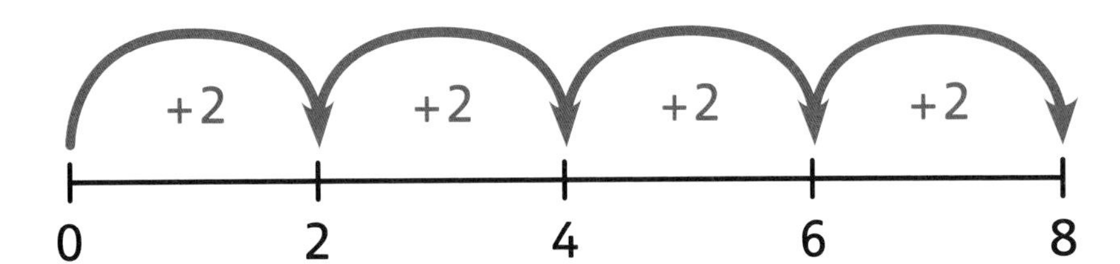

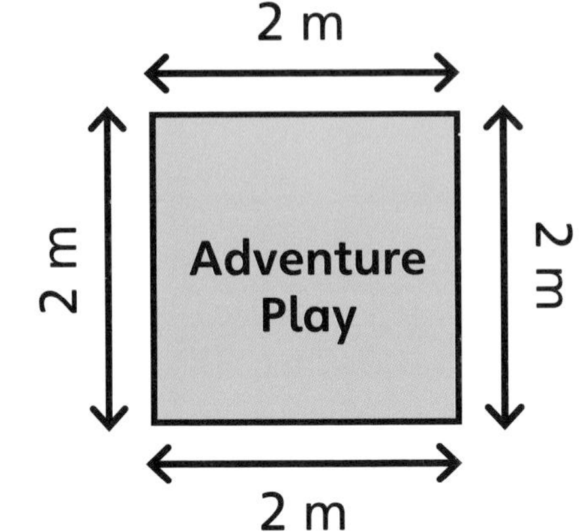

The perimeter of the adventure play area is ☐ metres.

2 Children run around the perimeter of the school playing field three times.

How many metres do they run?

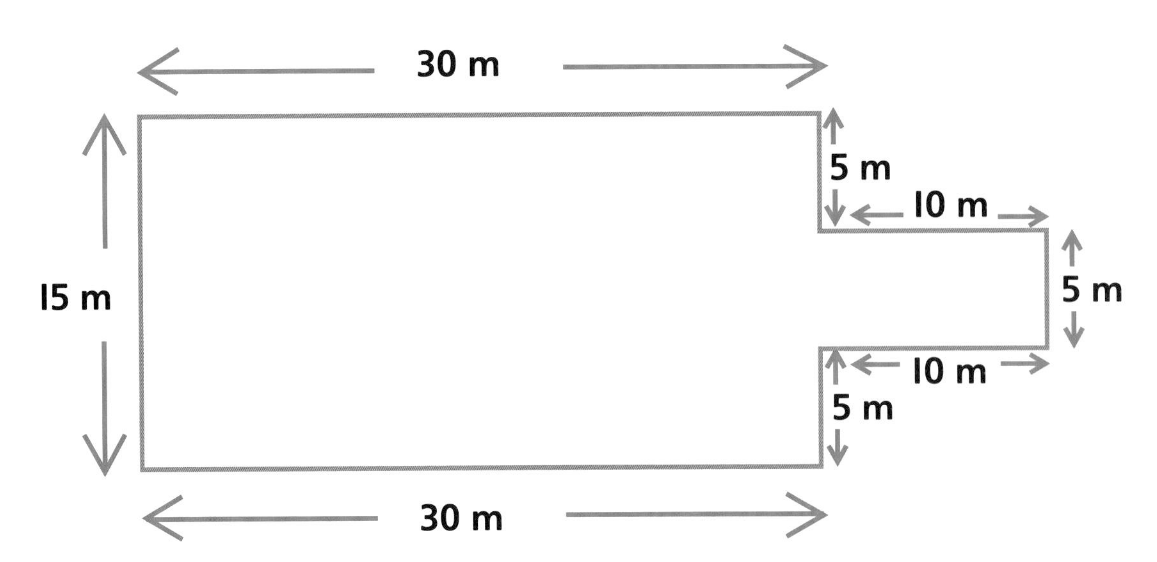

The perimeter of the playing field is ☐ metres.

The children run ☐ metres.

3 Reena makes this shape out of sticks.

What is its perimeter?

The perimeter of Reena's shape is ☐ cm.

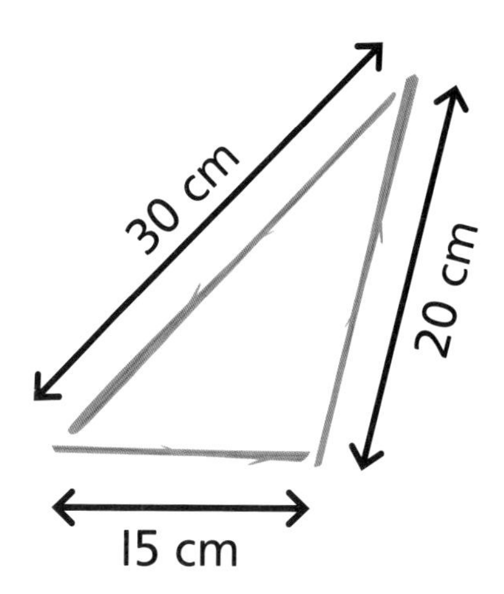

4 The school's nature area has four sides and a perimeter of 18 m.

CHALLENGE

Lexi has measured one side of the nature area. It is 6 m long.

Zac has measured another side of the nature area. It is 4 m long.

What could the other side lengths be?

I will start by working out how many metres the other two sides added together must be.

I wonder if the nature area is a rectangle.

The other side lengths could be ☐ m and ☐ m.

→ Practice book 3B p110

Problem solving – length 1

Discover

It could grow up to 3 times longer by the time it is an adult.
I think my snake could grow longer than 2 metres.
0 10 20 30 40 50 60 70 80 90 1 m

1 **a)** Is Andy correct? Could his snake grow longer than 2 m?

b) Six months later the snake is 1 m 45 cm long.

How much longer could it grow?

Share

a) You can show the problem with a bar model.

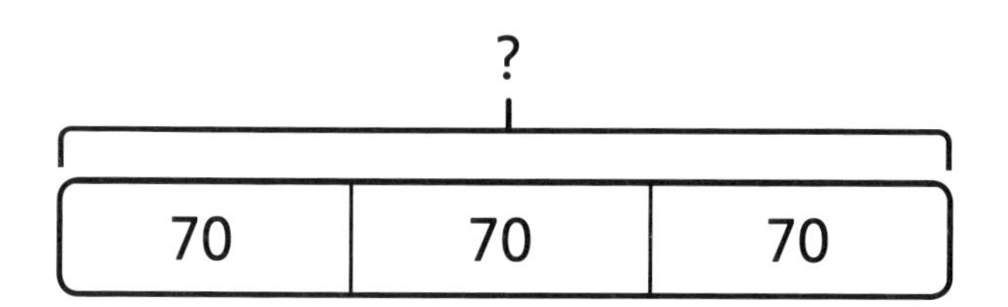

I used repeated addition.

70 + 70 + 70 = 210

70 cm × 3 = 210 cm

The adult snake could grow to 210 cm.

The parts are equal so I used multiplication.

I know that 7 × 3 = 21 so I worked out 70 × 3 = 210.

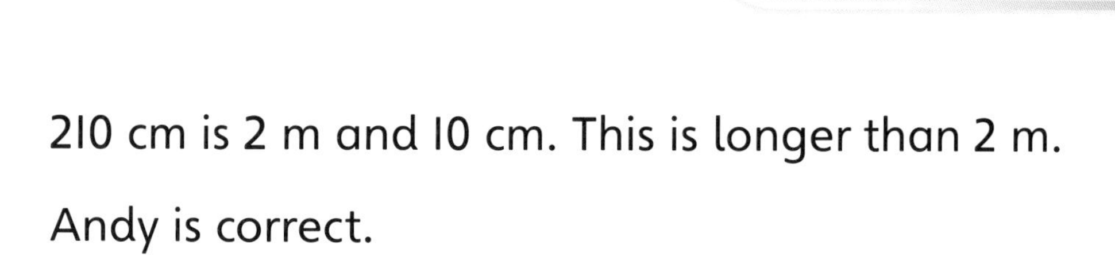

210 cm is 2 m and 10 cm. This is longer than 2 m.

Andy is correct.

b) 1 m 45 cm is equal to 145 cm.

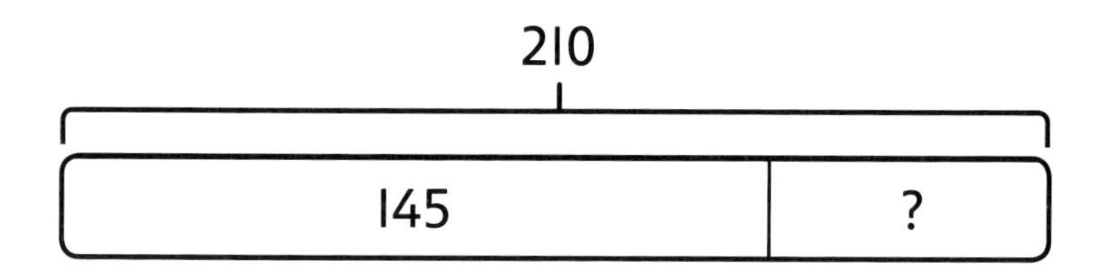

210 − 145 = 65

The snake could grow another 65 cm.

Think together

I will work out the m and the cm separately.

1 This wild snake is 1 m 50 cm long. It can grow up to 4 times as long.

How long could it grow?

0 10 20 30 40 50 60 70 80 90 1 m 10 20 30 40 50 60 70 80 90 1 m

?

1 m 50 cm	1 m 50 cm	1 m 50 cm	1 m 50 cm

4 × 1 m = [ ] m 4 × 50 cm = [ ] cm

4 × 1 m 50 cm = [ ] m [ ] cm

The snake could grow to [ ] m and [ ] cm long.

2 Isla has a pet snail that is 8 cm 2 mm long. Isla's snail is twice as long as Max's pet snail. How long is Max's snail?

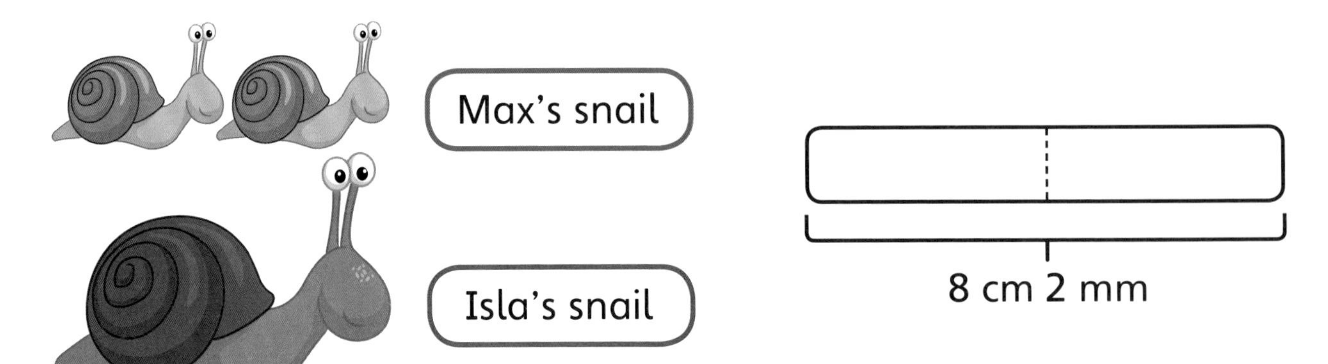

Max's snail is [ ] cm and [ ] mm long.

3 The budgie is half the height of the parrot.

How tall is the budgie?

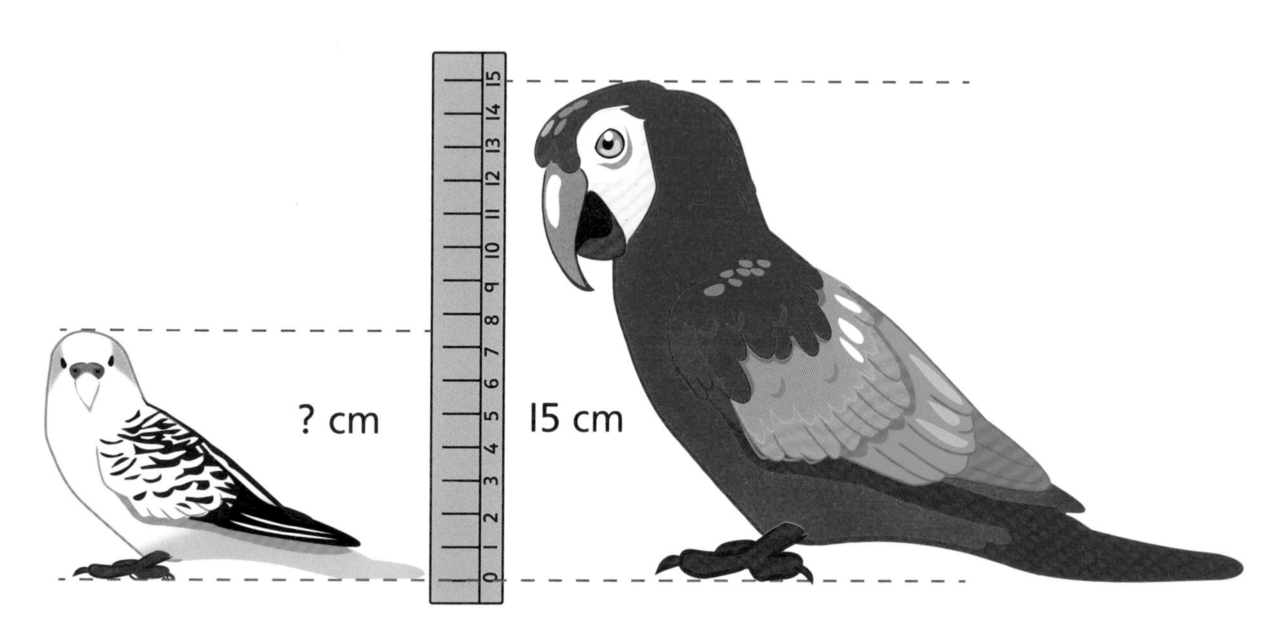

The budgie is ☐ cm and ☐ mm tall.

I could work out half if the parrot was 14 cm or 16 cm.

I will draw a bar model and think about cm and mm.

→ Practice book 3B p113

Problem solving – length ❷

Discover

1 **a)** How much skirting board should Toshi cut to fill the gap?

b) How many more cupboards could he fit into the gap?

Share

a) Each cupboard is 80 cm wide.

420 cm			
80 cm	80 cm	80 cm	? cm

I know that 4 m 20 cm is 420 cm. I will convert everything into centimetres for this subtraction.

$3 \times 80 = 240$. The cupboards take up 240 cm.

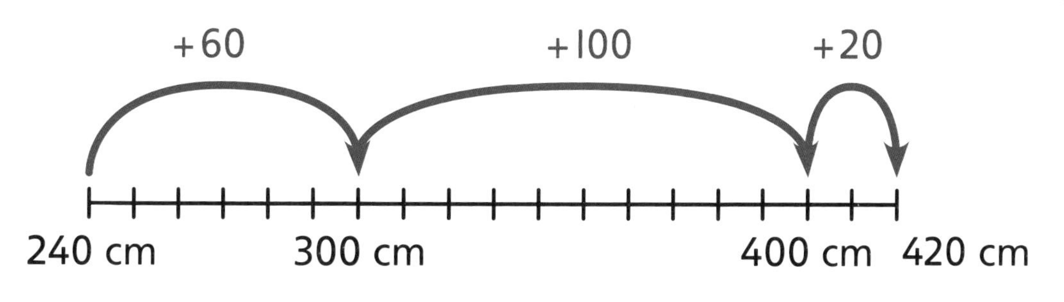

$240 + 180 = 420$ or $420 - 240 = 180$

Toshi needs to cut 180 cm of skirting board to fill the gap.

b) The gap is 180 cm.

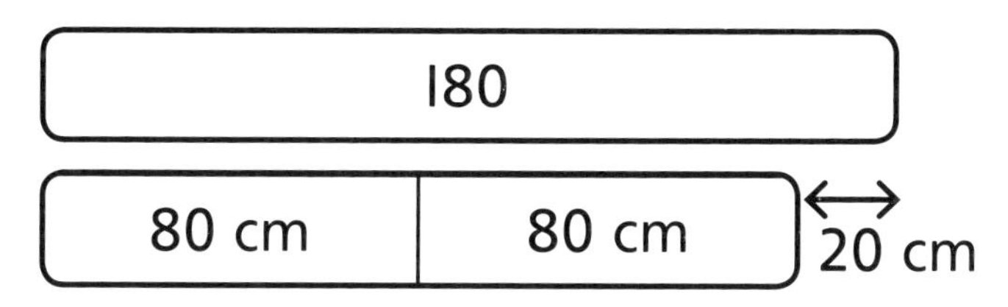

$2 \times 80 = 160$

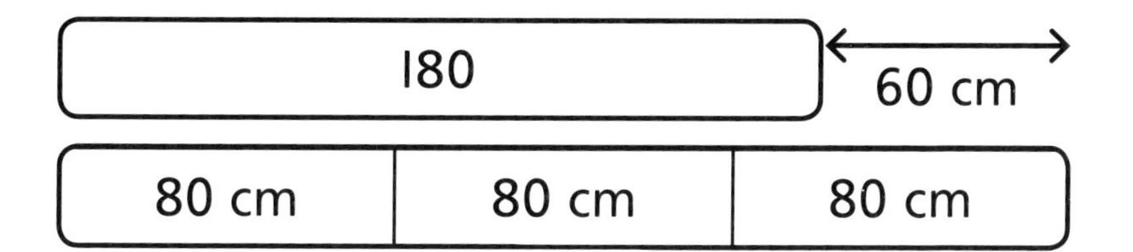

$3 \times 80 = 240$

Toshi could fit 2 more cupboards into the gap.

Think together

1 Holly has 8 m of wood.

How much will she have left over after making the book shelves?

?

1 m 25 cm	1 m 25 cm	1 m 25 cm	1 m 25 cm	1 m 25 cm

☐ × ☐ = ☐

☐ – ☐ = ☐

Holly will have ☐ of wood left over.

2 Jamie wants a wallpaper border around her bedroom door.

The door is 250 cm high.

How much wallpaper will she need for the top and both sides of the door?

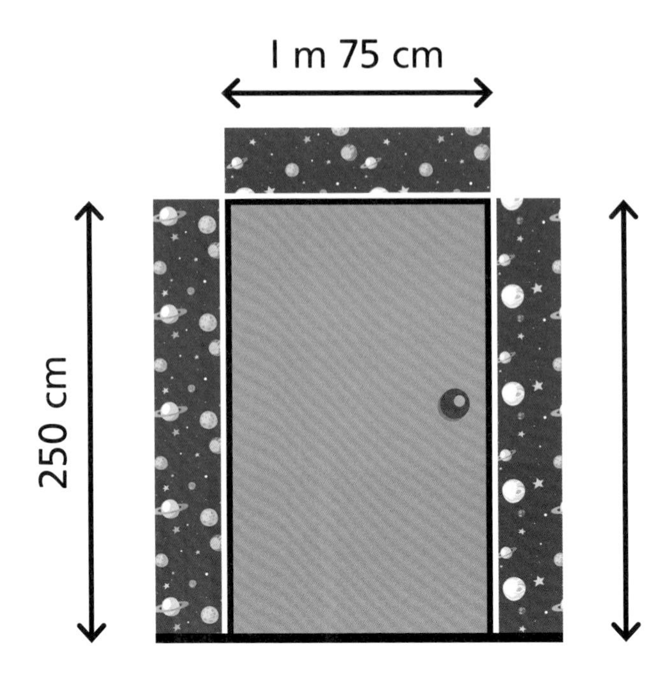

3 Jen builds two windows. One is twice the width of the other.

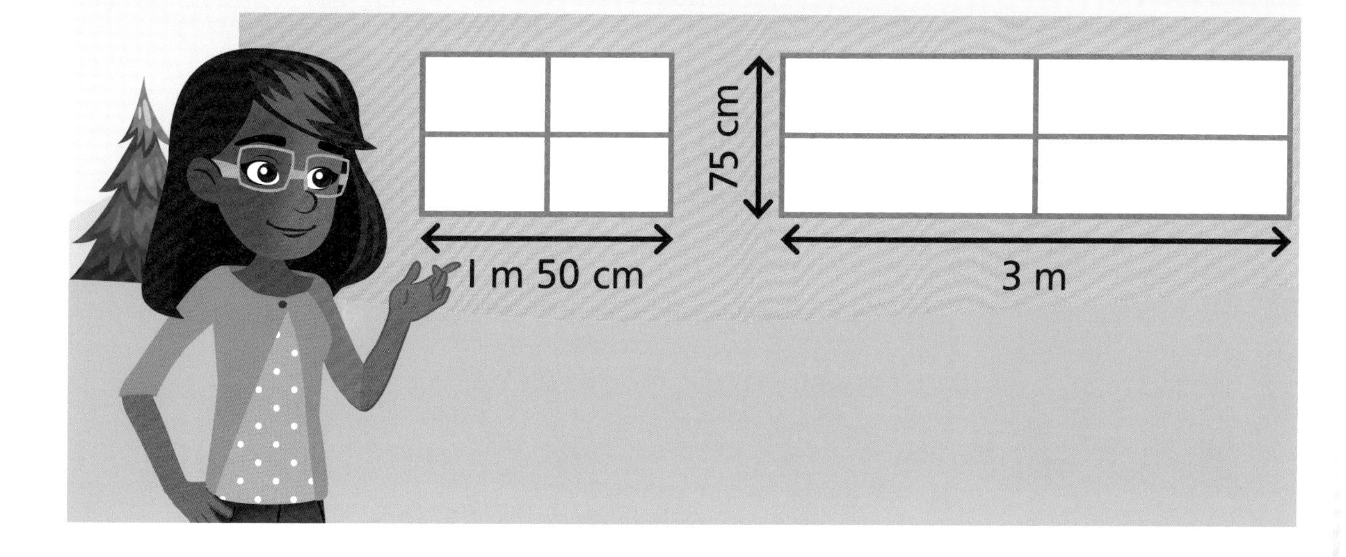

I think the bigger window will have double the perimeter of the smaller window.

Do you agree with Jen?

Discuss Jen's prediction and then calculate to check.

I will draw bar models for each calculation. Then I can compare the perimeters.

What do you notice?

→ Practice book 3B p116

End of unit check

1 Look at these lengths.

2 m 30 cm   256 cm   231 cm   1 m 96 cm   206 cm

Which statement is correct?

A 206 cm is the shortest, 256 cm is the longest.

B 1 m 96 cm is the shortest, 256 cm is the longest.

C 1 m 96 cm is the longest, 256 cm is the shortest.

D 2 m 30 cm is the longest, 206 cm is the shortest.

2 Which calculation has a total of 2 m 56 cm?

A 100 cm + 56 cm

B 210 cm + 46 cm

C 120 cm + 1 m 26 cm

D 210 cm + 46 mm

3 Which model represents the correct difference for 2 m 23 cm – 73 cm?

A

2 m 23 cm	
2 m 50 cm	0 m 73 cm

B

223 cm	
0 m 73 cm	1 m 53 cm

C

2 m 23 cm	
0 m 50 cm	0 m 73 cm

D

2 m 23 cm	
0 m 73 cm	1 m 50 cm

4 Which shape has a perimeter of 40 cm?

A

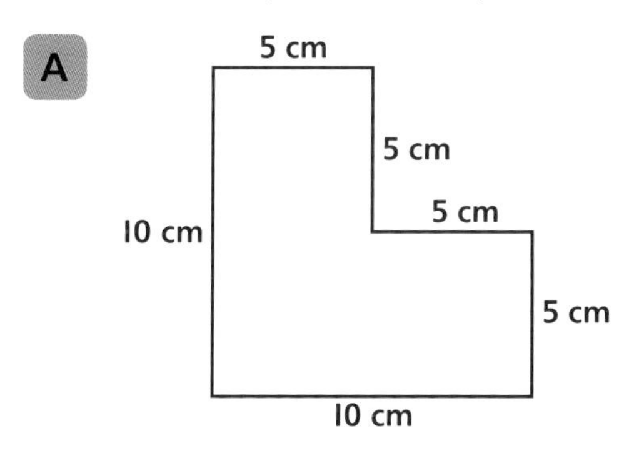

C

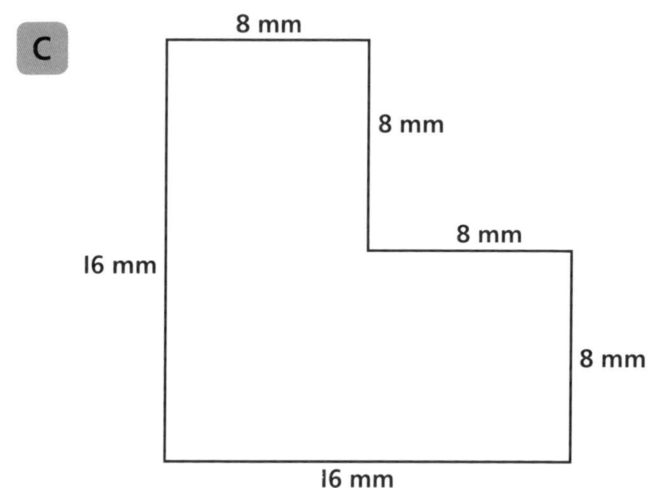

B

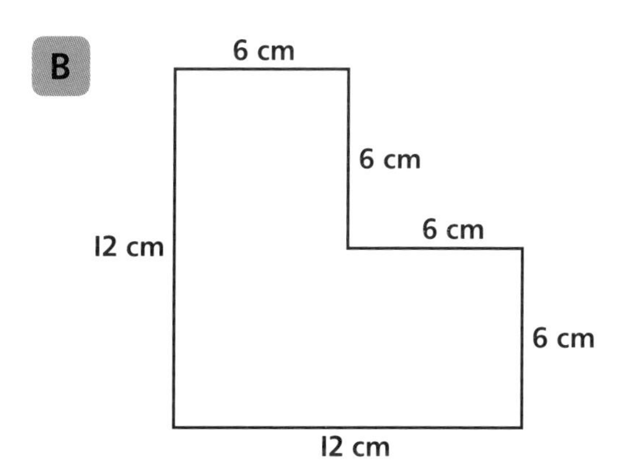

D

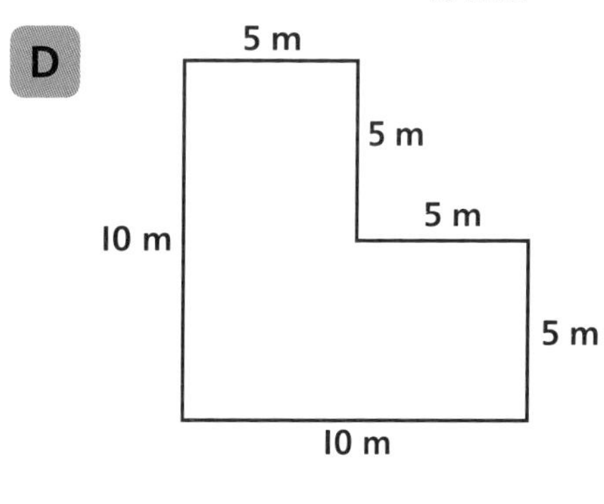

5 A rectangle has sides that measure 16 cm and 4 cm.
What is the total perimeter of the rectangle?

A 20 cm B 36 cm C 40 cm D 40 m

6 A stack of 10 identical boxes is 50 cm high.
Tim takes 3 boxes off the top. How high
is the stack now?

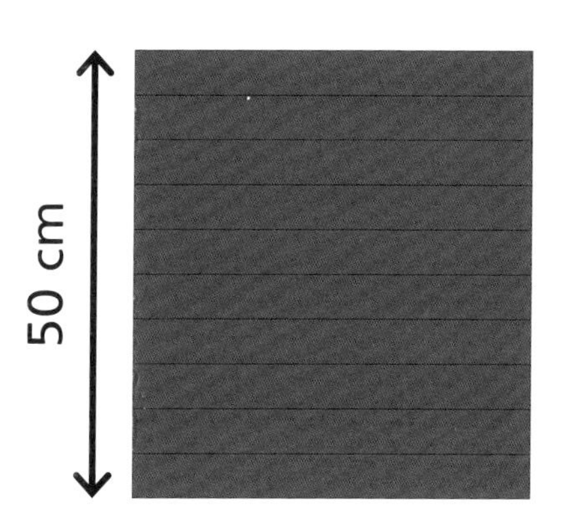

→ Practice book 3B p119

Unit 9
Fractions 1

In this unit we will …

- Make a whole with unit and non-unit fractions
- Explore tenths as fractions
- Understand fractions as numbers
- Calculate fractions of a set of objects

Do you remember what this is called?

How many parts has the whole been split into?

What is the value of one of the parts?

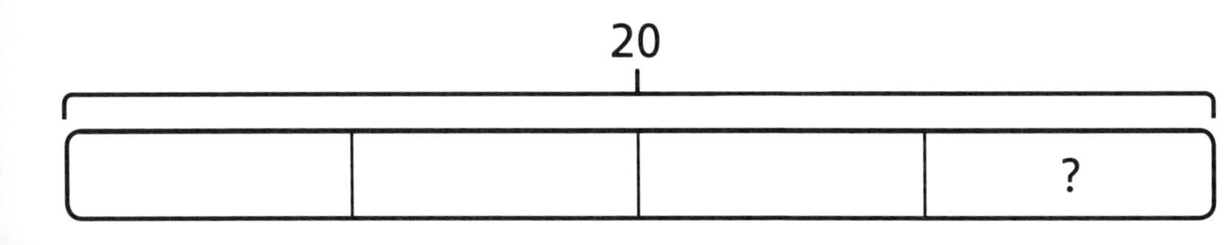

We will need some maths words. Which words have you used before?

equal **parts** **whole** **unit fraction**

equation **integer** **non-unit fraction**

numerator **denominator** **represent** **share**

group **mixed number** **whole number**

divide **set of objects** **multiply**

tenth **interval**

We need a number line too! What fraction is the arrow pointing to?

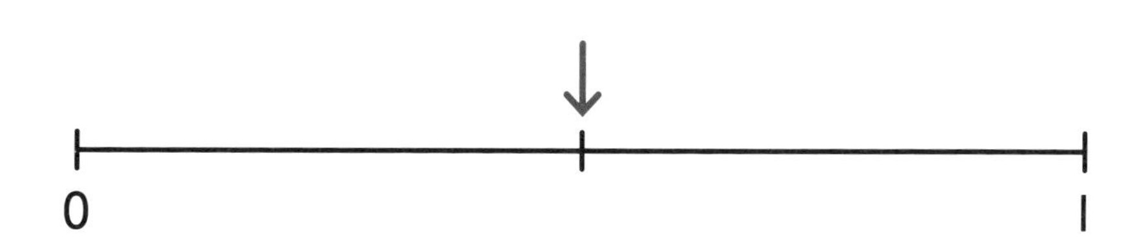

Unit and non-unit fractions

Discover

Amelia	Max	Isla	Zac

1 **a)** What fraction of the children are wearing glasses?

b) Max's kite is $\frac{1}{2}$ red and $\frac{1}{4}$ yellow.

What shape is the kite that Max is flying?

Share

a)

$\frac{1}{4}$ $\frac{3}{4}$

There are 4 children in total. The denominator is 4.

1 of the 4 children is wearing glasses. The numerator is 1.

$\frac{1}{4}$ of the children are wearing glasses.

b)

I will start by working out which of the kites are $\frac{1}{2}$ red.

Then I will work out which of these kites are also $\frac{1}{4}$ yellow.

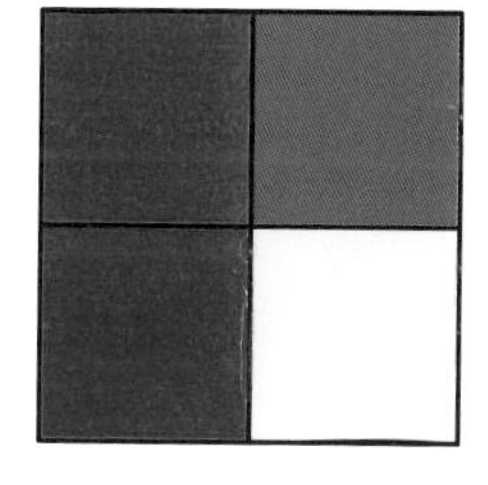

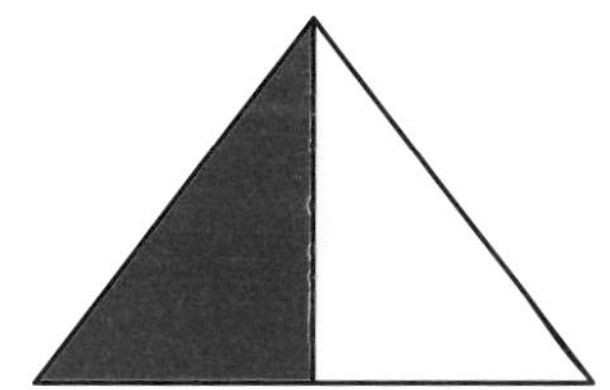

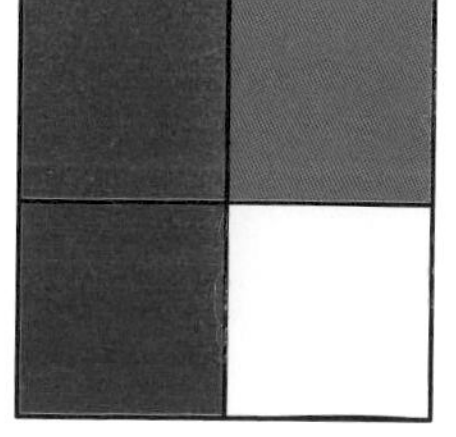

Both of these shapes are $\frac{1}{2}$ red.

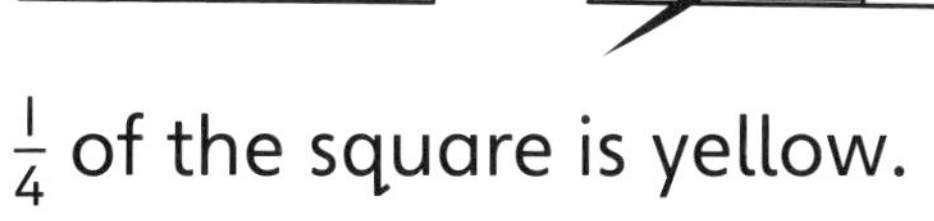

$\frac{1}{4}$ of the square is yellow.

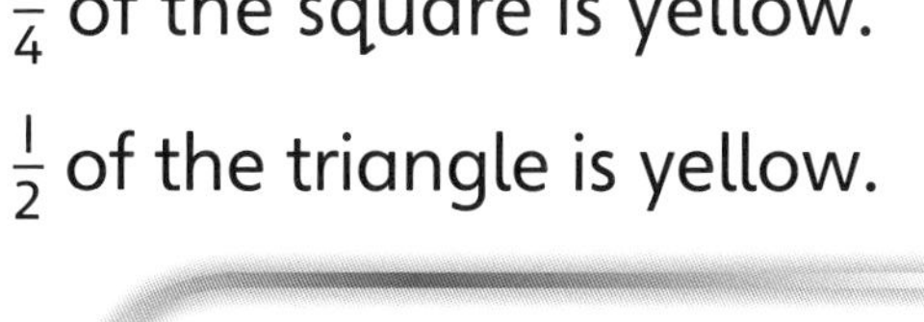

$\frac{1}{2}$ of the triangle is yellow.

The square is $\frac{1}{2}$ red **and** $\frac{1}{4}$ yellow.

Max is flying the kite that is shaped like a square.

The triangle is split into 2 equal parts (denominator). 1 of the parts is red (numerator). We say $\frac{1}{2}$ is red.

Think together

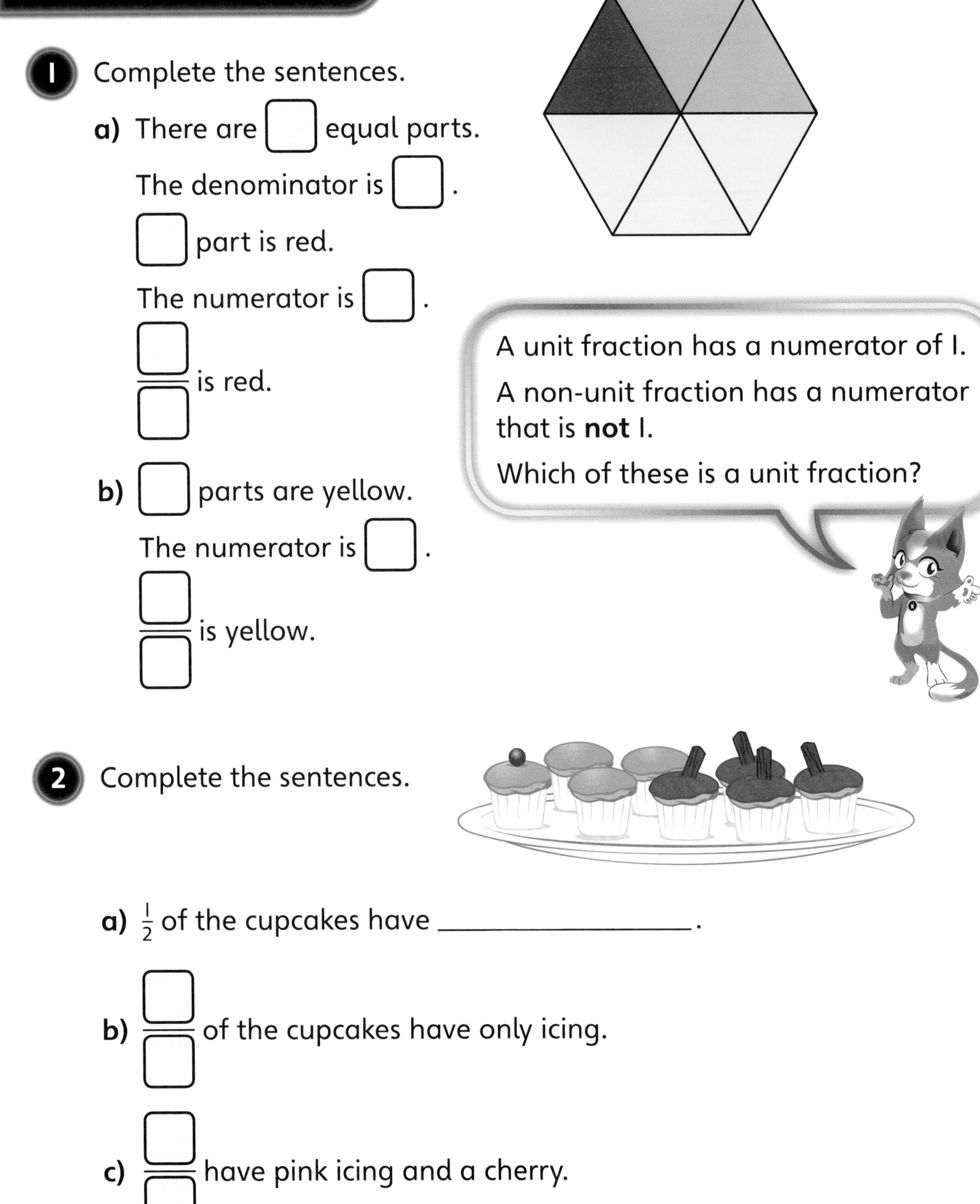

A unit fraction has a numerator of 1.
A non-unit fraction has a numerator that is **not** 1.
Which of these is a unit fraction?

1 Complete the sentences.

a) There are ☐ equal parts.

The denominator is ☐.

☐ part is red.

The numerator is ☐.

$\frac{\square}{\square}$ is red.

b) ☐ parts are yellow.

The numerator is ☐.

$\frac{\square}{\square}$ is yellow.

2 Complete the sentences.

a) $\frac{1}{2}$ of the cupcakes have ________________.

b) $\frac{\square}{\square}$ of the cupcakes have only icing.

c) $\frac{\square}{\square}$ have pink icing and a cherry.

3 Are these statements true or false?

a) $\frac{3}{5}$ of the shapes have 4 sides.

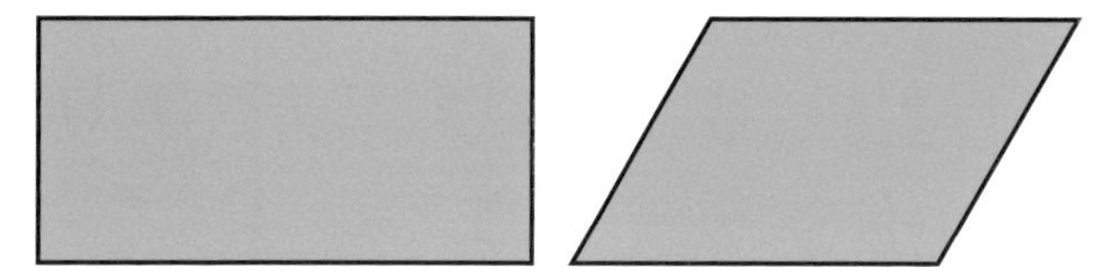

b) $\frac{5}{5}$ of the candles are lit.

c) $\frac{6}{6}$ of the apples are red.

4 Mo ate 3 pieces of apple pie.

What fraction of the pie did Mo eat?

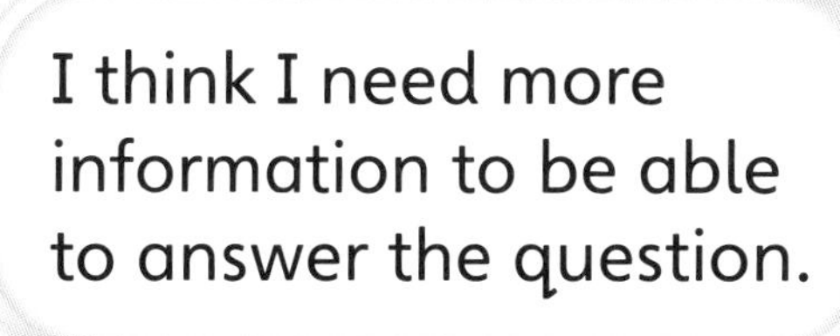

I think I need more information to be able to answer the question.

I wonder if there is more than one possible answer.

→ Practice book 3B p122

Making the whole

Discover

Only $\frac{1}{8}$ of an iceberg is above the water.

1 **a)** $\frac{1}{3}$ of the people on the boat are female.

What fraction of the people on the boat are male?

b) What fraction of the iceberg is under the water?

Share

a) $\frac{1}{3}$ of the people on the boat are female.

This is because 1 of the 3 people is female.

2 out of the 3 people on the boat are male.

This is written as $\frac{2}{3}$.

Two-thirds of the people on the boat are male.

$\frac{1}{3} + \frac{2}{3} = \frac{3}{3}$

$\frac{1}{3} + \frac{2}{3} = 1$

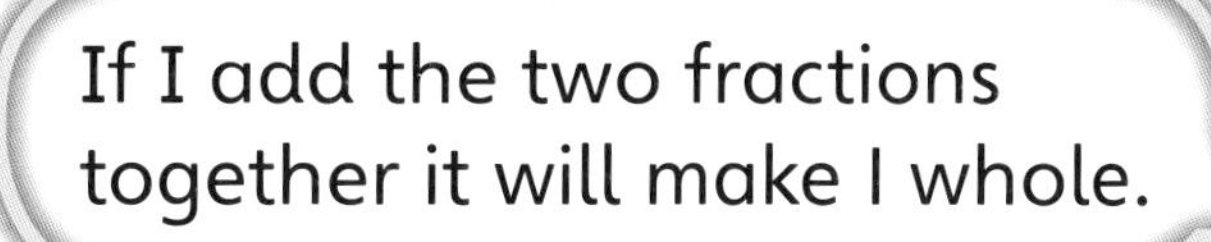

If I add the two fractions together it will make 1 whole.

b) The whole is split into 8 parts.

1 out of the 8 parts is above the water.

This is written as $\frac{1}{8}$.

7 out of the 8 parts are under the water.

This is written as $\frac{7}{8}$.

$\frac{1}{8} + \frac{7}{8} = \frac{8}{8}$

$\frac{1}{8} + \frac{7}{8} = 1$ whole

$\frac{7}{8}$ of the iceberg is under the water.

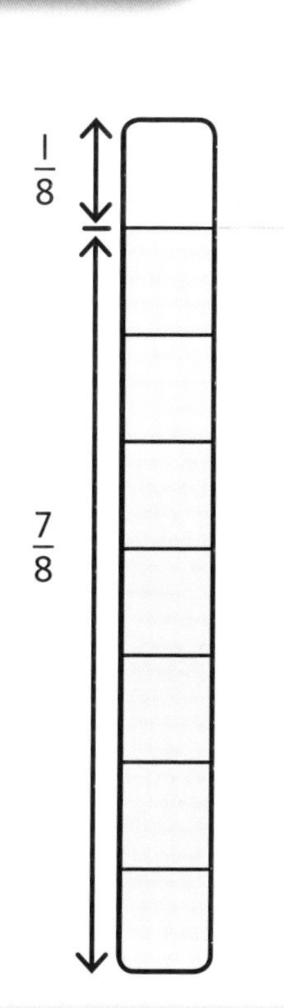

Think together

1 **a)** $\frac{4}{5}$ of the bottle is full of water.

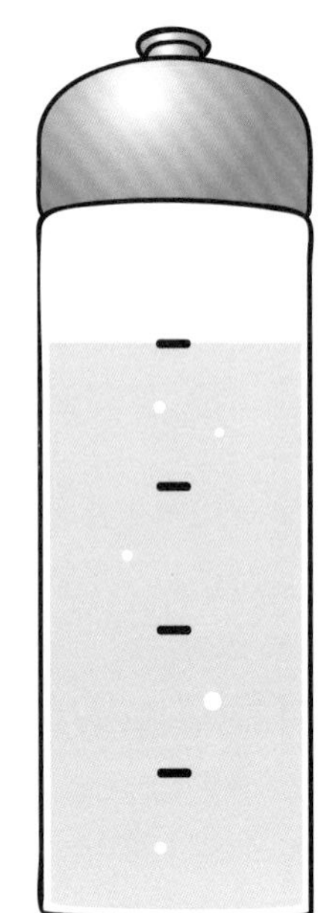

What fraction of the bottle is empty?

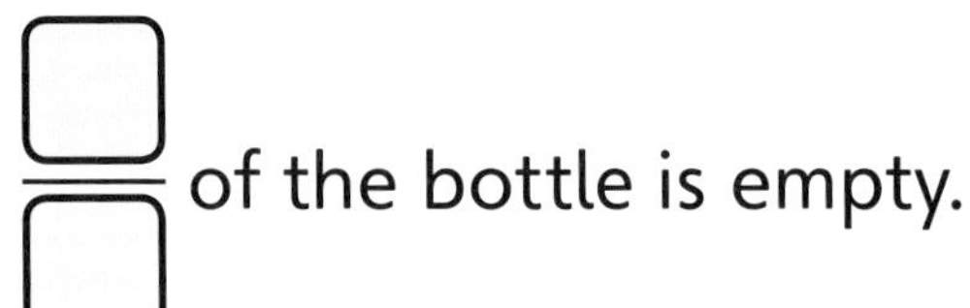

$\frac{\square}{\square}$ of the bottle is empty.

b) Work out the number sentence.

$\frac{4}{5} + \frac{\square}{\square} = 1$ whole

I represents the whole of the water bottle.

2 Aki has run $\frac{1}{6}$ of a race.

How much further does he have to run?

$\frac{1}{6} + \frac{\square}{\square} = 1$

Aki has $\frac{\square}{\square}$ of the race left to run.

3 Work out these number sentences.

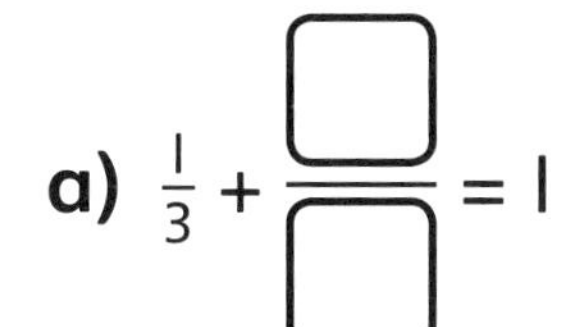

a) $\frac{1}{3} + \frac{\square}{\square} = 1$

b) $1 = \frac{4}{5} + \frac{\square}{\square}$

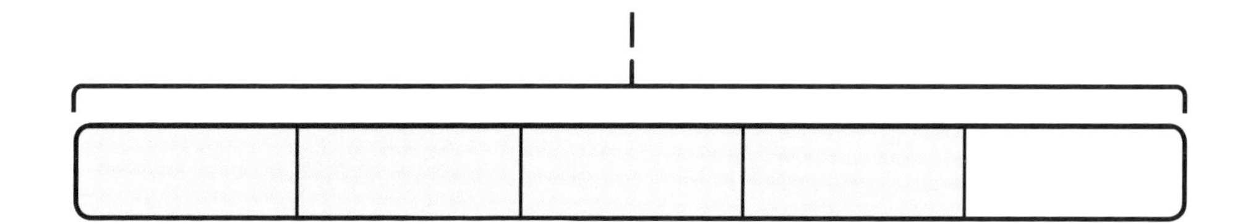

c) $\frac{\square}{\square} + \frac{4}{7} = 1$

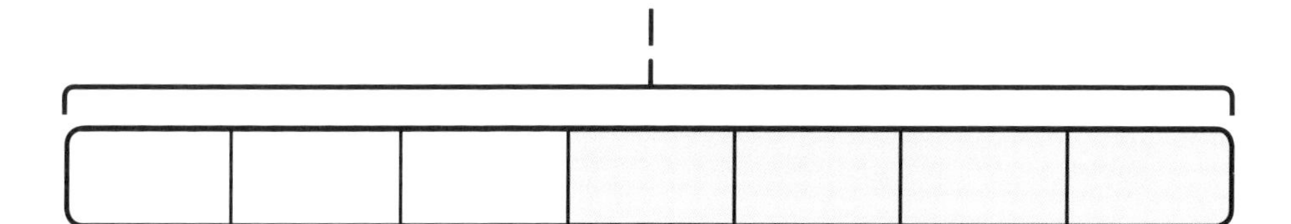

4 Which of the following number sentences are correct?

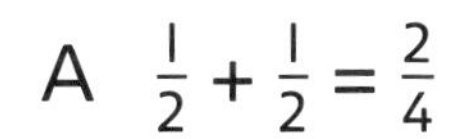

A $\frac{1}{2} + \frac{1}{2} = \frac{2}{4}$

B $\frac{2}{5} + \frac{3}{5} = 1$ whole

C $\frac{4}{7} + \frac{3}{7} = \frac{7}{7}$

I think I can explain the mistake in the incorrect number sentence.

→ Practice book 3B p125

Tenths 1

Discover

1 **a)** What fraction of the whole jigsaw is 1 piece?

b) Danny removes 2 pieces of the jigsaw. What fraction does he remove?

Is the answer the same no matter which pieces he removes?

Share

a) The jigsaw is split into 10 equal parts.

The denominator is 10.

One jigsaw piece is 1 part of the whole jigsaw.

The numerator is 1.

1 piece is $\frac{1}{10}$ of the whole.

$\frac{1}{10}$ is written as **one-tenth**.

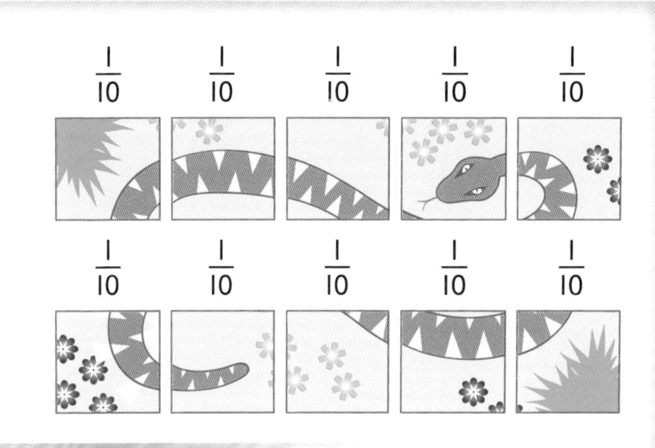

This number line goes up in $\frac{1}{10}$s.

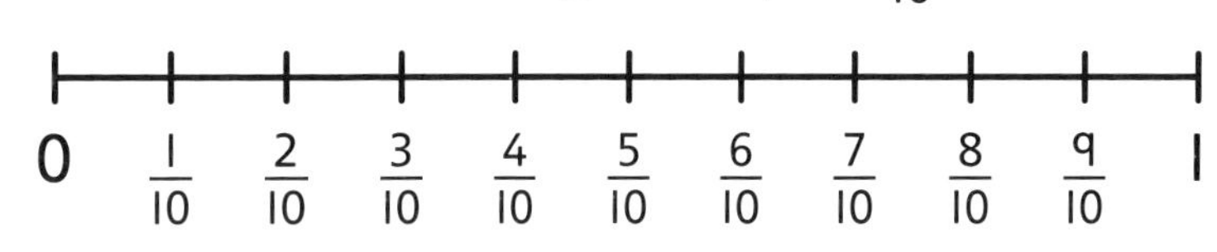

b) Danny removes 2 of the 10 pieces. This is $\frac{2}{10}$ or two-tenths of the whole.

There is more than one way to find $\frac{2}{10}$ of the whole.

All of the pieces of the jigsaw are the same size, so each piece is $\frac{1}{10}$ of the whole.

Taking any 2 pieces of the jigsaw will represent $\frac{2}{10}$ or two-tenths of the whole.

So, the answer is the same no matter which 2 pieces Danny removes.

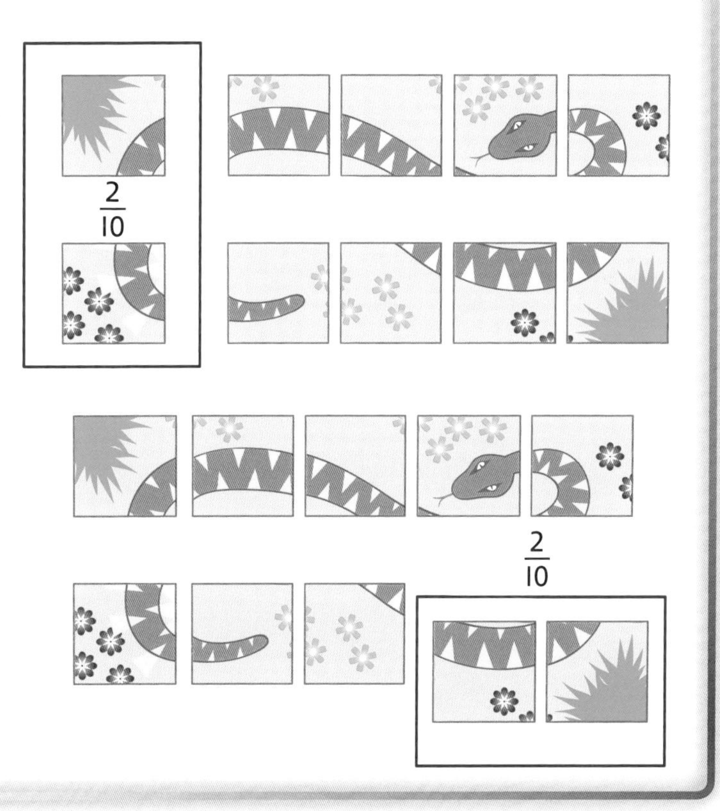

Think together

1 **a)** What will the next fraction on the number line be?

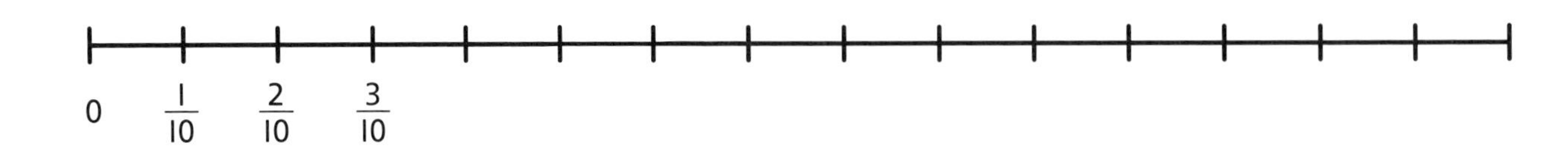

b) Count to the end of the number line.

What is the last number?

I know that $\frac{10}{10}$ is the same as 1 whole.

2 10p is $\frac{1}{10}$ of £1.

What fraction of £1 is 40p?

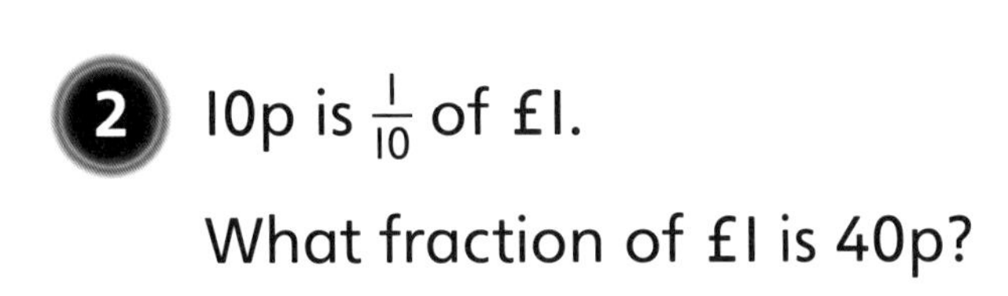

$\frac{1}{10}$

3 2 chocolate bars are each split into 10 equal pieces.

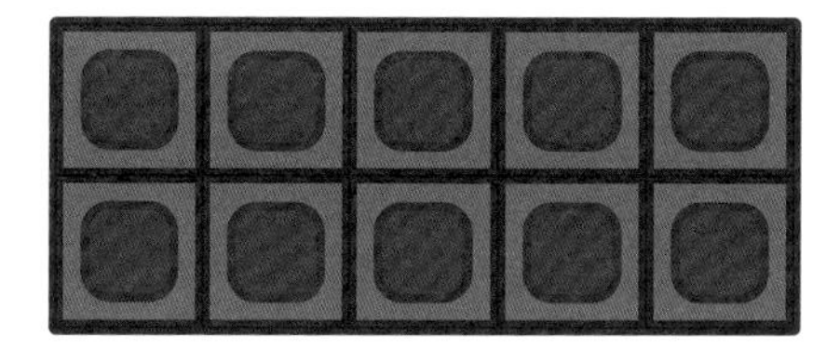 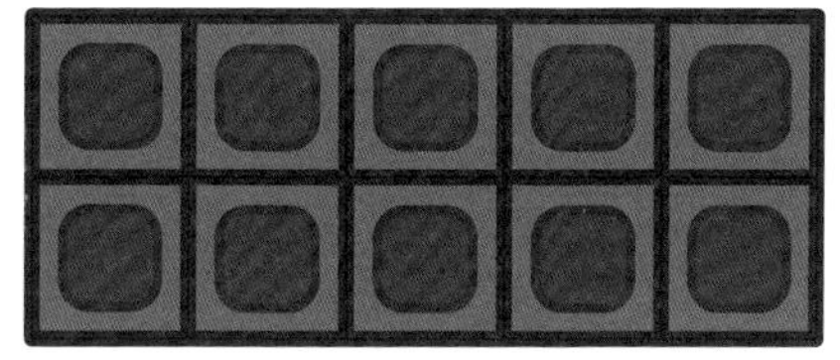

13 children eat $\frac{1}{10}$ of a bar of chocolate each.

What fraction of one of the chocolate bars is left?

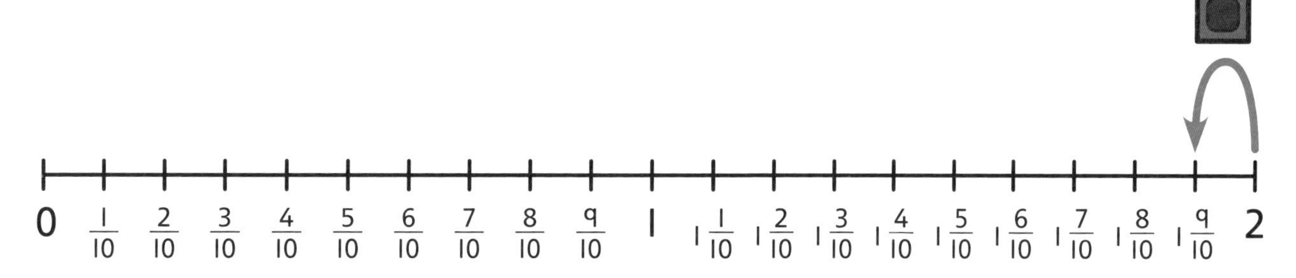

CHALLENGE

4 Do you agree or disagree with Reena?

The big pieces make $\frac{5}{10}$ of the whole jigsaw puzzle. The small pieces also make $\frac{5}{10}$ of the whole jigsaw puzzle.

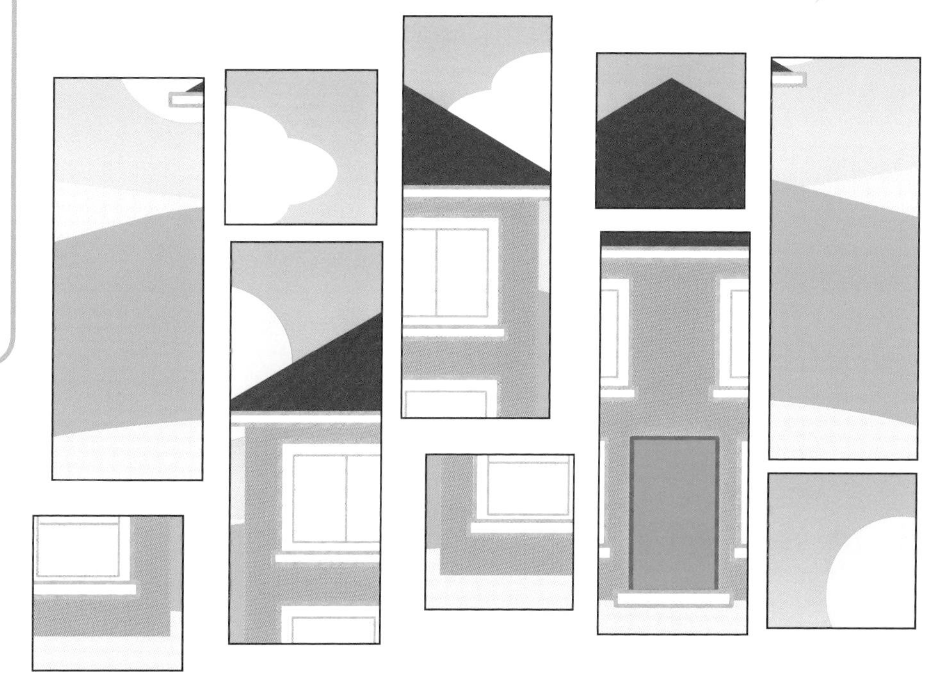

→ Practice book 3B p128

Tenths 2

Discover

I wonder if I can share the food equally between the bowls.

1 a) How much apple will each child get?

b) How much melon will each child get?

Share

There are 10 bowls so there is not enough for everyone to have 1 apple each. Maybe I will split each apple into 10 equal pieces.

a) These 10 pieces can be shared equally between the 10 bowls. Each piece is $\frac{1}{10}$ of an apple.

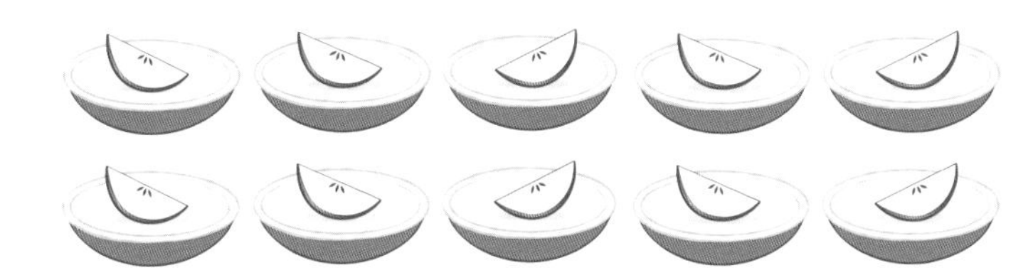

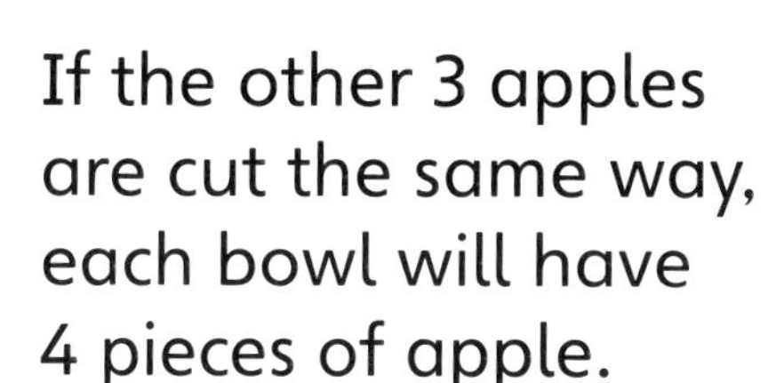

If the other 3 apples are cut the same way, each bowl will have 4 pieces of apple.

Each piece is $\frac{1}{10}$ so there are $\frac{4}{10}$ in each bowl.

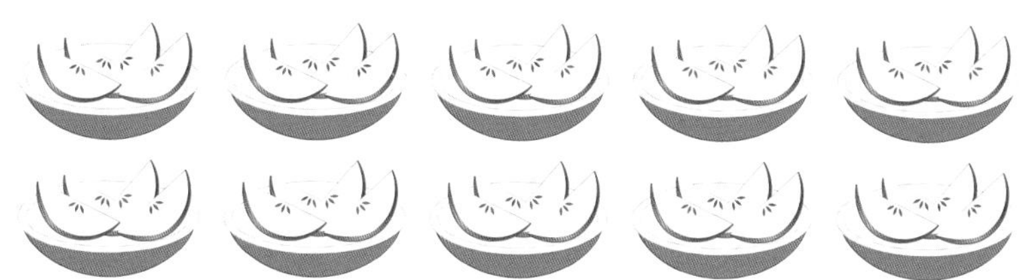

$4 \div 10 = \frac{4}{10}$

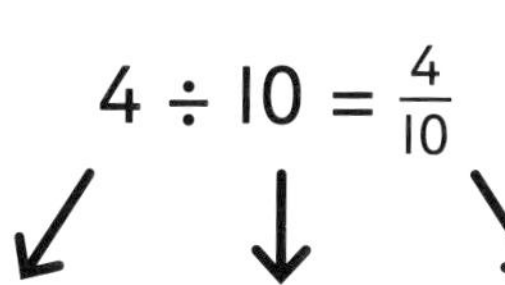

4 apples   10 bowls   fraction of an apple in each bowl

Each child will get $\frac{4}{10}$ of an apple.

b) If each melon is also split into 10 pieces there will be 20 pieces altogether, 2 for each bowl.

$2 \div 10 = \frac{2}{10}$

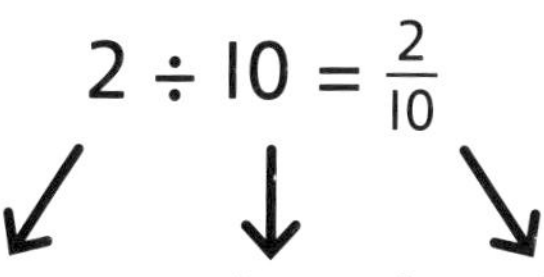

2 melons   10 bowls   fraction of a melon in each bowl

Each child will get $\frac{2}{10}$ of a melon.

Think together

1 **a)** How could each cake be shared between the 10 bowls?

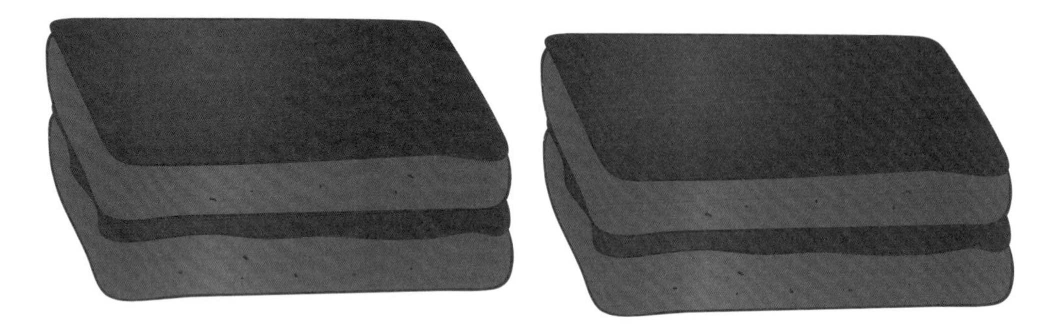

Each bowl will get ☐ of each cake.

b) If both the cakes were shared out, what fraction of a cake would each child get?

Each child would get ☐ cake.

I wonder if there are different ways I could share the cake.

2 The school athletics team has entered a 6 km relay race.

There are 10 children on the team. Each child must run the same distance.

What fraction of the whole distance must each child run?

Each child must run $\frac{\square}{\square}$ of the 6 km race.

3 1 stack of counters is shared equally on to a ten frame.

a) What fraction of the whole stack does each counter represent?

The stack has 10 counters. I will put one counter on each square of the ten frame.

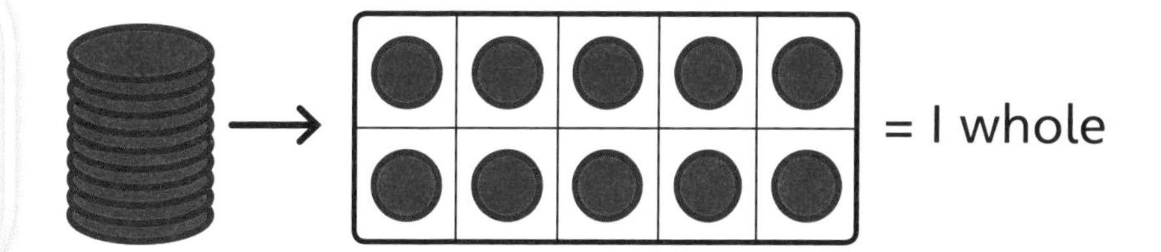

b) Complete the number sentence.

$1 \div \square = \frac{\square}{\square}$

c) 2 stacks of the same counters are shared onto a ten frame.

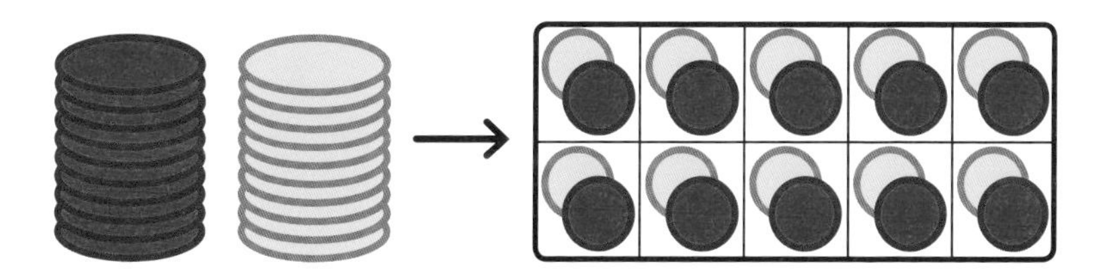

Explain how this picture shows that

$2 \div 10 = \frac{2}{10}$

d) How could counters and a ten frame be used to show

$3 \div 10 = \frac{3}{10}$?

→ Practice book 3B p131

Fractions as numbers ①

Discover

I am thinking of a number that one of the arrows is pointing to. Can you guess my number?
0
1

① **a)** How many equal parts has the number line been split into?

What does each interval on the number line represent?

b) What could Miss Hall's number **not** be?

What could Miss Hall's number be?

Share

a) The number line has been split into 7 equal parts.

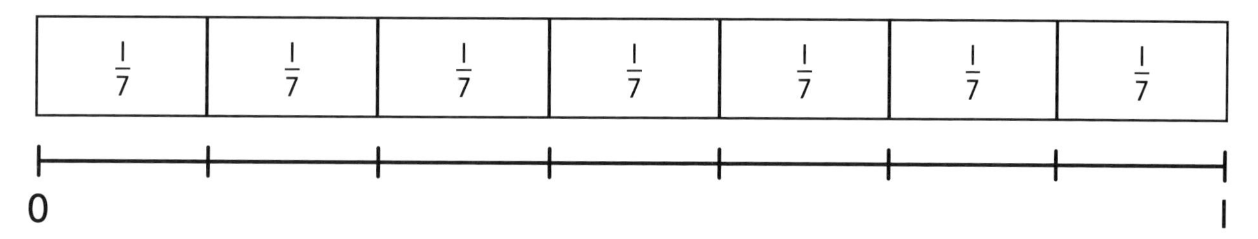

Each interval on the number line represents $\frac{1}{7}$ more than the previous interval.

b)

I can count up in $\frac{1}{7}$s from 0 to 1 and write the numbers on.

I know the numerator of each number is how many of the parts I have moved on from 0.

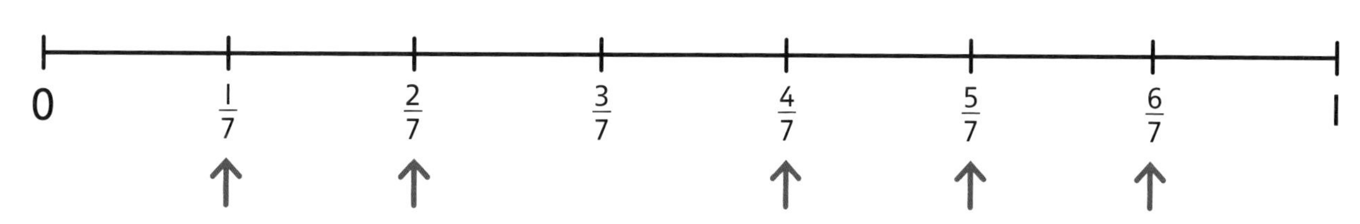

The numbers must have the denominator 7.

There is not an arrow on the 3rd interval. Miss Hall could not be thinking of $\frac{3}{7}$.

The number Miss Hall is thinking of cannot be 0, $\frac{3}{7}$ or 1.

Miss Hall's number could be $\frac{1}{7}$, $\frac{2}{7}$, $\frac{4}{7}$, $\frac{5}{7}$ or $\frac{6}{7}$.

Think together

1 Where would each of these numbers be placed on the number lines?

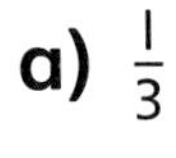

a) $\frac{1}{3}$

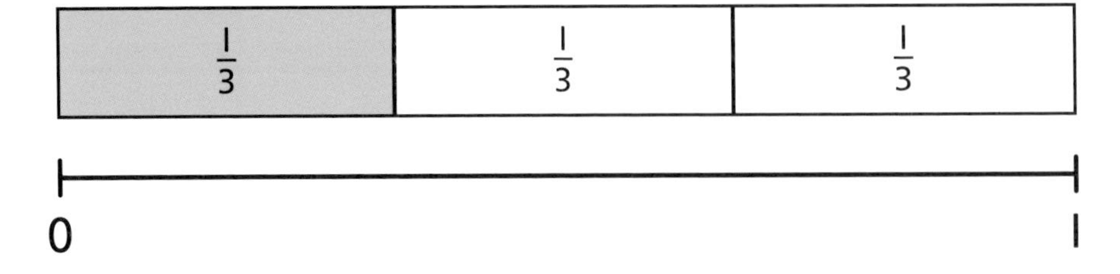

b) $\frac{3}{5}$

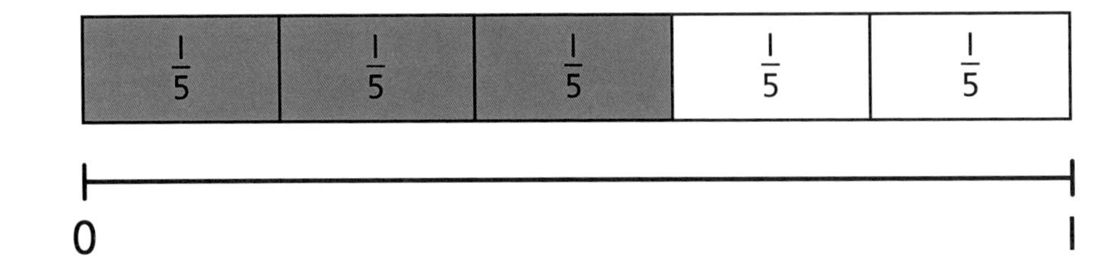

c) $\frac{3}{8}$

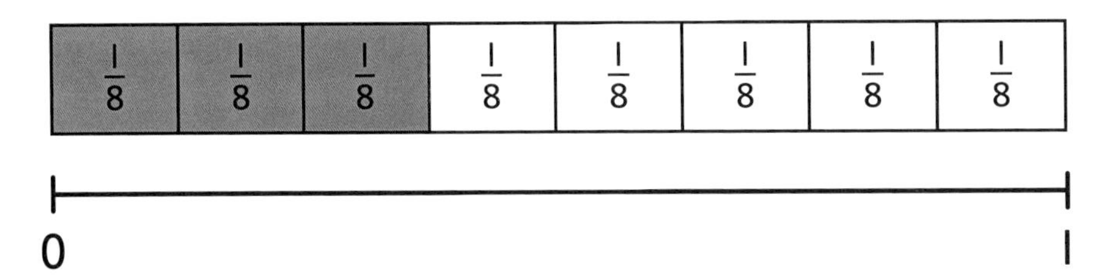

2 What fractions are shown at points A, B and C?

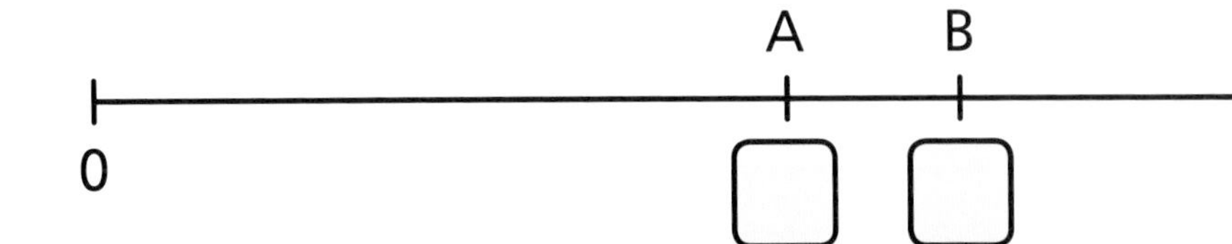

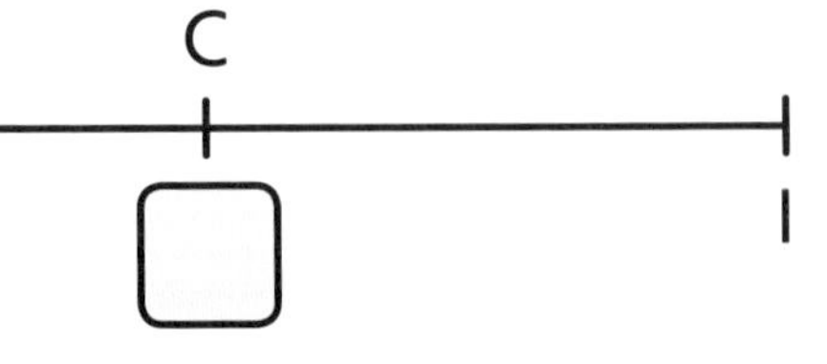

$\frac{1}{4}$	$\frac{1}{4}$	$\frac{1}{4}$	$\frac{1}{4}$

$\frac{1}{5}$	$\frac{1}{5}$	$\frac{1}{5}$	$\frac{1}{5}$	$\frac{1}{5}$

$\frac{1}{8}$	$\frac{1}{8}$	$\frac{1}{8}$	$\frac{1}{8}$	$\frac{1}{8}$	$\frac{1}{8}$	$\frac{1}{8}$	$\frac{1}{8}$

3 Which is larger, $\frac{2}{3}$ or $\frac{3}{5}$?

Use <, = or > to complete the number sentence.

$\frac{2}{3} \bigcirc \frac{3}{5}$

Is $\frac{3}{5}$ larger than $\frac{2}{3}$ because $3 > 2$?

I am going to place both numbers on a number line and use fraction strips to help me check.

4 You can only see part of these 0 to 1 number lines.

Each number line starts at 0 and finishes at 1.

Which is longer, number line A or number line B?

Explain how you know.

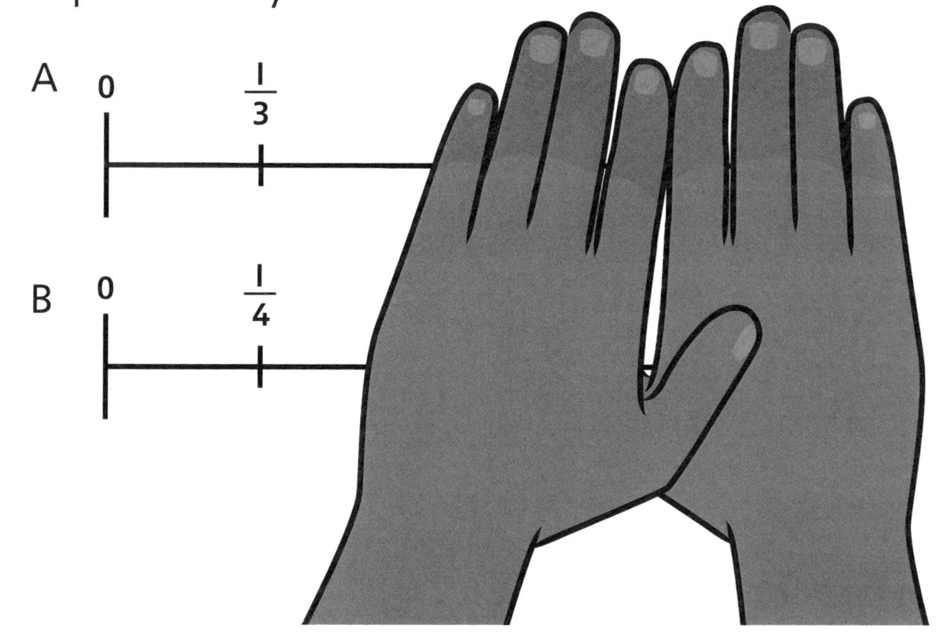

→ Practice book 3B p134

Fractions as numbers 2

Discover

1 **a)** Where will Lee's age go on the age chart? Who is the oldest?

b) How much older than Jamilla is Lee?

Share

a)

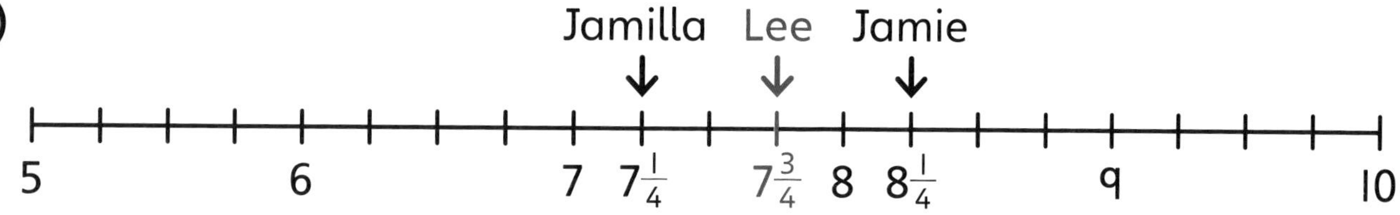

I started at 0 and counted up in quarters.

I started at 7 as this is the whole and I counted on in quarters from there.

Lee's age is between Jamilla and Jamie's ages. Jamie is the oldest at $8\frac{1}{4}$.

$7\frac{3}{4}$ is a **mixed number**. A mixed number is a whole number (7), and a fraction ($\frac{3}{4}$) combined.

b) Count on in quarters from Jamilla's age to Lee's age.

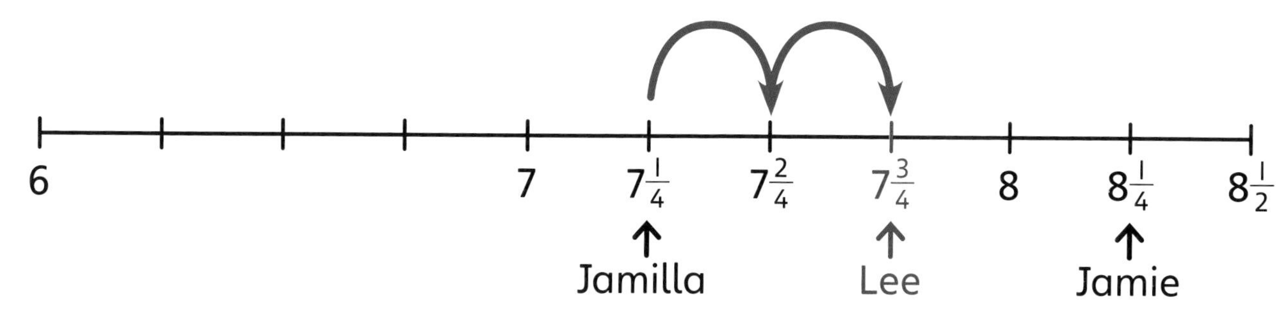

Lee is $\frac{2}{4}$ of a year older than Jamilla.

There are $\frac{2}{4}$ between Jamilla and Lee. $\frac{2}{4}$ is the same as $\frac{1}{2}$.

Lee is $\frac{1}{2}$ of a year older than Jamilla.

Think together

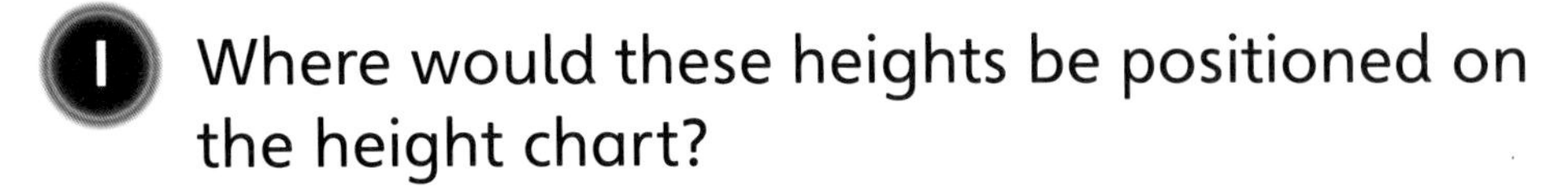

1 Where would these heights be positioned on the height chart?

Amelia's little sister is $\frac{3}{4}$ metre.

Toshi is $1\frac{3}{4}$ metres.

Kate is $1\frac{1}{4}$ metres.

I could use this height chart to help me work out what $\frac{3}{4}$ of a metre is.

2 m

1 m

0

2 What numbers are the arrows pointing to?

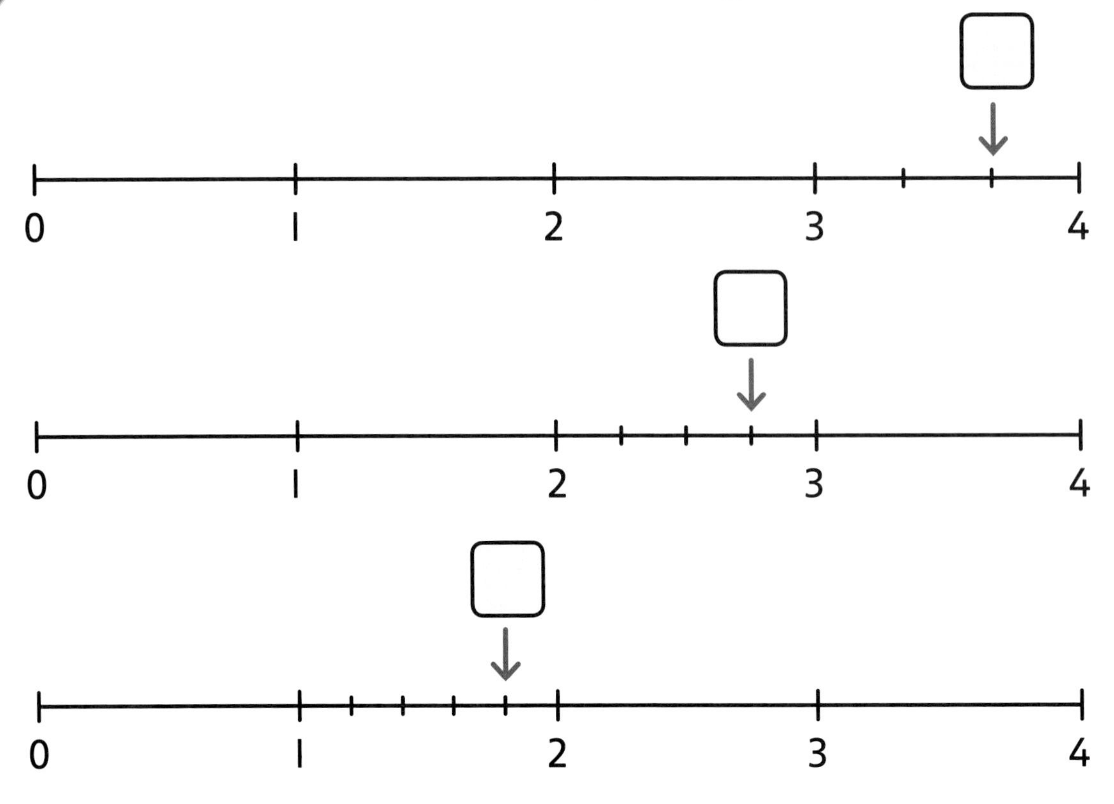

3 Point to where these numbers should be.

$1\frac{1}{3}$

$2\frac{3}{4}$

4 A rabbit jumps $\frac{2}{10}$ of a metre with every jump.

A hare jumps $\frac{3}{10}$ of a metre with every jump.

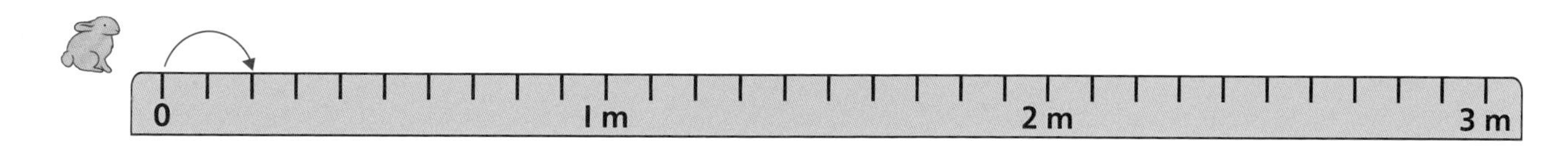

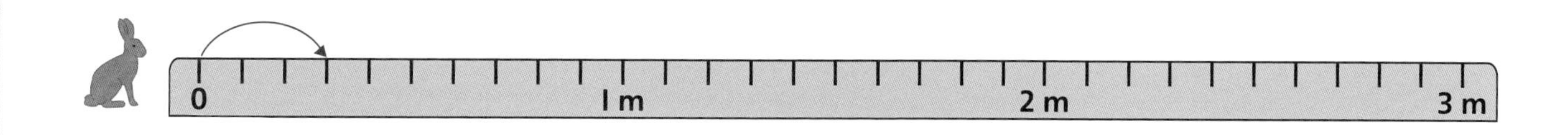

Will the rabbit ever land at the same position the hare has landed?

I will use my finger to continue the jumps of each animal, making sure that each jump is the correct size.

Then I will look to see which distances both animals landed on.

→ Practice book 3B p137

Fractions as numbers ③

Discover

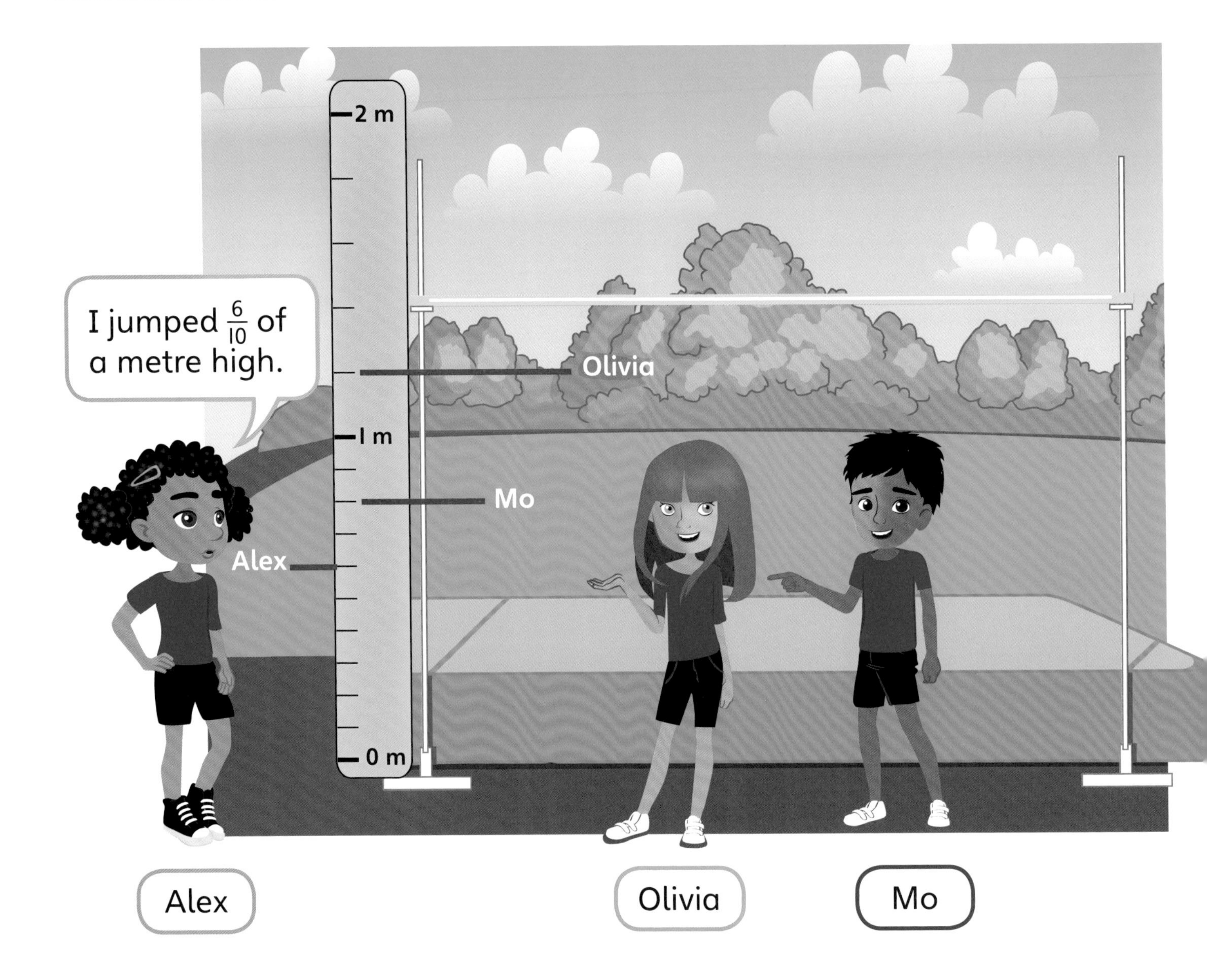

1 **a)** Alex, Mo and Olivia are practising the high jump. Alex's jump is the lowest at $\frac{6}{10}$ of a metre. Olivia's jump is the highest.

How high did Mo jump?

b) How high did Olivia jump?

Share

a) Between 0 m and 1 m has been split into tenths.

Alex jumped $\frac{6}{10}$ of a metre. Mo jumped $\frac{2}{10}$ of a metre higher than Alex.

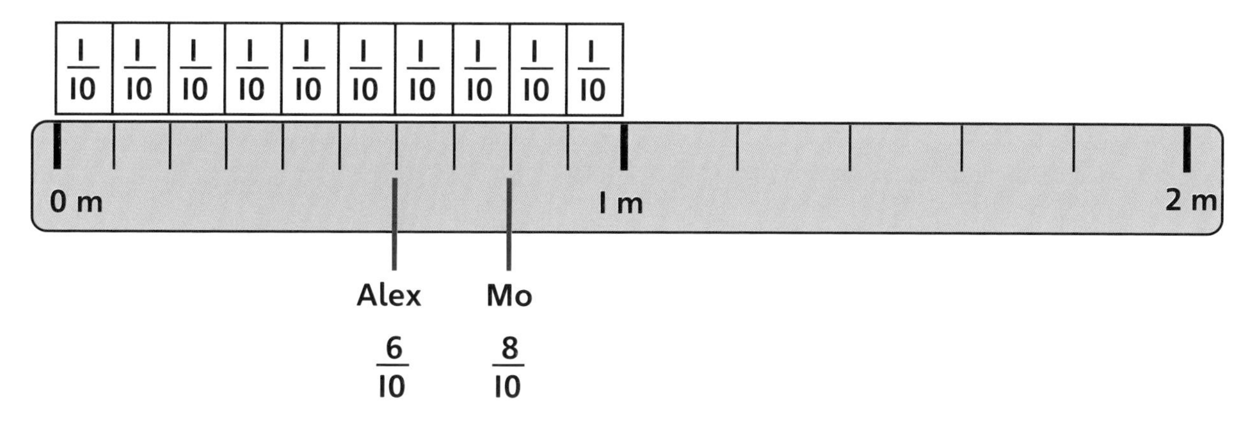

Mo's jump was $\frac{8}{10}$ of a metre high.

b)

There is 1 whole, so Olivia must have jumped $1\frac{1}{10}$ metres high.

There is 1 whole but there are only 5 parts between 1 m and 2 m, not 10. It has been split into fifths.

The denominator must be 5.

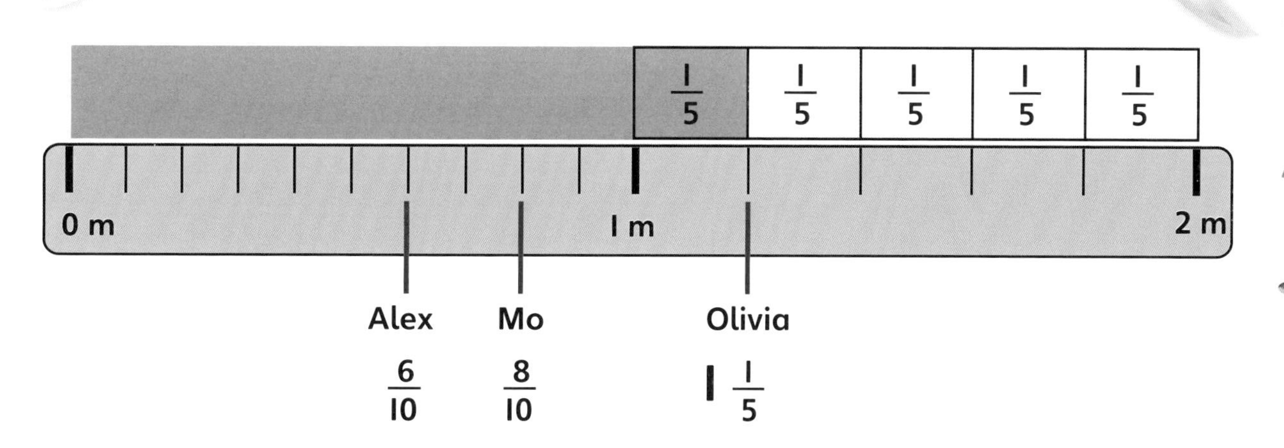

Olivia's jump was $1\frac{1}{5}$ metres high.

Think together

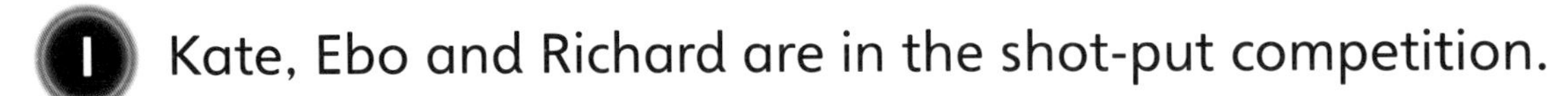

1 Kate, Ebo and Richard are in the shot-put competition.

Kate throws the shot $2\frac{5}{10}$ metres.

Ebo throws the shot $2\frac{9}{10}$ metres.

Richard throws the shot $1\frac{5}{10}$ metres.

On a number line, show your partner how far each shot has been thrown.

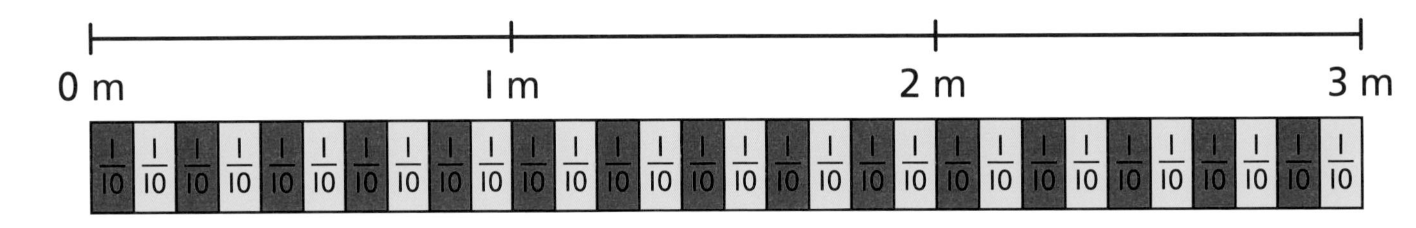

2 **a)** Point to where each number should be placed on the number line.

$\frac{7}{8}$ $1\frac{3}{8}$ $2\frac{4}{8}$

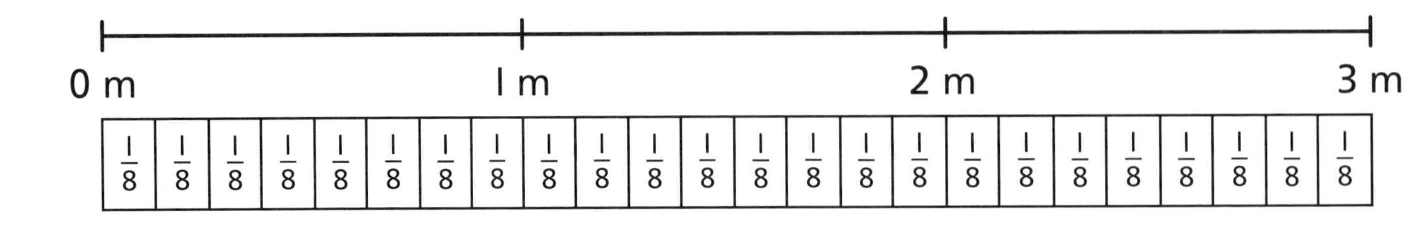

b) Are all three of the numbers mixed numbers?

3 **a)** Do you agree or disagree with Astrid?

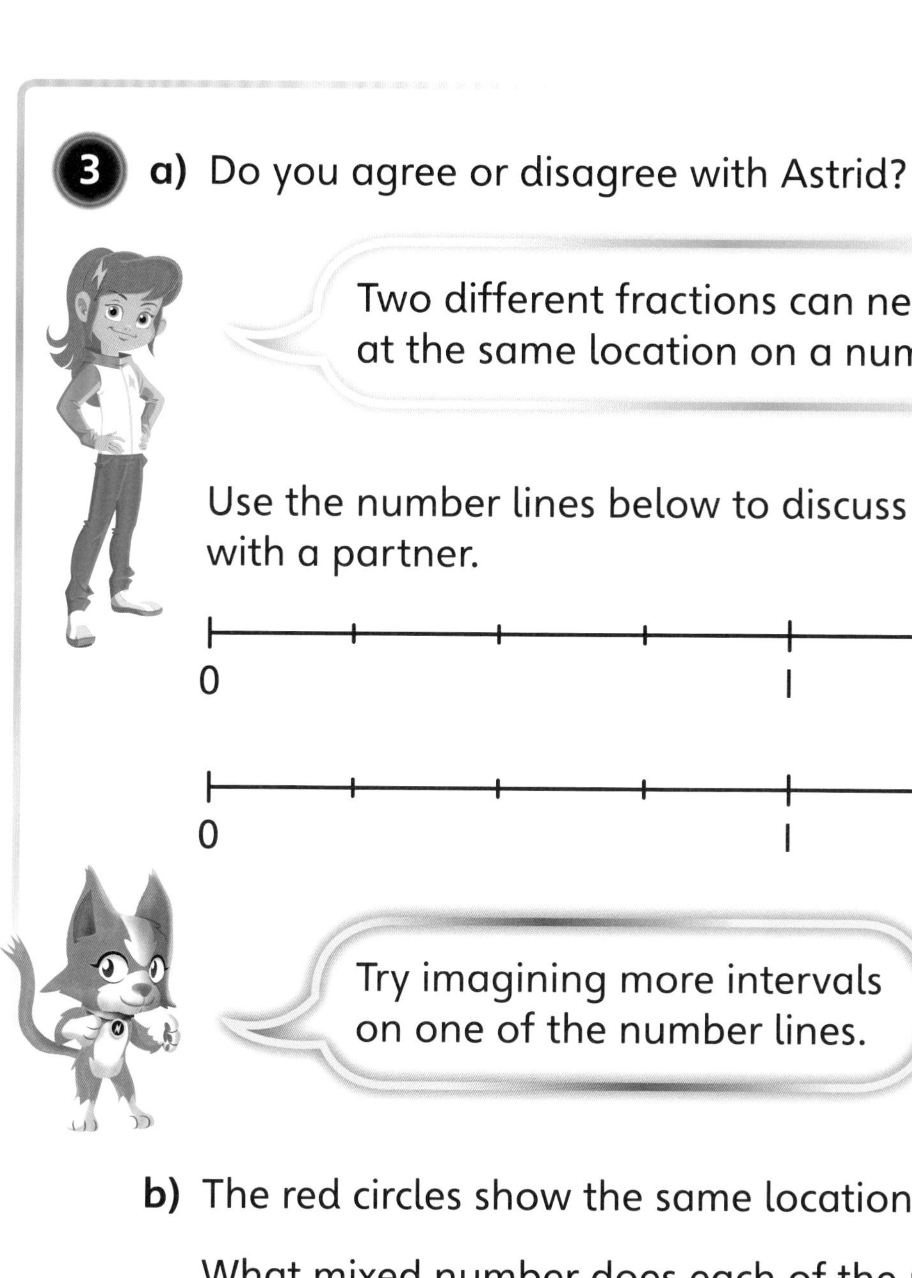

Two different fractions can never be placed at the same location on a number line.
Try imagining more intervals on one of the number lines.

Use the number lines below to discuss your answer with a partner.

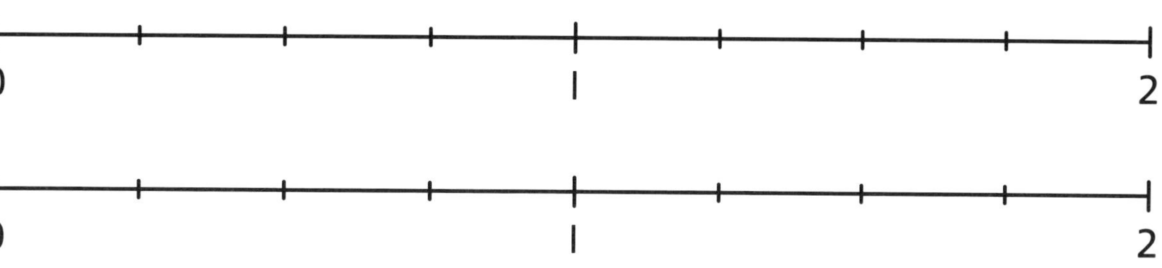

b) The red circles show the same location on the number lines.

What mixed number does each of the red circles show?

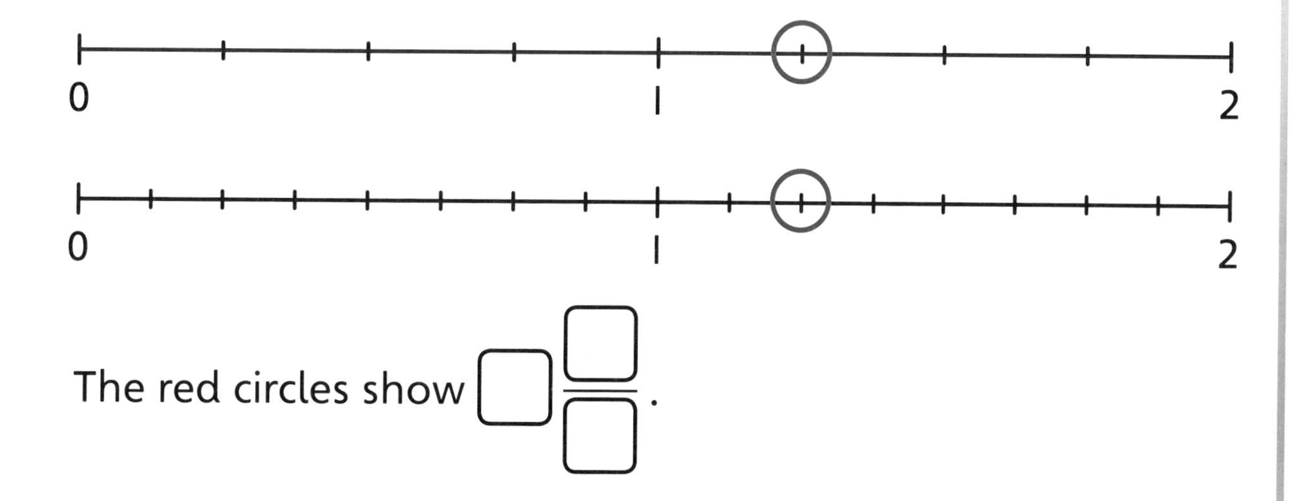

The red circles show $\square \frac{\square}{\square}$.

→ Practice book 3B p140

Fractions of a set of objects 1

Discover

RECIPE
Toppings for each cake:
$\frac{1}{3}$ bowl of marshmallows
$\frac{1}{5}$ bowl of peanuts
$\frac{1}{9}$ bag of chocolate swirls
Marshmallows
Peanuts
Chocolate swirls

1 **a)** There are 30 marshmallows in a bowl.

How many marshmallows are used on 1 cake?

b) There are 45 chocolate swirls in a bag.

How many chocolate swirls are used on 1 cake?

Share

I used counters to represent marshmallows.

a) There are 30 marshmallows in a bowl. $\frac{1}{3}$ of a bowl of marshmallows are used on 1 cake.

The denominator is 3. This means the whole must be split into 3 equal parts.

I shared the counters between the number of parts equally.

30 marshmallows

$\frac{1}{3}$	$\frac{1}{3}$	$\frac{1}{3}$

$\frac{1}{3}$ means the number of objects in 1 of the 3 parts.

$\frac{1}{3}$ of 30 is 10.

10 marshmallows are used on 1 cake.

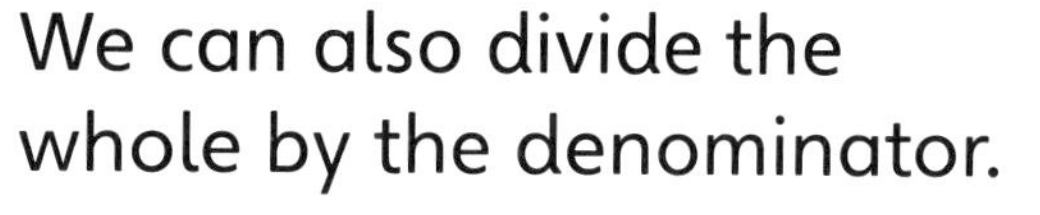

We can also divide the whole by the denominator.

$30 \div 3 = 10$

b) There are 45 chocolate swirls in a bag. $\frac{1}{9}$ of the chocolate swirls are used on 1 cake.

The denominator is 9. This means there are 9 equal parts.

$45 \div 9 = 5$

$\frac{1}{9}$ of $45 = 5$

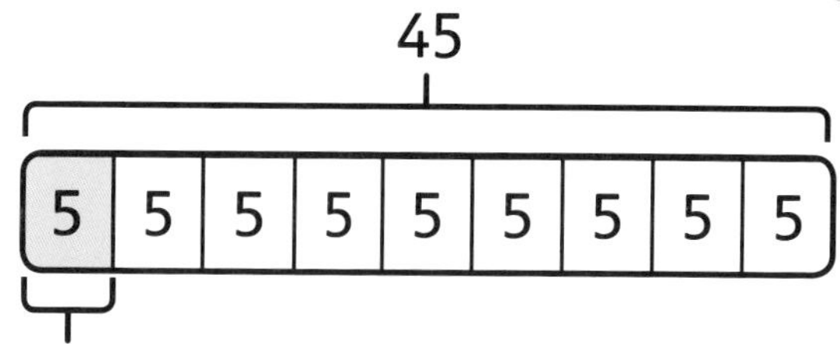

5 chocolate swirls are used on 1 cake.

Think together

1 Which representation shows $\frac{1}{4}$ of 20?

A

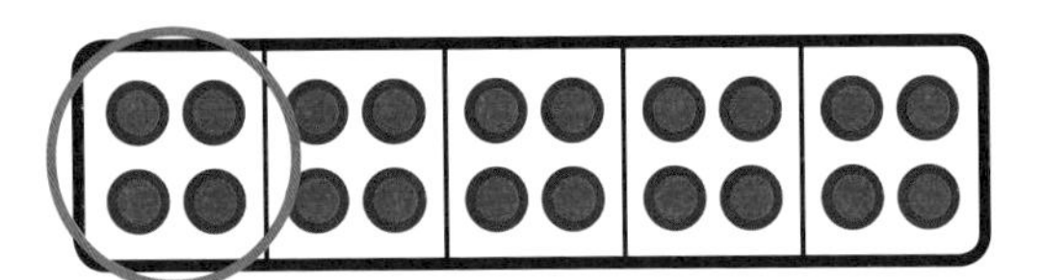

B

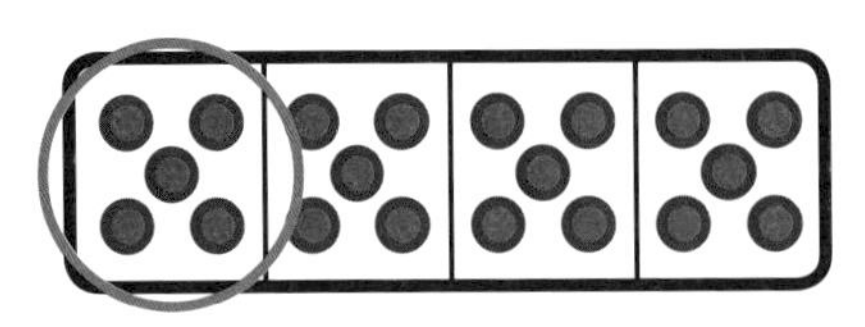

C

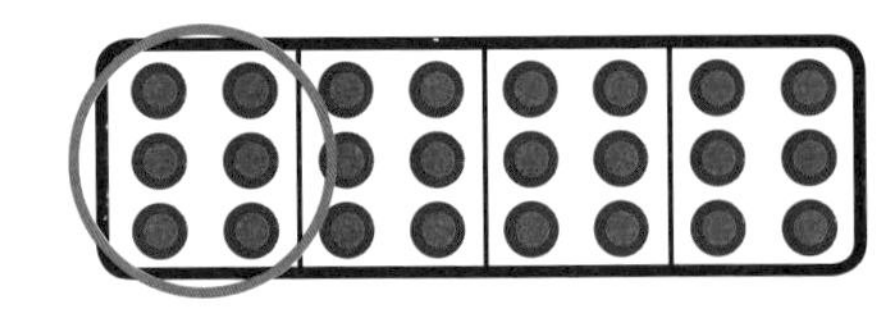

Representation ☐ shows this.

2

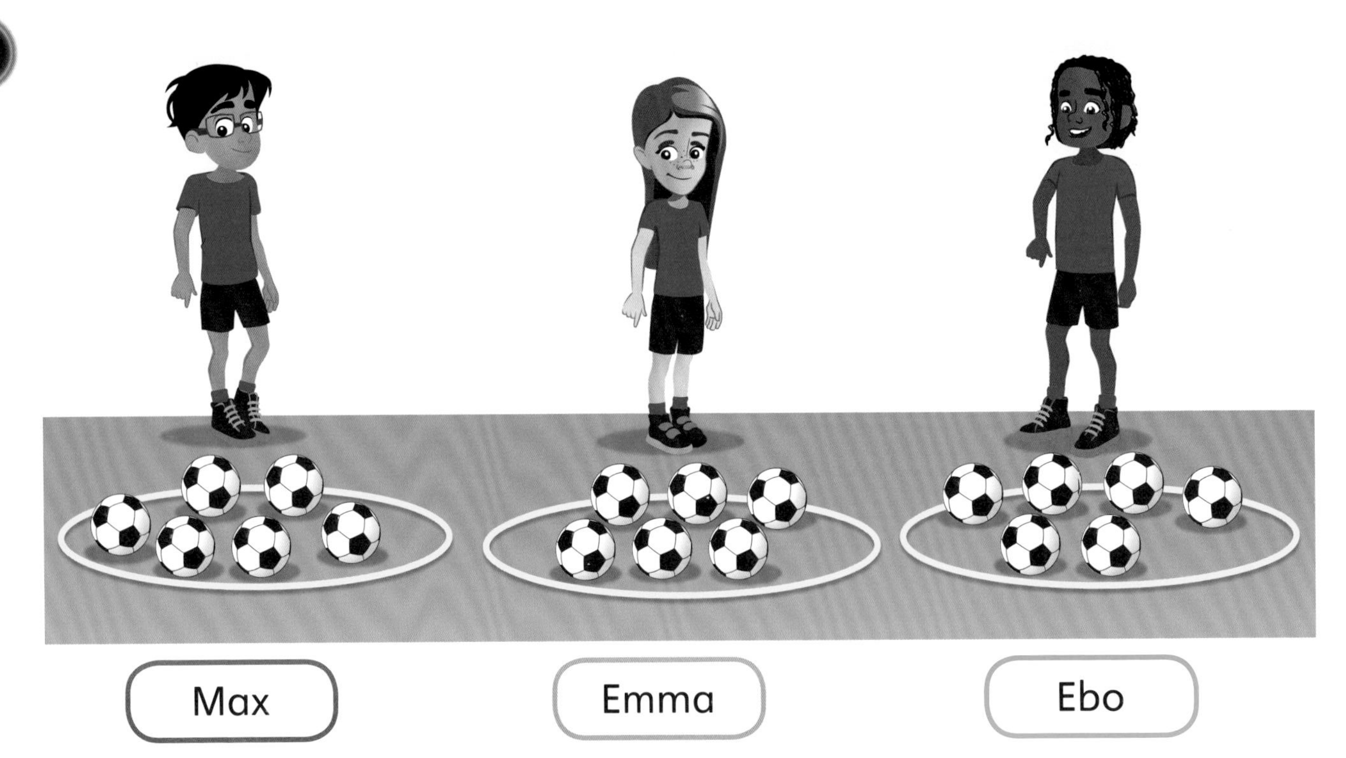

a) There are 18 footballs in total. Max, Emma and Ebo each think they are pointing to $\frac{1}{3}$ of 18.

$\frac{1}{3}$ of 18 is ☐.

b) Who is correct? Why?

_______________ is correct because _______________________________

3 Jamie has taken 3 brownies from a bag.

This is $\frac{1}{5}$ of the bag of brownies.

How many brownies were in the bag to start with?

There were ☐ brownies in the bag to start with.

4 Andy has won a prize in a raffle.

He can choose between 2 prizes.

Which prize will give Andy more money?

A

B

I would choose the one with the largest number of pound coins.

I would calculate the fraction of each amount to find which has the greater value.

☐ will give Andy more money.

→ Practice book 3B p143

Fractions of a set of objects 2

Discover

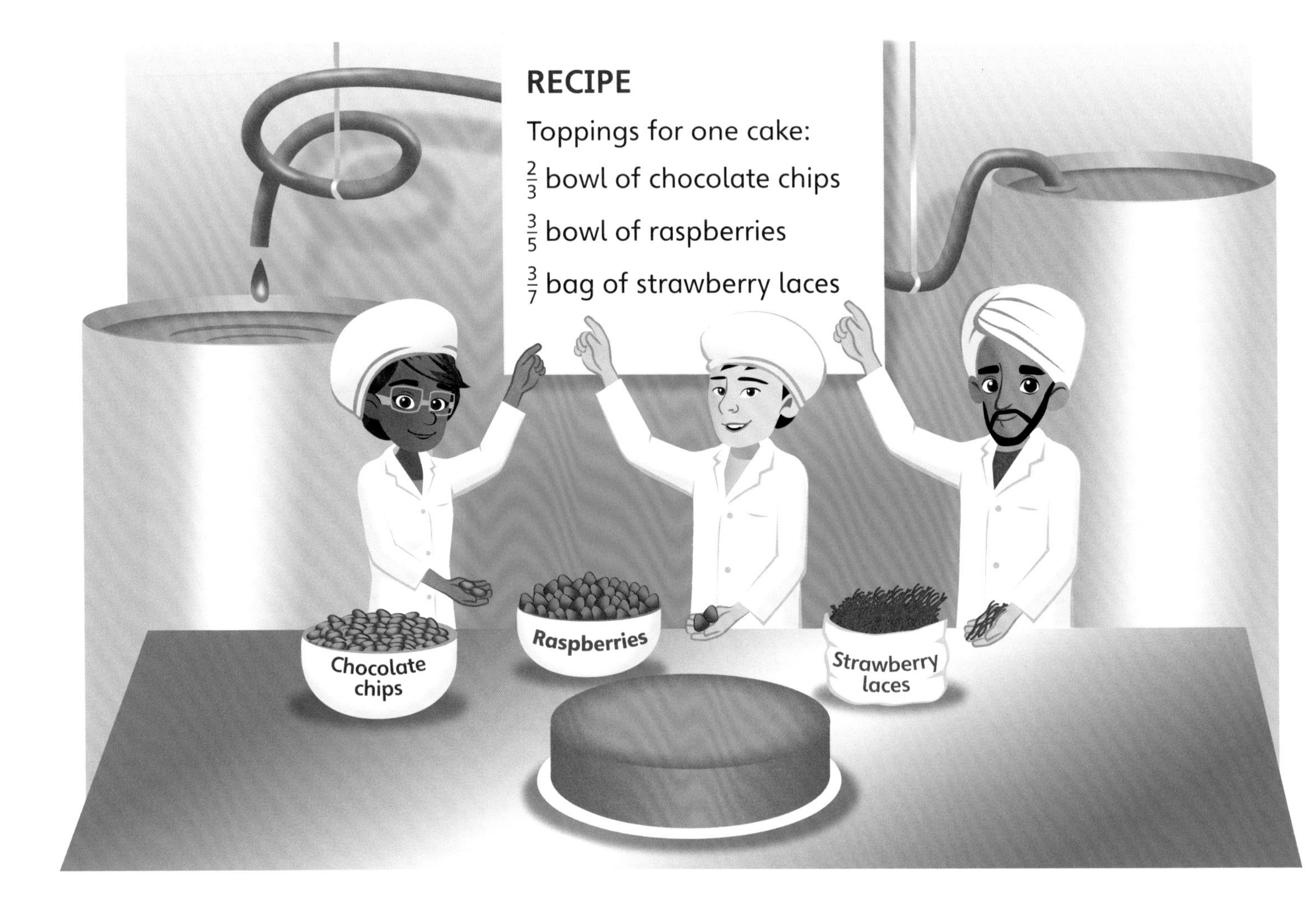
RECIPE
Toppings for one cake:
$\frac{2}{3}$ bowl of chocolate chips
$\frac{3}{5}$ bowl of raspberries
$\frac{3}{7}$ bag of strawberry laces
Chocolate chips
Raspberries
Strawberry laces

1 **a)** There are 35 raspberries in a bowl.

How many raspberries are used on 1 cake?

b) There are 35 strawberry laces in a bag.

How many strawberry laces are used on 1 cake?

Share

I used counters to represent the raspberries and shared these between the number of parts.

a) There are 35 raspberries in a bowl.

$\frac{3}{5}$ of a bowl of raspberries are needed.

The denominator is 5. This means the whole must be split into 5 parts.

$35 \div 5 = 7$

There are 7 in each part.

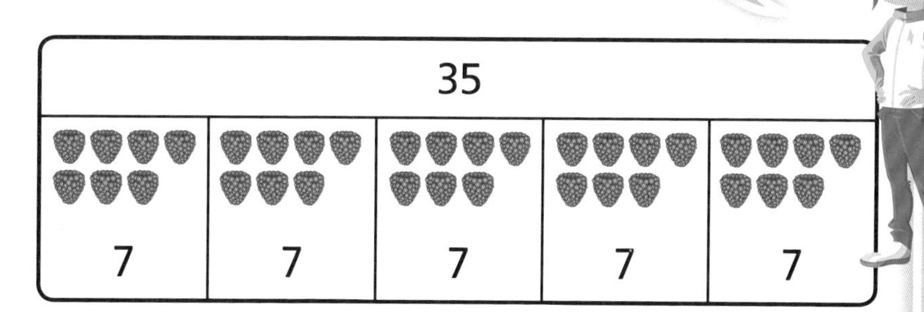

The numerator is 3, so 3 of the parts must be used.

$3 \times 7 = 21$ $\frac{3}{5}$ of $35 = 21$

21 raspberries are used on 1 cake.

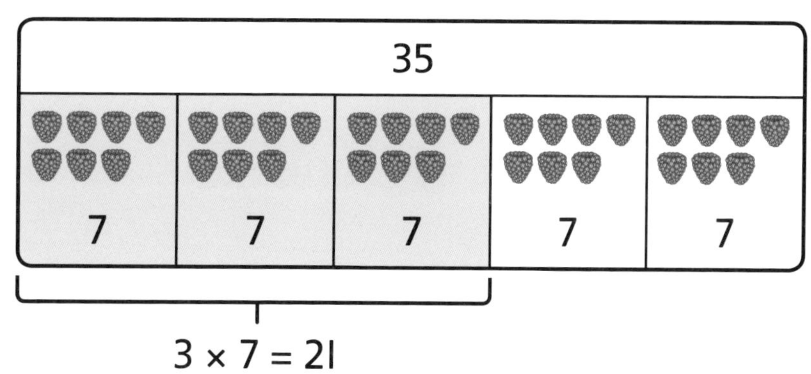

b) There are 35 strawberry laces in a bag.

$\frac{3}{7}$ of the laces are used on 1 cake.

The denominator is 7, so the whole must be split into 7 equal parts.

$35 \div 7 = 5$

There are 5 in each part.

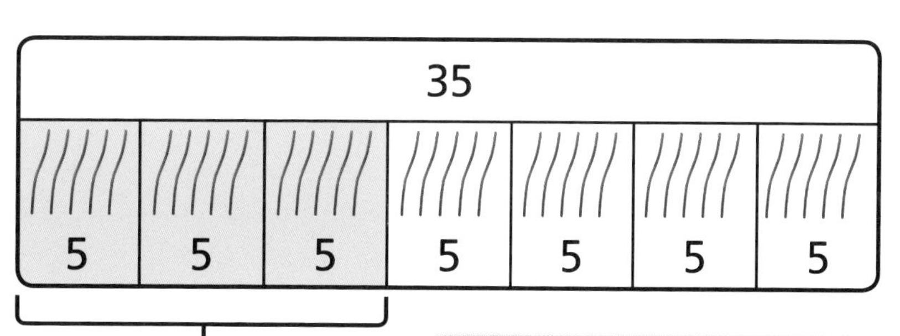

The numerator is 3, so 3 of the parts must be used.

$3 \times 5 = 15$ $\frac{3}{7}$ of $35 = 15$

15 strawberry laces are used on 1 cake.

I can see a link between these two calculations and a times-table fact.

Think together

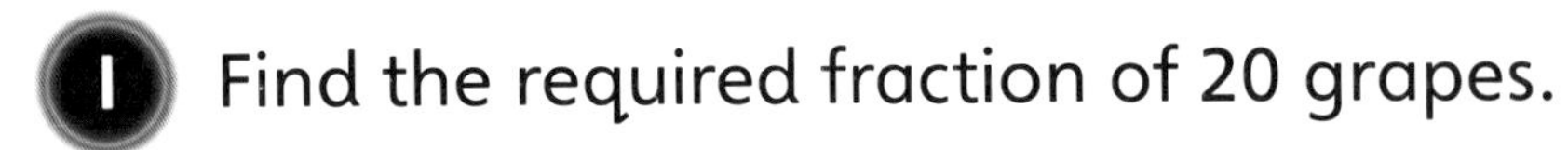

1 Find the required fraction of 20 grapes.

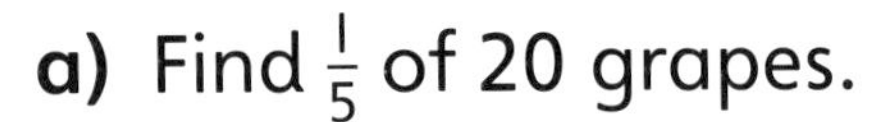

a) Find $\frac{1}{5}$ of 20 grapes.

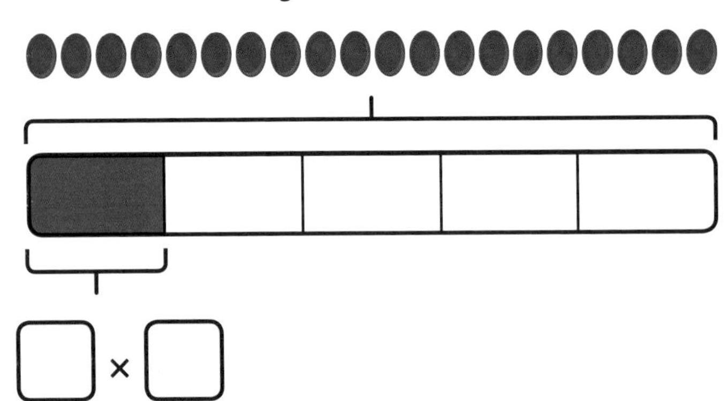

$\square \times \square$

$\frac{1}{5}$ of 20 grapes = $\square$ grapes.

b) Find $\frac{3}{5}$ of the grapes.

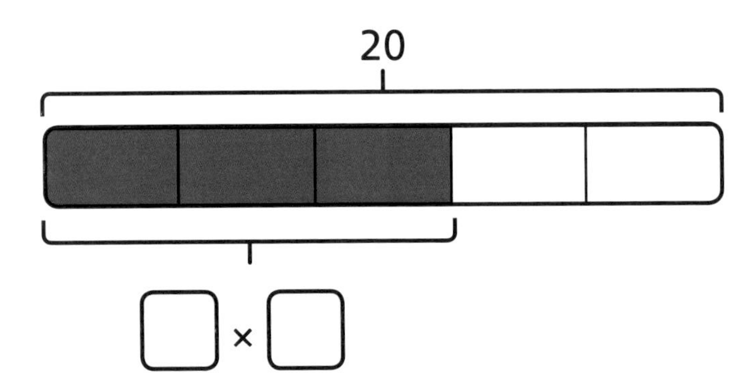

$\square \times \square$

$\frac{3}{5}$ of 20 grapes = $\square$ grapes.

c) Find $\frac{2}{5}$ of 20 grapes.

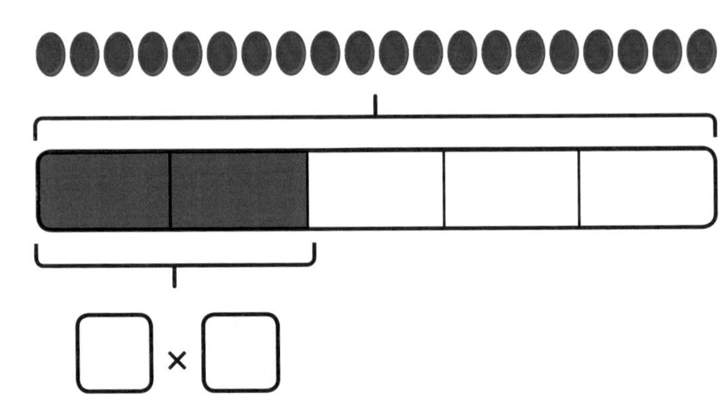

$\square \times \square$

$\frac{2}{5}$ of 20 grapes = $\square$ grapes.

d) Find $\frac{4}{5}$ of the grapes.

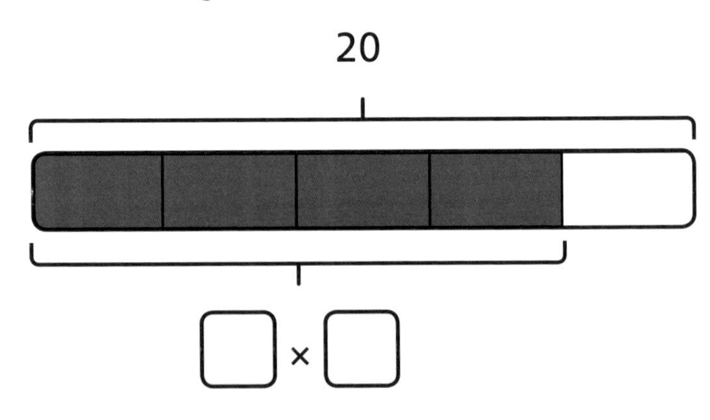

$\square \times \square$

$\frac{4}{5}$ of 20 grapes = $\square$ grapes.

I can use the previous answers to help me calculate the final answer.

2 With your finger, circle $\frac{2}{3}$ of these objects.

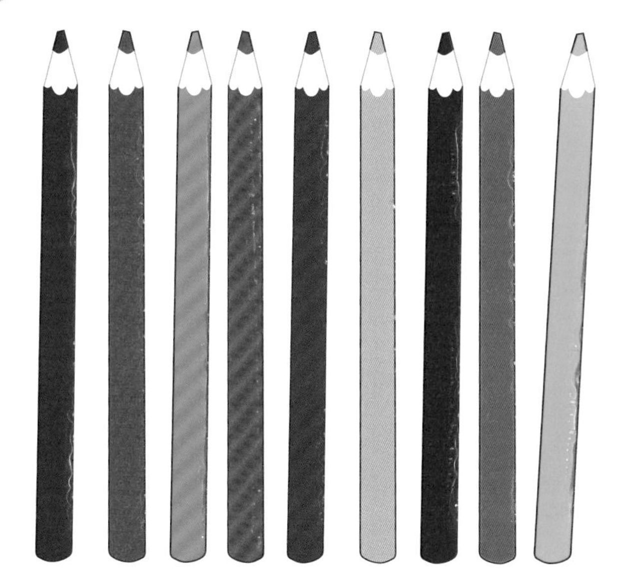

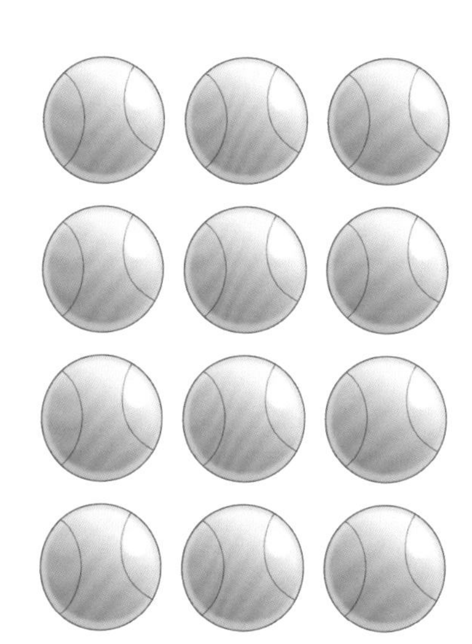

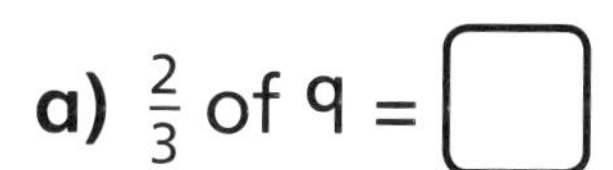

a) $\frac{2}{3}$ of 9 = ☐

b) $\frac{2}{3}$ of 12 = ☐

CHALLENGE

3 Use these facts to find the missing answers.

a) $\frac{1}{4}$ of 16 apples = 4 apples $\frac{3}{4}$ of 16 apples = ☐ apples

b) $\frac{1}{9}$ of 45 oranges = 5 oranges $\frac{5}{9}$ of 45 oranges = ☐ oranges

c) $\frac{1}{10}$ of 30 kiwis = 3 kiwis $\frac{7}{10}$ of 30 kiwis = ☐ kiwis

I can use the unit fraction of each group of objects to help me calculate the non-unit fraction of the same amount.

→ Practice book 3B p146

Fractions of a set of objects 3

Discover

1 **a)** The whole bag of cat food is shared equally between all of the cats.

How much food will 2 of the cats get in total?

b) There are 8 dogs in the animal home.

This is $\frac{2}{5}$ of the total number of animals.

How many animals are there altogether?

Share

a) There are 5 cats.

The whole must be split into 5 equal parts.

500 g				
100 g	100 g	100 g	100 g	100 g

First calculate how much food 2 cats get.

This will calculate $\frac{2}{5}$ of 500 g.

First find the unit fraction.

500 g ÷ 5 = 100 g

100 g × 2 = 200 g

2 cats will get 200 g of food in total.

I can find $\frac{1}{5}$ and then multiply it by the numerator.

b) 8 dogs represent $\frac{2}{5}$ of the animals in the home.

You need to work backwards to complete this problem.

To find the total number of animals, first find what $\frac{1}{5}$ is.

If 8 represents $\frac{2}{5}$, then $\frac{1}{5}$ is 8 ÷ 2

8 ÷ 2 = 4

There are 5 parts in the whole.

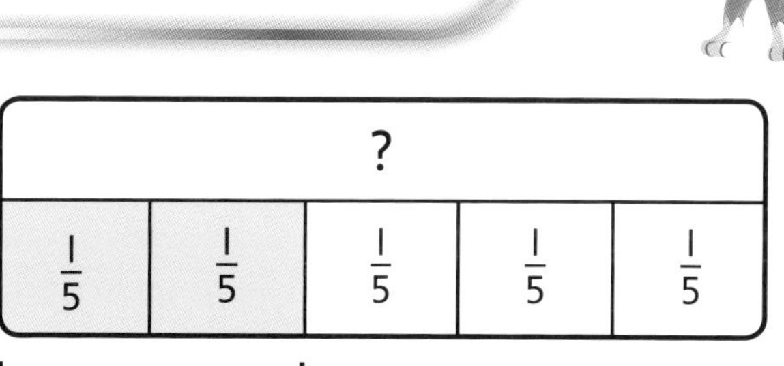

8 dogs

4 × 5 = 20

There are 20 animals altogether.

?				
4	4	4	4	4

Think together

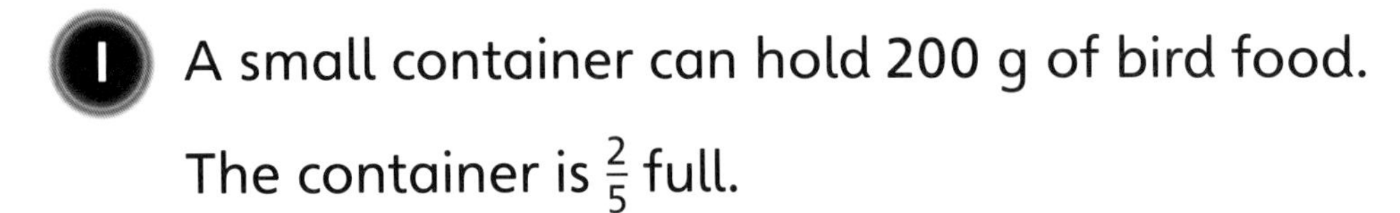

1 A small container can hold 200 g of bird food.

The container is $\frac{2}{5}$ full.

How much bird food is in the container?

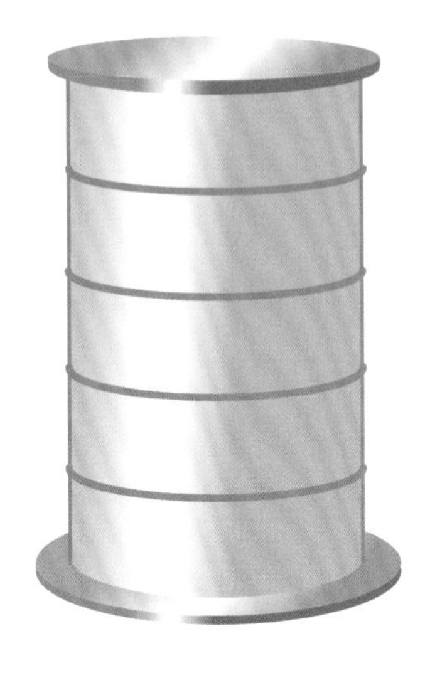

200g				
▒	▒			

$\square \div \square = \square$

$\square \times \square = \square$

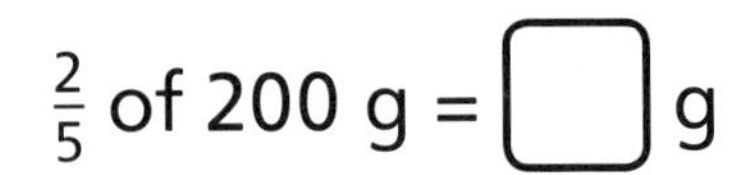

$\frac{2}{5}$ of 200 g = $\square$ g

$\square$ g of bird food is in the container.

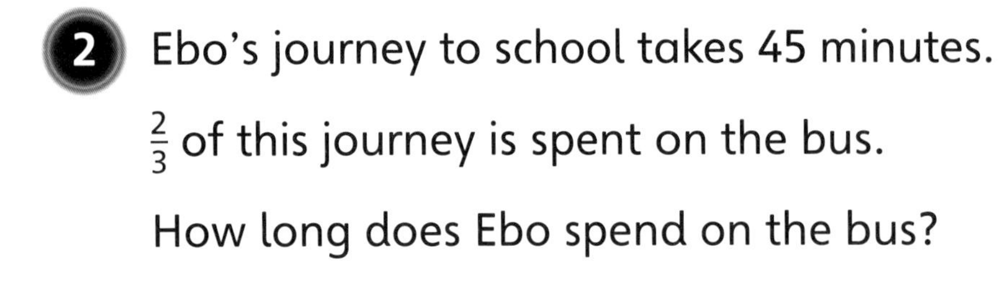

2 Ebo's journey to school takes 45 minutes.

$\frac{2}{3}$ of this journey is spent on the bus.

How long does Ebo spend on the bus?

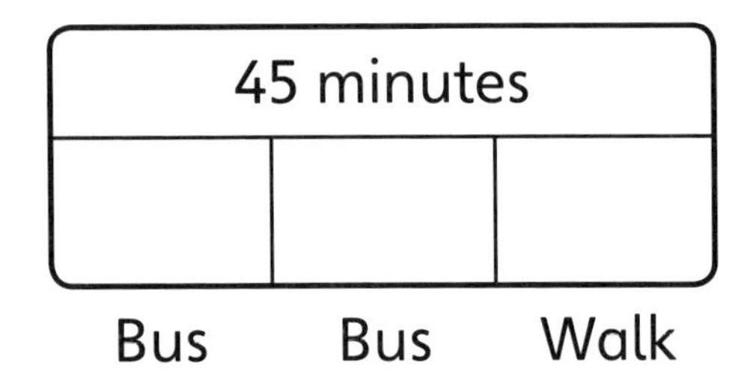

45 minutes		
Bus	Bus	Walk

$\frac{2}{3}$ of 45 minutes = $\square$ minutes

Knowing that $\frac{1}{3}$ of 45 minutes = 15 minutes can be used in two different ways to help me find the answer.

CHALLENGE

3 **a)** Mo runs a race.

After 20 metres he has run a quarter of the race.

How long is the race?

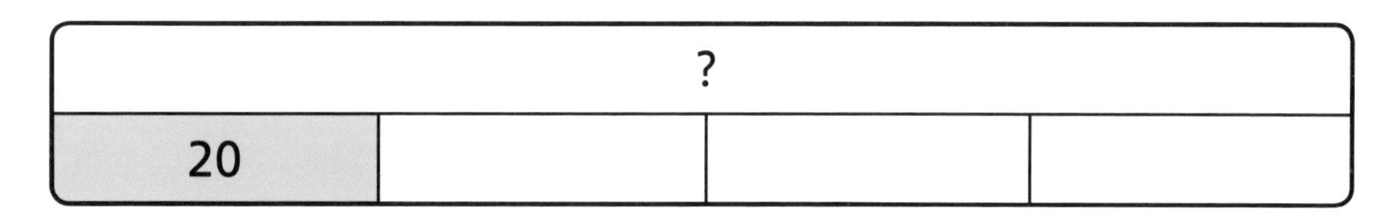

The race is ☐ metres.

This time I think I am working out the whole amount. I need to do something different.

b) Danny takes part in a sack race.

After 18 metres he has gone $\frac{2}{3}$ of the distance.

How long is the sack race?

The race is ☐ metres.

I am going to use a bar model to help me.

→ Practice book 3B p149

Problem solving – fractions

Discover

1 **a)** What fraction of the monkeys are in the trees?

b) The zookeeper has 20 fish. She feeds $\frac{2}{5}$ of the fish to the penguins at midday.

She feeds the rest of the fish to the penguins at 6 pm.

How many fish do the penguins get at 6 pm?

Share

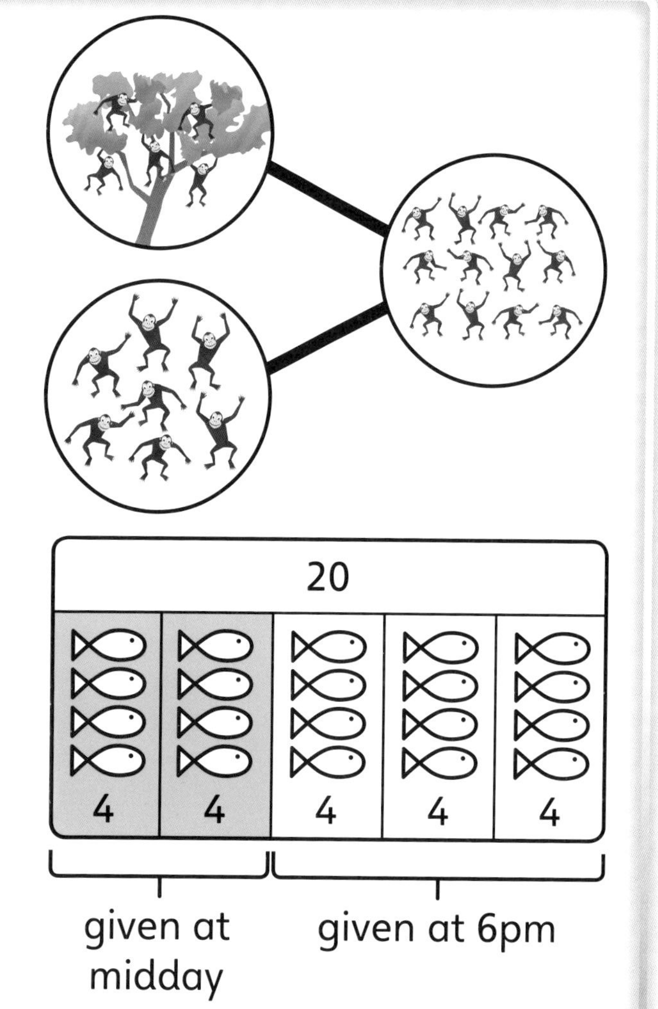

a) 5 monkeys are in the trees.

7 monkeys are on the ground.

There are 12 monkeys altogether, so the whole is 12.

$\frac{5}{12}$ of the monkeys are in the trees.

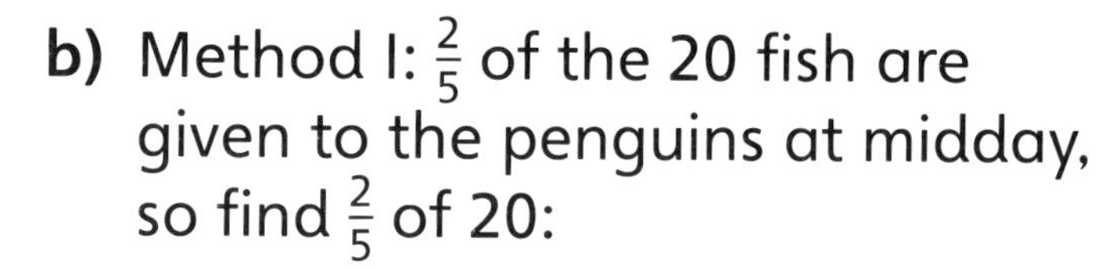

b) Method 1: $\frac{2}{5}$ of the 20 fish are given to the penguins at midday, so find $\frac{2}{5}$ of 20:

$20 \div 5 = 4$ (This is $\frac{1}{5}$ of 20.)

$4 \times 2 = 8$ (This is $\frac{2}{5}$ of 20.)

The penguins are given 8 fish at midday.

$20 - 8 = 12$

The penguins are given 12 fish at 6 pm.

Method 2: The penguins are given $\frac{3}{5}$ of the fish at 6 pm, so find $\frac{3}{5}$ of 20:

$20 \div 5 = 4$ (This is $\frac{1}{5}$ of 20.)

$4 \times 3 = 12$ (This is $\frac{3}{5}$ of 20.)

The penguins are given 12 fish at 6 pm.

I think I could find the number of fish given at 6 pm by calculating a different fraction of the whole.

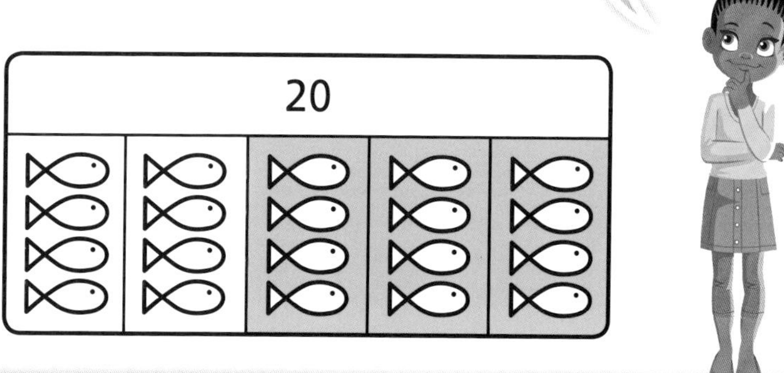

Think together

1 There are 10 penguins.

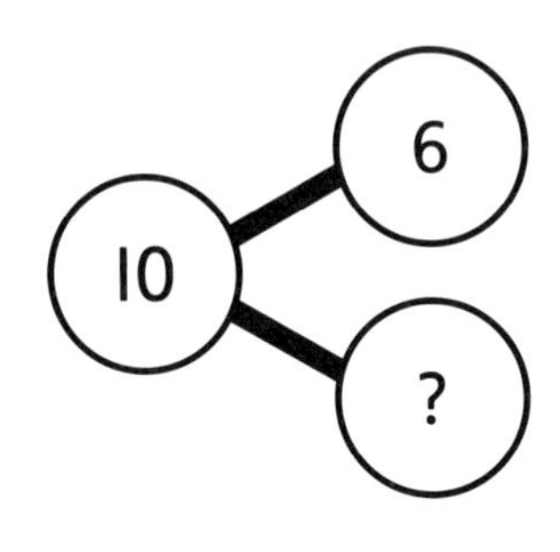

a) How many of the penguins are diving into the water?

☐ penguins are diving.

b) What fraction of the penguins diving?

$\frac{\square}{\square}$ of the penguins are diving.

2 There are 30 frogs.

$\frac{2}{6}$ are orange, $\frac{3}{6}$ are green and the rest are yellow.

How many yellow frogs are there?

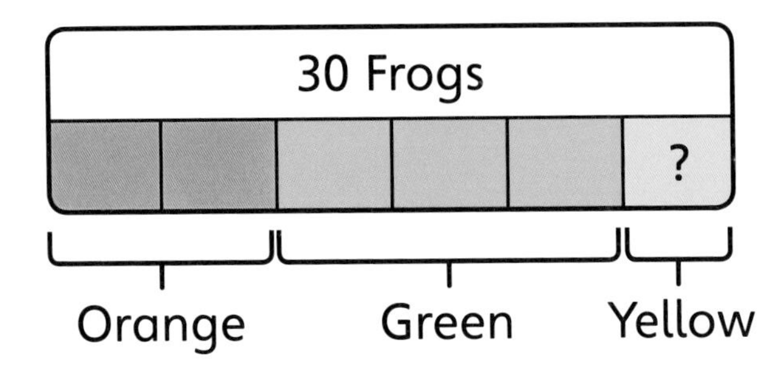

There are ☐ yellow frogs.

3 In the zoo kitchen there is $\frac{1}{4}$ of a 500 g bag of carrots and $\frac{3}{4}$ of a 200 g bag of carrots.

The zebras need 350 g of carrots. Are there enough carrots?

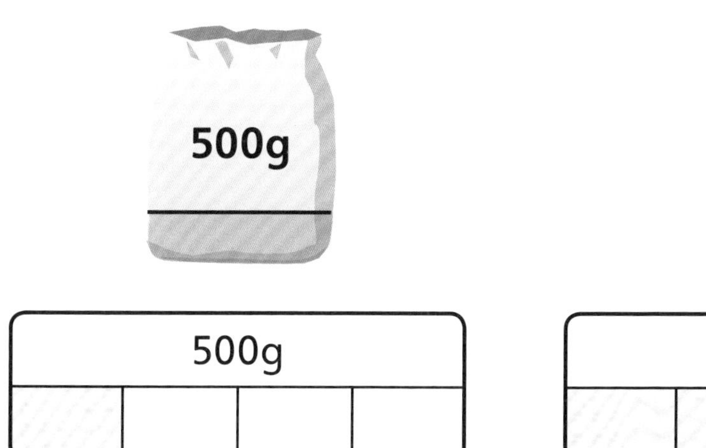

4 This is $\frac{3}{8}$ of a bucket of fish.

I wonder what representations I can draw to help work out the answer.

How many fish would be in a full bucket?

→ Practice book 3B p152

End of unit check

1 What fraction of the shape is shaded?

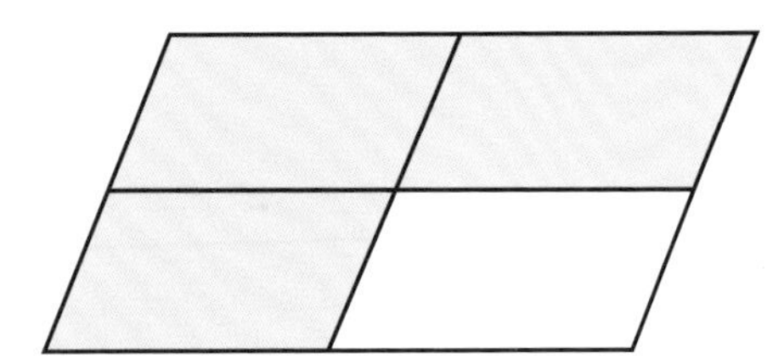

A $\frac{1}{4}$ B $\frac{3}{1}$ C $\frac{1}{3}$ D $\frac{3}{4}$

2 $\frac{2}{7} + \frac{\square}{\square} = 1$

A $\frac{8}{10}$ B $\frac{5}{7}$ C 3   D $\frac{7}{7}$

3 There are 4 melons on a tray.

They are cut up and shared equally between 10 people.

What fraction of a melon does each person get?

A $\frac{1}{10}$ B $\frac{4}{10}$ C $\frac{5}{10}$ D $\frac{10}{4}$

4 What number is the arrow pointing to?

0 ... 1

A $\frac{5}{6}$ B 5   C $\frac{3}{4}$ D $\frac{1}{6}$

5 What number is the arrow pointing to?

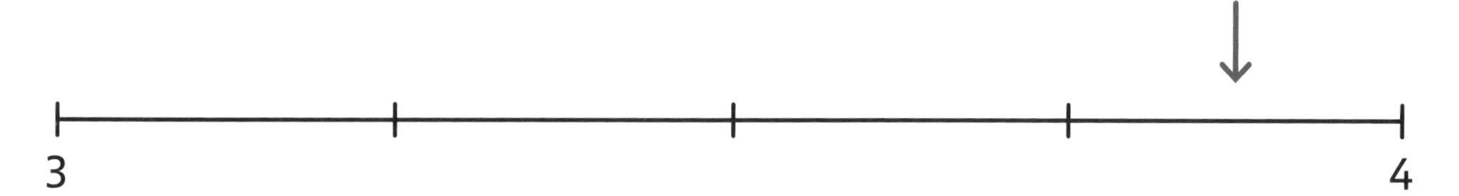

A $\frac{7}{8}$ B $3\frac{3}{4}$ C $3\frac{7}{8}$ D $3\frac{9}{10}$

6 Some seals are fed $\frac{7}{8}$ of a bucket of 64 fish.

How many fish do the seals receive?

A 8 fish B 32 fish C 16 fish D 56 fish

7 Max has 44 counters.

$\frac{1}{4}$ of the counters are red. The rest are blue.

How many of the counters are blue?

→ Practice book 3B p155

It is always good to learn new things!

It is fun to find new ways to do things too!

Wow, we have solved some difficult problems!

Yes, we have! Can we find even better ways to solve problems?

These maths adventures were great!

Yes! Let's find some more!

What do we know now?

Can you do all these things?

- Multiply and divide a 2-digit number by a 1-digit number
- Add and subtract amounts of money
- Interpret pictograms, bar charts and tables
- Measure length and perimeter
- Order fractions on a number line
- Find a fraction of a set of objects

Some of it was difficult, but we did not give up!

Now you are ready for the next books!